The Institution of Civil Engineers'

# Arbitration Practice

**The Institution of Civil Engineers'**

# Arbitration Practice

Geoffrey Hawker
*Chartered Civil Engineer and Barrister*

John Uff
*Chartered Civil Engineer and Queen's Counsel*

Charles Timms
*Chartered Civil and Mechanical Engineer*

Thomas Telford, 1986

Published by Thomas Telford Ltd, Telford House, PO Box 101, 26–34 Old Street, London EC1P 1JH, England

First published 1986

British Library Cataloguing in Publication Data:

Hawker, Geoffrey
   The Institution of Civil Engineers' arbitration
   practice.
   1. Civil engineering—Contracts and specifications
   —Great Britain   2. Arbitration and award—
   Great Britain
   I. Title   II. Uff, John   III. Timms, Charles
   IV. Institution of Civil Engineers
   624      KD1641

ISBN: 0 7277 0247 5

Set in Linotron Bembo by Tradespools Ltd, Frome

Printed in Great Britain by Redwood Burn Limited, Trowbridge, Wiltshire

# CONTENTS

*Contents*

## Appendices

# FOREWORD

It may be that, as a Judge, I have a distorted view of some aspects of life, but I cannot imagine a civil engineering contract, particularly one of any size, which did not give rise to some disputes. This is not to the discredit of either party to the contract. It is simply the nature of the beast. What is to their discredit is if they fail to resolve those disputes as quickly, economically and sensibly as possible.

The courts and arbitrators, respectively representing the public and private sectors in the business of disputes settlement, have for long worked in harmony, each recognising that the other has an essential part to play. In the context of civil engineering disputes, the main burden falls, and will always fall, upon arbitrators. It therefore behoves all who enter into such contracts to understand the arbitral procedures available. First and foremost amongst these is the newly revised Arbitration Procedure of the Institution of Civil Engineers.

This work approaches this Procedure with an admirable blend of the practical and the theoretical, guiding the reader through what would otherwise appear to be a jungle of technicalities with a skill which reveals the true simplicity and practical sense of the system. One of the great advantages of arbitration as a means of disputes settlement is that it can be tailored to the needs of particular types of dispute and, within that general approach, can provide many optional variations. However, as with all sophisticated machinery, a handbook is essential if full advantage is to be taken of all the available facilities. I welcome this volume as such a handbook.

John Donaldson
THE MASTER OF THE ROLLS

# AUTHORS' PREFACE

The original 1973 edition of the ICE Arbitration Procedure with its notes for guidance was welcomed as a concise and readable summary of arbitration practice as it then existed. This 1983 edition is much enlarged and, for reasons touched on later, contains many powers and procedures not previously available. The need for extended notes for guidance led to publication of the Procedure itself as a separate document, and this is available as an insert to the printed Conditions of Contract. The work of expanding the notes has resulted in this book, which offers both guidance on the Procedure and a general introduction to civil engineering arbitration.

Our intention has again been to produce a concise, readable and—above all—useful book for those who find themselves embroiled in civil engineering disputes. We do not seek to supplant the standard works on arbitration or construction law. Rather have we concentrated on the practical problems which experience has shown can lead to difficulty.

In preparing the book we have greatly appreciated the support of our colleagues on the Institution's Arbitration Advisory Board and the Advisory Committee on Contract Administration and Law. The chapters on Scotland owe much to the assistance of Bill McLeish and Bernard Abbott FFICE, Alistair Hamilton, Solicitor, and Michael Weir, of the University of Strathclyde, also to Arthur Allen FICE and James Arnott, Solicitor, who offered useful advice. Similarly, Tony Greeves FICE from Belfast and Max Abrahamson, Solicitor, from Dublin were most helpful with regard to Irish matters. Our thanks are also due to Harry Jones, Secretary to all the relevant Institution Committees. Finally, we are grateful to Sir John Donaldson, Master of the Rolls, for his support in launching the 1983 Rules and for contributing the Foreword to our book.

Our intention has been to state the law as it was on 1st April, 1985.

G.F.H.
J.F.U.
C.C.T.

# TABLE OF CASES

# TABLE OF STATUTES

# ENGINEERING ARBITRATION

# Chapter 1

# INTRODUCTION

The Institution of Civil Engineers' (ICE) Arbitration Procedure owes its existence to the arbitration agreement in the fifth edition of the ICE Conditions of Contract. Clause 66(1) of those Conditions[1] refers to ". . . the Institution of Civil Engineers' Arbitration Procedure (1973) or any amendment or modification thereof being in force at the time of the appointment of the arbitrator . . ." and an ad hoc drafting committee was accordingly created to produce it.

The resulting document—eventually published in 1976 as the familiar "Red Book"—contained the Procedure itself together with notes for guidance and various forms, precedents and appendices. The Procedure covered only the steps leading up to the Hearing, including the appointment of the arbitrator, preliminary meetings and typical orders for directions. The notes for guidance went somewhat further and included sections on the powers of the arbitrator, the conduct of the Hearing and the preparation of the award. However, neither the Procedure nor the notes for guidance affected or added to the existing powers available to the arbitrator.

Following the passing of the Arbitration Act 1979 a subcommittee of the ICE Arbitration Advisory Board was set up to redraft the Procedure to take account of the changes brought about by the new Act. At the same time, it was apparent that substantial changes had occurred in both the law and the practice applying to construction disputes. Throughout the 1970s the potential liabilities of most parties involved in works of civil engineering construction had been greatly enlarged, particularly in the field of tort. Litigation and arbitration had each become much more complex, prolonged and expensive. And, with the advent and continuance of high interest rates, the advantage to debtors of delaying payment and the corresponding damage to creditors had increased to make speed of critical importance. In the light of this, the subcommittee was asked to extend its review to include all aspects of civil engineering arbitration.

A particular problem pointed out by several commentators was that large-scale arbitration, with legal representatives appearing on both sides, was becoming indistinguishable from litigation, but with the disadvantage that an arbitrator had to be paid whereas the parties could obtain the services of a Judge and court-room free of charge. Arbitrators were being required to act like Judges, including listening to expert evidence being extracted from witnesses by and debated between lawyers. The problem had developed to the point where many lawyers were advising their clients that

---

[1] The revised Clause 66, revised in March, 1985, now refers to the ICE Arbitration Procedure (1983): see Chapter 6.

litigation was to be preferred to arbitration as being often both quicker and cheaper; or that, if arbitration could not be avoided, the arbitrator should be a lawyer.

Faced with this situation, the subcommittee took the view that engineering arbitration conducted as if it were litigation might well prove unsatisfactory, if only because an engineer-arbitrator is not and cannot be expected to act like a Judge. Moreover, if engineering arbitration were to remain viable, it must be capable of mobilising those special features which distinguish it from and give it an advantage over litigation. The solution adopted by the subcommittee was therefore to try to give to the arbitrator and to the parties effective control over the proceedings, and to allow the possibility of saving time and costs by making best use of the arbitrator's specialist abilities.

As the new Procedure was substantially longer than the 1973 version it was decided to publish the Procedure itself as a separate document, and to produce this Practice to replace the earlier "notes". Thus the new Procedure and this Practice together replace the 1973 publication.

## Outline of the 1983 Procedure

The purpose of the ICE Arbitration Procedure is twofold. First, it sets out a uniform procedure for making reference to arbitration and for the appointment of arbitrators. Secondly, and more important, it aims to provide powers and procedures which will encourage the parties, either under the direction of the arbitrator or by agreement, to find the most appropriate means for identifying the real issues underlying their dispute or difference which need to be ventilated.

A particular feature of the Rules contained in the Procedure is the adoption of a large measure of flexibility. This is necessary since engineering disputes may range from matters essentially legal in character to those which are largely technical. In the latter case there are particular Rules which allow the arbitrator to use to the full his own technical expertise free from undue involvement with non-technical advocates.

The Procedure creates a range of new powers available to the arbitrator, either at the instigation of the parties or sometimes at his own instigation. In addition, there are special procedures available to assist in the economical resolution of particular kinds of dispute.

## New powers

Among the new powers given to the arbitrator is the important power to make a "summary award" (Rule 14). This is a substantial extension of the power to make an interim award under s. 14 of the Arbitration Act 1950 and is analogous to the High Court's power of summary judgment under Order 14 of the Rules of the Supreme Court. Parties need no longer be deterred from arbitration by the thought of inevitable delays of months or years before monies due can be released.

Other new powers given to the arbitrator include much tougher powers to enforce compliance with interlocutory orders. It has always been a source of delay and dismay that arbitrators had no effective "teeth" to see that their directions were obeyed. Under the new Rules the arbitrator has express powers to debar a party from relying on matters in respect of which he is in default (Rule 11.4), to order the deposit of money as security (Rule 6.1) and to proceed with a hearing should a party fail to appear (Rule 15.4). The arbitrator is also given extensive powers to control and direct the way in which the parties present their cases and over the conduct of the Hearing generally (Rules 12, 13, 15 and 16). These controls will allow the arbitrator to direct the Hearing towards those points and issues which he considers to be of greatest importance.

## Special Procedures

At the heart of the new Procedure is an arsenal of three special procedures available to the parties and to the arbitrator in circumstances where traditional procedures are inappropriate. The first of these is the *Short Procedure* (Part F). This can apply to any dispute, but is more suited to disputes where the amount of money at issue is limited. It consists essentially of a submission with documents together with a short summary hearing at which further evidence may be adduced. It is envisaged that the process will take no more than about three months from beginning to end, and that costs will not normally be awarded.

The second new procedure may apply in any dispute where there are technical issues and the parties rely on expert advisers. The *Special Procedure for Experts* (Part G) is intended to create a new type of forum comprising the arbitrator and the experts retained by the parties who, without the intervention of lawyers, review together the technical evidence and issues. Following this, the arbitrator makes a binding award upon the issues of fact. This process may be embarked upon at any stage in the proceedings. But in a case which turns on technical issues, it would be more appropriate to invoke the procedure at the outset.

The third new procedure deals with *Interim Arbitration* (Part H), i.e. arbitration which proceeds before completion of the Works. Clause 66(2) of the ICE Conditions of Contract defines the circumstances in which interim arbitration may take place.[1] These include claims under Clause 12 (adverse physical conditions or artificial obstructions) or the withholding of any certificate. One of the problems with existing procedures was that, in the absence of means to speed up an interim hearing, such arbitrations were often still unresolved when the Works were completed, thus defeating the object of the early start. The new Procedure lays down particular rules for arbitrations conducted during the course of the Works. Unless the parties otherwise agree, the dispute is required to be brought to a conclusion at or before completion of the Works. To achieve this, the arbitrator is given power to direct the use of Parts F or G (otherwise available only at the choice of the parties) and to make various types of finding appropriate in the circumstances, including an "interim decision" which may be re-opened after completion.

## Control by engineers

One effect of the new Procedure should be to allow greater involvement in the arbitration process by engineers. By tradition, lawyers not only deal

---

[1]   The revised Clause 66 removes all bars to interim arbitration: see Chapter 6.

with the issues of law which arise in a case but also undertake the conduct and management of the case as a whole. The engineer's role may thus be restricted to the giving of evidence, if and when requested to do so. In formal litigation this arrangement is often both desirable and necessary. But an engineering arbitration usually arises out of a dispute which has been managed and conducted by and between engineers, at least to the stage of a Clause 66 reference.

Under the new Procedure a more balanced approach to the resolution of such disputes becomes possible. It may be that some parties will wish to retain a lawyer in overall charge of the case, with the engineers taking over for part of the proceedings where appropriate. But equally it is open to the parties or their engineers to keep control of the case, bringing in their lawyers for specific tasks when required. In this way the particular skills of each profession may be deployed to the best advantage.

*Chapter 2*

# DISPUTE TO APPOINTMENT

**The arbitration agreement**

Every arbitration is based on two separate contracts. The first is an agreement between the parties to refer their disputes to arbitration; this is usually called the "arbitration agreement". The second is an agreement between the parties on the one part and the arbitrator on the other by which the arbitrator agrees to determine the disputes and the parties agree to pay his fees. The second agreement is sometimes called the "appointment" to distinguish it from the arbitration agreement.

The arbitration agreement may form part of some other contract between the parties or may be a separate contract entered into for the purpose. Clause 66[1] of the ICE Conditions of Contract is an example of the first of these. The arbitration agreement will often contain terms setting out the powers which the arbitrator may exercise and it will usually state how the arbitrator is to be appointed. Alternatively, the arbitrator's powers may be defined or qualified in the contract of appointment, which may also set out the terms on which the arbitrator is to act, including his right to payment.

**The three essentials**

Parties in dispute sometimes attempt to set up their own informal arbitration without recourse to lawyers or to formal appointments. Provided that three essential elements are present, such arrangements may well suffice. The status in law of the tribunal so created does not depend on formality, either in the appointment of the arbitrator or in the conduct of the arbitration. Indeed, it is possible to create a tribunal which will produce a proper arbitration despite the parties' intention to avoid a legally binding result. Conversely, an intended arbitration may prove not to be an arbitration at all, and the loser may not be bound by the result.

To achieve a valid arbitration, three elements must be present. These are

(*a*)  a dispute between the parties must exist;

(*b*)  the parties must agree to refer the dispute for decision by a third party; and

(*c*)  the parties must be legally bound by the result.

Thus, for example, the adjudication of a dispute on pay or conditions between an employer and a trades union representing his employees is not a true arbitration (despite the misuse of that term in popular usage) since the "award" of the adjudicator is not binding upon the trades union concerned. Similarly, an agreement to refer the valuation of a property to an outside expert in connection with the renewal of a lease will only result in an

---

[1]  This Clause has recently been revised: see Chapter 6.

arbitration if the parties have first disagreed on what that valuation should be. If the situation is that the parties do not know and want the expert to decide for them, then the expert is likely to be a valuer and not an arbitrator, even though the parties may be bound by the result.

An arbitration under Clause 66 of the ICE Conditions of Contract satisfies the three requirements, since it arises from the Engineer's formal decision on some matter referred to him under Clause 66(1) and a subsequent challenge thereto by one of the parties. Clause 66 is itself an agreement to refer the matter to a third party and the arbitrator's award is thereby made final and binding upon the parties.[1]

### The reference to arbitration

Even though a valid arbitration agreement may already exist and a dispute may have arisen, one of the parties must still take some formal step to initiate the proceedings. This is usually known compendiously as "the reference" but it may consist of a number of different stages. First, it may be necessary to give the other party formal notice of the dispute. Secondly, steps must be taken to nominate a specific individual as arbitrator, which in itself may take place in several stages. Finally, the chosen arbitrator must accept the appointment. The second and third stages can be taken before a dispute has arisen, either by naming the arbitrator in the original contract (although this is unusual), or by appointing an arbitrator to determine all disputes whether already in existence or arising thereafter. Where an appointment is needed a party may put forward his nomination at the same time as he gives notice of the dispute.

### Notice of the dispute

Under the ICE Conditions of Contract a dispute must first be referred to the Engineer for his formal decision under Clause 66(1). The Clause then provides that

"Such decisions shall be final and binding upon the Contractor and the Employer unless either of them shall require that the matter be referred to arbitration as hereinafter provided ... the Employer or Contractor may within three calendar months after receiving notice of such decision or within three calendar months after the said period of three months[2] ... require that the matter shall be referred to ... arbitration. ..."

The effect of these words may be vital to either or both parties. A decision deemed to be final and binding in this way cannot be re-opened by the Court[3] and, if neither party requires the matter to be referred to arbitration before the period of three months provided for that purpose, the right to do so will also be lost, leaving the dissatisfied party with no remedy whatsoever.

---

[1] It is also in the tribunal's own interest that he be a true arbitrator as here defined. Should one of the three elements be wanting, he will be a mere conciliator or valuer and, as such, liable in negligence to the parties or to any third party suffering damage by his actions. A true arbitrator, on the other hand, will in general enjoy immunity from suit analogous to that of a Judge.

[2] i.e. the three months within which the Engineer ought to give his decision.

[3] *Kaye* v. *Hosier & Dickinson* [1972] 1 W.L.R. 146.

The Contract provides no exceptions to this rule. However, it seems that, even if notice to refer the Engineer's decision to arbitration is not given in time, the decision can be challenged if it contains a patent error[1] or embodies a point of law.[2] Alternatively, the time for reference to arbitration may be extended by the Court under s. 27 of the Arbitration Act 1950 if "... undue hardship would otherwise be caused ...". But "undue hardship" means more than the loss of a potential claim and the Court will not lightly grant an extension of time under the Section.[3]

The above matters apply when the Engineer has given a decision under Clause 66(1) and the parties have failed to challenge it. But Clause 66(1) also appears to provide the same result where the Engineer fails to give any decision within the three months provided for that purpose and notice of arbitration is not given within a further three months. This raises several issues. First, it may be argued that if no decision is given the requirement for a decision as a condition precedent to arbitration can no longer apply and the parties should be able to proceed to arbitration at any time subsequently. Secondly, what is the position if the Engineer does give a decision, but after the three months' period has expired? A decision which fails to comply precisely with the requirements of the Clause ought not in principle to be a bar to further proceedings, but, on the other hand, is the second three months' period to run in that event from the date of the decision or from the expiry of the first three months' period? The safest course is to give notice of arbitration as soon as the first three months' period has expired without a decision.

It follows that it is important for the parties to know whether a decision under Clause 66(1) has in fact been given by the Engineer.[4] He will, of course, have given many decisions on various matters during the course of the Works. But, unless the matter in question has been referred to him for decision under Clause 66(1) as distinct from any other provision of the Contract, time will not run. In particular, it is not open to the Engineer to stipulate that a particular decision is given under Clause 66(1) unless the matter has been so referred, as the effect of such action would otherwise be to deprive a party of his rights under the Contract. It is thought that if a party can show that he has failed to challenge a decision within the time allowed because of a genuine misunderstanding about its status, the Court would be likely to exercise its power to grant an extension of time under s. 27 of the Arbitration Act 1950.

## Limitation Acts

Another important aspect of giving notice of arbitration is that it operates as the deemed commencement of proceedings for the purposes of the Limitation Acts.[5] The notice is equivalent to the issue of a Writ in the High

---

[1]   i.e. an error "on the face" of the decision.

[2]   See Keating's *Building Contracts* (4th edn), p. 546.

[3]   *Liberian Shipping Corp. "Pegasus"* v. *A. King & Sons Ltd.* [1967] 2 Q.B. 86, and Keating, *op. cit.*, p. 546.

[4]   *Monmouth County Council* v. *Costelloe & Kemple* [1965] 63 L.G.R. 429; 5 B.L.R. 83.

[5]   Limitation Act 1980, s. 34. The requirement is for "notice requiring [the other party] to appoint an arbitrator or to agree to the appointment of an arbitrator". See also s. 29(2) of the Arbitration Act 1950.

Court. If a party wishes to proceed in the High Court but the possibility exists that there may be an application for a stay of proceedings,[1] a "protective" notice of arbitration may be given which will operate irrespective of the actual commencement of proceedings in Court. The fact that a party applying for a stay of proceedings may intend to rely on a limitation defence when arbitration proceedings are commenced is not a ground for refusing to stay the proceedings in Court.[2]

## Nomination of the arbitrator

The procedure for obtaining the nomination of an arbitrator is covered in detail in the new Procedure.[3] The parties may, and frequently do, agree upon their own choice of arbitrator. Once an individual is nominated he must accept the appointment before he becomes the arbitrator, and it is not unknown for the nominee to fail to agree terms with the parties. Detailed notes on this and other problems, together with those which arise if the parties cannot agree on their own choice of arbitrator, are given in the commentary.[4]

## Two or more arbitrators

Both the new Procedure and Clause 66 envisage the appointment of a sole arbitrator and most civil engineering arbitrations are of this form. However, although unusual, other forms of tribunal are possible and may be appropriate in particular circumstances. This can be achieved either by an appropriate amendment to Clause 66 when the original Contract is made or by entering into a separate agreement when notice of arbitration is given.

The most useful form of multiple tribunal for civil engineering disputes is where each party appoints his own arbitrator. Such two-man tribunals are well known in maritime arbitration and need no elaboration here.[5] The main advantages are that disputes over appointment are avoided, and the choice of two arbitrators with differing (but relevant) expertise can minimise the need to adduce expert evidence.[6]

However, should the two arbitrators fail to agree, English law requires them to appoint an umpire. This can give rise to its own problems[7] and can be costly, but if the parties also adopt the maritime practice of being represented before the umpire by their respective erstwhile arbitrators final resolution of the disputes will be facilitated because the ex-arbitrator advocates will be well seized of the evidence and arguments.

If the parties wish to avoid the problems which can arise if two arbitrators disagree, they could each appoint their own arbitrator as before and then

---

[1] S. 4 of the Arbitration Act 1950.
[2] *Bruce* v. *Strong* [1951] 2 K.B. 447.
[3] See p. 53, *post.*
[4] See p. 54, *post.*
[5] See *Russell on Arbitration* (20th edn), p. 124 *et seq.*, or Mustill & Boyd's *Commercial Arbitration*, p. 151.
[6] The saving in the cost of expert evidence should more than cover any increase in the tribunal's fees.
[7] See, for example, Gibson-Jarvie & Hawker's *Guide to Commercial Arbitration under the 1979 Act*, p. 40.

either agree on a Chairman or direct the arbitrators to appoint one.[1] The resulting triumvirate should then be able to bring in a majority award. However, in the event that each of the three arbitrators holds a different view there would still be no effective majority. It would therefore be prudent for the Chairman to be given a casting vote so that a final award is obtainable no matter what the circumstances.

Other forms of multiple tribunal can be devised but are unlikely to be found useful in connection with civil engineering arbitration.

## Interim arbitration

Clause 66(1) of the ICE Conditions of Contract provides that no steps shall be taken in the reference until after completion or alleged completion of the Works unless both parties agree in writing or the dispute is one which falls within the scope of Sub-Clause (2). The exceptions under the Sub-Clause cover disputes under Clause 12 (adverse physical conditions or artificial obstructions) or Clause 63 (forfeiture) or the withholding by the Engineer of any certificate or any portion of retention money. The inclusion of disputes about the withholding of certificates is a wide exception and may cover certificates under any Clause of the Contract which, on one view of the question, ought to have been given.[2]

The right to immediate or "interim" arbitration will be particularly important where a decision may have an important bearing on the manner in which the remainder of the Works are to be constructed. This is obviously the case where there is a dispute as to the validity of forfeiture. Equally, where a substantial claim arises under Clause 12 at an early stage of the Works, each party needs to know whether the claim is allowable so that appropriate and timely action can be taken to minimise any increase in the cost of the Works. Again, an interim arbitration under Clause 12 will often be commenced while a substantial portion of the work below ground remains to be done. An early decision will clearly be particularly useful to the Employer and the Engineer in considering whether the design of the Works or the methods to be used in their construction should be altered.[3]

A full discussion of the procedures to be followed in conducting interim arbitrations is contained in the commentary.[4]

## The function of the Engineer

Under the ICE Conditions of Contract the Engineer is appointed by the Employer and is empowered to give instructions, to control the Works and

---

[1] This form of tribunal could formerly be confused under English law with the two-arbitrator-and-umpire pattern. This has now been rectified by s. 6(2) of the Arbitration Act 1979.

[2] See *A. E. Farr* v. *Ministry of Transport* [1960] 1 W.L.R. 956, but see also *Costain International* v. *A.G. of Hong Kong* [1983] 23 B.L.R. 48.

[3] In such cases a decision on liability only may suffice, issues of quantum being adjourned until after the Works have been completed.

[4] See Chapter 10.

to make decisions which under the terms of the Main Contract[1] are binding upon Employer and Contractor alike unless and until rescinded or varied by an arbitrator. He is not a party to the Contract and is required to "hold the balance" and to act fairly between the parties. At the same time he acts as the Employer's agent or representative, empowered to act on the Employer's behalf, and receives his remuneration from the Employer. Where the Employer is a public sector body or Authority the Engineer is also often a full-time employee of the Employer.

Instructions and decisions given by the Engineer during the course of the Contract may well give rise to disputes between the Employer and the Contractor. Again, where the Engineer has himself designed the Works or is responsible for producing working drawings, inadequacies in the former or lateness in delivering the latter may well give rise to claims. As has already been stated, before such disputes can be taken to arbitration they must first be referred back to the Engineer for review.[2]

There is no time limit for this referral. The Contractor may therefore accept the Engineer's initial rejection of his claims for the time being. He may await further developments, such as the collection of additional evidence or records, or the outcome of other or alternative claims. Such inaction will not prejudice the final outcome, as the Engineer's jurisdiction to deal with claims at first instance (i.e. other than under Clause 66(1)) extends at least up to the date of the Final Certificate.

From the Engineer's point of view, when a matter is referred to him under Clause 66 he should attempt to give a decision which will assist the parties. No procedure for arriving at a Clause 66 decision is laid down, but the Engineer should do his best to make a fresh and genuine assessment of the dispute, despite the fact that it will often have arisen out of some earlier decision of his own. He is now no longer dealing with a "claim" submitted to him under some other clause of the Contract, but with a "dispute" between the parties to the Contract. For example, he may have rejected a claim on the ground that he was not satisfied that the claim had been made out. But when it returns to him for a Clause 66 decision he must re-assess the claim on its merits and come to a fair and balanced decision. If he feels able also to state his reasons, so much the better, as this cannot fail to assist the parties when they come to consider whether or not they wish the matter to be referred to arbitration.

While the Engineer has a general duty to act fairly and impartially and to hold the balance between the parties in his administration of the Contract, this does not make him an arbitrator. His functions under Clause 66(1) have sometimes been referred to as "quasi-arbitral", but to think of them in those terms can be misleading. Thus, unlike a true arbitrator, the Engineer is not bound by the rules of natural justice, nor is he bound to hear or receive submissions from both parties before reaching his decisions (although he may often be well advised to do so). He should, nevertheless, be careful to

---

[1] This is not necessarily so in the case of a sub-contract, but there the Main Contractor usually has power to pass on the Engineer's instructions, so the practical effect will be broadly the same. For a general statement of the Engineer's duties see the check list in Appendix VIII.

[2] See p. 6, *ante.*

avoid the appearance of acting merely as a "rubber stamp". This is particularly important when either or both of the parties employ auditors or other outside experts to monitor progress, or where the Employer's internal organisation is such as to bring pressure to bear upon the Engineer or his staff.[1]

In operating the Clause 66(1) procedures the Engineer may be required to adjudicate matters for which it is alleged that he or his staff have been to blame. But, while it may be difficult for him wholly to detach himself or to ignore his own possible liability in such cases, he must still strive to maintain his impartiality.

Finally, once arbitration has commenced, the Engineer may and often will be called upon to give evidence before the arbitrator. Both the ICE Conditions of Contract and the ICE Arbitration Procedure provide for this.[2] Thus, in reaching his decision under Clause 66 he should do so in such a manner that he will if necessary be able to explain and justify his position in the witness box. In addition, the Employer will usually rely heavily on the Engineer's advice and guidance in formulating his case.

---

[1]  The correct relationship between Engineer and auditor is set out in the recent pamphlet *Joint Statement: Engineers and Auditors* by the Institution of Civil Engineers and the Chartered Institute of Public Finance and Accountancy.

[2]  Clause 66(1)(b) of the ICE 1973 Conditions of Contract; Clause 66(6) of the ICE 1985 Conditions of Contract; Rule 8.2 of the Procedure.

*Chapter 3*

# APPOINTMENT TO AWARD

**Use of the ICE Arbitration Procedure (1983)**

The circumstances in which the ICE Arbitration Procedure may be applied to an arbitration under the ICE Conditions of Contract are set out in Clause 66 of the Conditions and in Rule 26 of the Procedure. It may also be applied to arbitrations under the FIDIC Conditions or the "Blue Form"[1] or, indeed, to any kind of arbitration if the parties so agree. Where the parties so agree before the arbitrator is appointed he will be bound by that agreement, but in all other cases the arbitrator's agreement should normally be obtained.[2]

The effect of Clause 66 and Rule 26 is that the ICE Arbitration Procedure will become binding in the following circumstances:

    (*a*) the parties may expressly agree to adopt the Procedure before appointing an arbitrator;

    (*b*) an arbitrator appointed by agreement may require the parties to agree to the Procedure (so that if they do not he may decline the appointment);[3]

    (*c*) upon a Presidential appointment, the Procedure may be directed to apply, which will bind both the parties and the arbitrator;[4]

    (*d*) a Presidential appointee, where the president has not directed the application of the Procedure, may himself require the parties to agree to it;

    (*e*) the parties may agree to the Procedure at any time after the appointment of an arbitrator, subject to his consent.

It is anticipated that, where the parties do not of their own motion agree to the Procedure, Presidential appointments will contain a direction that it shall apply,[5] and that any arbitrator appointed by agreement from the ICE List of Arbitrators will normally stipulate that the parties accept the Procedure as a condition of his appointment.

---

[1] The Form of Sub-Contract issued by the Federation of Civil Engineering Contractors (the "FCEC Form"). A new version was issued in September, 1984.

[2] Since it may be argued that, once validly appointed, the arbitrator is, by s. 12(1) of the Arbitration Act 1950, wholly in charge of procedure and it is then too late for the parties to change his authority by a subsequent agreement between themselves.

[3] Rule 26.1(c).

[4] Clause 66(1) and Rule 26.1(b).

[5] Within the Institution both the Arbitration Advisory Board and the Advisory Committee on Contract Administration and Law have recommended that the President should always include such a direction unless there are pressing reasons to refrain. See also the new Clause 66 (Chapter 6).

## The arbitrator's power to control the proceedings

Unless the parties have agreed before his appointment that a particular procedure shall apply, the arbitrator has a wide discretion both at common law and under s. 12 of the Arbitration Act 1950 to direct and control the proceedings.[1] Provided that he observes the rules of natural justice[2] he may conduct the enquiry as he sees fit,[3] even including in appropriate circumstances a right to refuse to hear Counsel.[4] An arbitrator may also hear evidence *de bene esse*,[5] and is not to be deemed incapable of disregarding matters which he may subsequently find inadmissible.[5]

Many of the powers set out in the new Procedure are already available to an arbitrator by statute or under common law. To these have been added a number of other powers which would normally be exercised by the High Court in relation to an action in that Court. Taken as a whole, these powers are remarkably wide, but no more so than those contained in the arbitration rules of many other bodies.[6] There is in principle no objection to an arbitrator's powers being enlarged in this way and, while the Court does have jurisdiction to deal with complaints that particular rules of procedure may be inconsistent with the basic requirements of arbitration law, the scope for objection is narrow.[7]

Powers already available to an arbitrator are included in the new Procedure, first, to achieve a comprehensive code and, secondly, to encourage arbitrators to use all the powers available to them. Experience indicates that many arbitrators seldom make use of many of their existing powers to control the proceedings. It is to be hoped that, in future, engineering arbitrators will take charge of and direct arbitrations with the same concern for efficiency and economy as they would apply to the management of their Clients' affairs in the normal course of business. For this to be achieved in practice, arbitrators must understand the full extent of their powers and must be prepared to apply them robustly. The ICE will continue to play its part through the training and examination of engineers in arbitration practice and theory. For better or worse, the day of the amateur arbitrator, however gifted, is long past.

## Statutory powers

Existing statutory powers affecting arbitrations fall into three groups and are largely contained in s. 12 of the 1950 Act and s. 5 of the 1979 Act.[8] The first group covers powers given to an arbitrator *per se;* the second comprises powers or actions which may be taken by the High Court in support of arbitration; the third are those additional powers which the High Court

---

[1]   See *Bremer Vulkan* v. *South India Shipping* [1981] A.C. 909, *per* Lord Diplock at pp. 983, 985 and Lord Scarman at p. 999.

[2]   See p. 19, *post*; also Mustill & Boyd's *Commercial Arbitration*, p. 252.

[3]   *Tillam* v. *Copp* (1847) 5 C.B. 211.

[4]   *Macqueen* v. *Nottingham* (1861) 9 C.B. 792.

[5]   *F. C. Whitley & Sons* v. *Clwyd C. C.* [1983] 22 B.L.R. 48.

[6]   See, for example, the *Rules of the International Court of Arbitration* (London).

[7]   For example, the Court will not intervene on the ground that the rules complained of permit the use of evidence normally considered inadmissible, or because legal representation is excluded (*Henry Bath* v. *Birgby Products* [1962] 1 Lloyds' Rep. 389).

[8]   See Appendix I.

may give to an arbitrator on request.

The first three subsections of s. 12 apply unless a contrary intention is expressed in the arbitration agreement.[1] By these subsections the arbitrator has power to take evidence on oath or affirmation and to administer oaths to or take affirmations of the parties and their witnesses. It is generally of advantage to take evidence on oath, if only because the act of being sworn helps to draw attention to the serious nature of the proceedings.

Again, subject to the proviso, s. 12(1) requires the parties to the reference and all persons claiming through them to produce before the arbitrator all documents within their possession or power which may be required or called for. Production of documents is expressly covered in the new Procedure.[2] The subsection also requires that the parties ". . . shall . . . do all other things which during the proceedings . . . the arbitrator . . . may require . . .". This requirement is very wide, such that it could be said to cover almost anything which the arbitrator might order. The provision has not been used by arbitrators in the past to any great extent in directing the course of proceedings. It does, however, give ample support to the vesting in arbitrators of wide specific powers.

The remainder of s. 12 empowers the High Court to assist the parties or the arbitrator by compelling witnesses to attend before the arbitrator under subpoena.[3] The Court is also given by s. 12(6) ". . . the same power of making orders . . . as it has for the purpose of and in relation to an action or matter in the High Court . . ." in respect of security for costs, discovery of documents, interrogatories, the taking of evidence by affidavit or on commission, interim injunctions and other "precautionary" remedies. Some of these powers are given to the arbitrator by the new ICE Procedure.[4] S. 12(6) is, however, subject to a proviso that the powers it gives the Court are not to prejudice any power which may be vested in the arbitrator of making similar orders himself.

Finally, s. 5 of the 1979 Act empowers the High Court to make an order extending the arbitrator's powers if any party to the arbitration fails to comply with any order made by the arbitrator within the time specified in that order or, if no time is specified, within a reasonable time. If there has been no such failure the High Court can do nothing, and the arbitrator must enter upon the reference and strive to make progress without the Court's help. But once a party is in default either the arbitrator himself or the other party to the reference may apply to the Court for an appropriate order, and the Court may then grant to the arbitrator (subject to any conditions which the Court may see fit to apply) power to continue with the reference ". . . in default of appearance or of any other act by one of the parties in like manner as a Judge of the High Court might continue with proceedings in that court where a party fails to comply with an order of that court or a requirement of rules of court . . .". By virtue of s. 5(5) the parties cannot agree to exclude

---

[1]  If the contrary intention is not expressly included in the arbitration agreement these powers vest in the arbitrator. Thus the parties cannot later agree to exclude them, and certainly not after the arbitrator's appointment has been completed (and see p. 56 *et seq., post*).
[2]  Rules 11.2, 13.1, 16.3 etc.
[3]  S. 12(4); see also s. 12(5).
[4]  Rule 6.1.

the High Court's power to extend the arbitrator's powers in this way, but such extension is not to derogate from any other powers he may have.

While these three groups of statutory powers overlap each other and also the arbitrator's common law powers, their characteristics are different. Thus the first group are powers which vest automatically in the arbitrator unless the parties agree that they shall not. The second group are powers which the High Court can itself use to assist the arbitration. Conversely, the third group are powers which the High Court can hand down to the arbitrator for him to use at his own discretion.

It will be seen that the powers given to arbitrators are frequently based on or derived from powers available to the High Court in litigation. High Court rules and procedures are set out in the Rules of the Supreme Court (RSC) which are republished periodically with extensive notes and commentaries in the Supreme Court Practice (commonly known as the "White Book"). This volume will often be of great assistance to arbitrators. Nevertheless, the Supreme Court Rules do not bind arbitrators and it is often appropriate to use other procedures. This is because there are fundamental differences between arbitration and litigation. One such difference arises in that the Court will wait for the parties themselves to invoke its assistance by issuing a summons or motion; if the parties stay quiescent the Court will seldom intervene of its own motion. But in arbitration the tribunal can and often should take positive action to progress the reference[1] whether the parties wish it or not. Thus the practice of some legal advocates in trying to persuade the arbitrator to follow High Court Rules in all circumstances should in general be resisted.[2]

## Interlocutory matters

The procedures which may be employed from the arbitrator's appointment to the commencement of the Hearing are covered in detail in the commentary[3] to Part C of the ICE Arbitration Procedure. However, a few of the more important points are discussed here because of the profound influence they can have in minimising delay and expense.

## The preliminary meeting

Rule 10.1 makes a preliminary meeting usually mandatory upon the arbitrator and the parties alike and requires it to be held as soon as possible after the arbitrator's appointment is completed. Opinions among practitioners are often sharply divided on the desirability of holding any meeting so early in the reference. Some see such a meeting as an opportunity to become acquainted with the arbitrator and the parties' representatives, while others consider it to be an expensive waste of time. It is true that at this stage the arbitrator will know little of the issues between the parties and may on that account have difficulty in knowing what directions are most appropriate. On the other hand, particularly where the parties have retained

---

[1]  See *Bremer Vulkan* v. *South India Shipping* [1981] A.C. 909 *per* Lord Diplock at p. 984.

[2]  Where the arbitrator decides, on a particular point, to follow the "White Book", it may be appropriate to make an order under s. 12(1) *by analogy with* the appropriate RSC procedure.

[3]  See Chapter 8.

Solicitors unfamiliar with arbitration, time and cost may be saved if the arbitrator's views and intentions are made known as early as possible, so that undue emphasis is not given to matters which may later prove to be of little or no importance to the real issues.

A timely preliminary meeting should thus be the rule rather than the exception. This will give the arbitrator an early opportunity to enlarge his knowledge of the matters with which he is to deal, and to guide and inform the parties and their representatives on how he wishes them to achieve most progress at least cost. The matters which need to be discussed at the preliminary meeting are considered later, in detail.[1] The meeting may also be used to raise any other matters which need to be settled. Thus, where the arbitrator's fees have not already been settled he may find it convenient to deal with them in open hearing rather than in protracted correspondence. The arbitrator may also use this opportunity to enquire whether the parties have entered or intend to enter into an exclusion agreement under s. 3 of the Arbitration Act 1979.[2] And, in general, the arbitrator should try to discover, if necessary by direct questioning, the nature of the disputes or differences to be brought before him, how they have arisen and what are likely to be the real matters at issue.

Finally, there will always be some cases where a preliminary meeting is inappropriate, for instance, where one of the parties is resident overseas. In such cases Rule 10.3 allows the parties to agree directions and to submit them to the arbitrator, who may then approve them without convening a preliminary meeting. But the parties cannot themselves choose to dispense with a preliminary meeting unless the arbitrator so agrees.

## Pleadings or statements of case

It often happens that one or both parties have prepared detailed technical submissions when referring the matters at issue to the Engineer under ICE Clause 66(1). The best and most efficient means of submitting such matters to the arbitrator may be simply to add a title page or back sheet to the Clause 66(1) papers. If, instead, the original papers are passed to a Solicitor who then instructs Counsel to draft formal pleadings, a great deal of time and cost will be expended. Moreover, the issues which eventually reach the arbitrator may differ from those which were put to the Engineer.

It is prudent to have the Clause 66(1) papers checked by lawyers if matters of law are likely to arise, and this examination may well throw up further issues.[3] But, should further issues be found, they can easily be covered by an addendum to the original papers, and the temptation to recast the whole case should in most cases be resisted. That is not to say that some editing and pruning of the original submission should not be attempted. But the wholesale translation of the original text into a new form is to be avoided.

Another feature to be avoided is the proliferation of demands for "further and better particulars". If the original pleading or statement has been

---

[1] See p. 63, *post.*

[2] See p. 42, *post.*

[3] Clause 66(1) expressly allows for this by providing that ". . . neither party shall be limited in the proceedings before such arbitrator to the evidence or arguments put before the Engineer for the purpose of obtaining his decision . . .".

properly prepared, no further particulars should be necessary to enable the other party to know the case he has to meet and to prepare his own pleading or statement in reply. Requests for particulars are sometimes regarded by arbitrators, not without some justification, as a means of causing delay, or as attempts at "fishing" for the evidence which the other side will adduce as proof of his case. More insidious is the request intended to embarrass rather than to inform. Arbitrators should be alert to such devices and should be firm in suppressing them. It may well be expedient on occasion to direct that no requests for further and better particulars shall be served without first applying to the arbitrator for leave to do so. The arbitrator should then examine and, if necessary, ask for elucidation of the draft request and should only approve those parts which seem to him to be necessary.

## Procedural meetings

Unlike the preliminary meeting, which Rule 10 makes virtually mandatory, procedural meetings are to be called only when the arbitrator deems them to be necessary. It is curious that parties or their advisers may at one stage oppose the holding of any meetings and at another stage insist that one be convened. The arbitrator must try to hold the balance between what he deems to be necessary and what one or even both parties may wish to occur. Thus, while Rule 12.1 empowers the arbitrator to call a procedural meeting, Rule 12.2 allows him to refuse a request for such a meeting and to deal with the subject matter of the request in some other way.

A recent development in the Official Referees' Court is worthy of note. This is the convening of what is in effect a final procedural meeting shortly before Trial to discuss procedure at the Trial itself. Some arbitrators have used this device and have found that useful savings in time and cost at Hearing can thereby be achieved. However, interlocutory meetings are in general attended only by Solicitors or, at the most, junior Counsel, even where it is intended to retain leading Counsel for the Hearing. If a "pre-Hearing" procedural meeting is to achieve its objectives, it is vital that those who are to conduct the Hearing should attend. No purpose will be served if Solicitors or junior Counsel agree on one procedure, only to find at the Hearing that leading Counsel take a different view.

## Summary awards

The topic of summary awards is fully covered in the commentary.[1] The procedure is new to arbitration but familiar in the High Court. If it is properly used, it should commend arbitration to those who consider that procedural delays constitute a form of economic harassment. The procedure should also encourage the settlement of disputes by disposing of matters on which there is little serious disagreement, thereby reducing to a minimum the amount of money at issue.

## The Hearing

The Hearing, again, is fully covered in the commentary.[2] The following

---

[1]   See p. 71, *post.*
[2]   See p. 73, *post.*

notes therefore deal with the arbitrator's general duties in conducting the Hearing.

An arbitrator has a duty to hear the parties and to make an adequate note of the proceedings for the purpose of his award and the giving of reasons. But, contrary to popular belief, the arbitrator need not remain silent during the Hearing. He will invariably assist the parties by indicating what is in his mind. If he has missed some essential point the advocates can make good the omission. If he is inclined to decide in favour of one party, the other will have an opportunity to make sure that his case has not been overlooked.

The arbitrator should not express any view until he is in a position to grasp the issues. But he need not wait until he has heard both sides. If an argument seems, on its face, to be correct, the arbitrator may helpfully so indicate. This will avoid repetition. It is often helpful to deal with submissions by asking the parties in turn what they have to say on a particular point. The overriding principle is that neither party should be deprived of the right of advancing any argument. This does not mean, however, that they may advance their arguments at any time or in any sequence that they choose. It is a matter for the arbitrator's judgement, bearing in mind the views of the advocates and the interests of the parties, how he directs the course of argument or submission. It is also helpful, before passing from an issue, for the arbitrator to ask the parties whether there is anything further that they wish to say on that matter.

Clearly, the arbitrator must seek to follow and to understand the evidence and arguments put before him. He should also seek to understand their relevance to the issues to be determined. In both respects the arbitrator is entitled to and should, where appropriate, ask questions of witnesses and advocates to ensure that he has a proper understanding of the case.

The duty of an arbitrator may be summarised as requiring him to comply with the generally accepted rules of "natural justice". There is no comprehensive or fixed definition of natural justice. But it has been suggested that it requires the arbitrator

(*a*) to act fairly between the parties, without bias;
(*b*) to be and be seen to be impartial;
(*c*) to pay and be seen to pay careful attention to any evidence or arguments; and
(*d*) to keep the parties fully informed of what he is doing and proposes to do.[1]

He must also be careful to hear both parties and should not normally take evidence or hear addresses from one party without the other party's being present.

---

[1] Mustill & Boyd's *Commercial Arbitration*, p. 252.

# Chapter 4

# THE AWARD AND AFTER

Once the Hearing is at an end the arbitrator will consider the evidence and the submissions of the parties. He will then make and publish his award together, where appropriate, with reasons.[1] The parties and their representatives have nothing further to do at this stage of the proceedings. However, it may sometimes happen that, after the Hearing has closed, one party may wish to adduce further evidence or to address the arbitrator further on certain issues. Or a party may feel that the arbitrator is likely to find in favour of his opponent and for this reason may seek to have the Hearing re-opened.

The arbitrator must be on his guard against unmeritorious attempts to re-open issues or to prolong argument on matters which should have been dealt with in full at the Hearing. Nevertheless, where fresh evidence comes to light after the close of the Hearing and the party seeking to rely on it cannot reasonably be blamed for not introducing it earlier, or where a point material to the issues emerges only after the Hearing has closed,[2] the arbitrator can and probably should take it into account. However, the other party must be given an opportunity to deal with and to reply to any further submissions and, in the case of new evidence, to adduce evidence in refutation. Application to adduce further evidence or argument may be made by either party at any time up to the moment that the award is actually made.

### Time for making the award

No time limit for making the award is prescribed in Clause 66 nor, in general, does the new Procedure do so; save that, where the Short Procedure is adopted, the award must normally be made and published within one calendar month following the conclusion of the meeting under Rule 20.4.[3] The arbitrator may extend the time limit if the circumstances make this reasonable, but he is under a statutory duty "... to use all reasonable despatch in ... making an award ...".[4] An arbitrator who fails to do so may be removed by the High Court on the application of any party to the reference.[4] Conversely, if a time limit is prescribed and the parties do not agree to an extension, the Court can enlarge the time limit "... whether

---

[1]  See p. 79, *post*.
[2]  In a complex dispute important points may only be identified when the events at the Hearing are reviewed later at leisure.
[3]  Rule 20.5; see also Rule 24.3 and pp. 84 and 93, *post*.
[4]  Arbitration Act 1950, s. 13(3).

the time has expired or not . . .".[1] But the Court will be slow to exercise this power without good reason.

The arbitrator should thus make and publish his award as soon as he can reasonably do so but should not allow a desire for speed to impair the thoroughness of his consideration of the matters at issue. In a reasonably complicated matter which has been properly presented and argued at the Hearing it should normally be feasible to produce a fully reasoned award well within three months of the conclusion of the Hearing. In a straightforward and short issue the Court often gives judgment within a day or so of the Trial and, while an arbitrator cannot be expected to match the expertise of a professional Judge, there is no reason why he should not aim to do likewise.

### Form of the award

The award need not be in writing. But it is desirable that it should be, if only to avoid the difficulties likely to be encountered in proving the terms of an oral award. Similarly, there is no prescribed form for the award. Provided that all the essentials of a valid award are present, any convenient form may be used. Discussion of the various forms which may be followed can be found in the various standard works on arbitration.[2] However, it is suggested that some degree of formality in the layout of the award and in the words used is desirable. The effect of the award is usually to deprive one party of what he thought were his legal rights, and the award should accordingly display an appropriate degree of gravity.

### Essentials of a valid award

To be valid every award must:

(a) be *final* with respect to the matters it purports to determine, so that there is no need for further judicial enquiry thereon; a "final award" must therefore settle all the points raised under the arbitration agreement which have not been determined by some earlier "interim award";

(b) be *certain*: the parties must know exactly what decisions the arbitrator has taken and it must be clear what, if anything, is to be done to implement the award; if money is to be paid, the amount and currency must be specified[3] and the payor and payee identified; if action other than payment of money is ordered the action must similarly be fully described and the time for performance laid down;

(c) be *consistent*, that is, it must not be ambiguous or contradictory: care is particularly necessary where there are many different issues to be determined or where a final award follows several interim awards;

(d) be *possible*: the requirements of the award must be both physically and legally capable of performance.[4]

---

[1] Arbitration Act 1950, s. 13(2).

[2] See, for example, *Russell on Arbitration* (20th edn), ch. 16 and app. 9; see also Appendix VI.

[3] If the actual amount to be paid is not stated, it will suffice if the award contains directions enabling the parties to calculate the amount to be paid without ambiguity.

[4] An award is not incapable of performance merely because the party ordered to pay damages has insufficient resources to enable him to do so.

Taking the reference as a whole, the arbitrator will not normally become *functus officio* until he has determined all the matters put to him by the parties.[1] Conversely, an award must not purport to decide matters which have not been put to him. Thus, for example, if the parties have referred only issues of liability, an award which purports also to determine quantum will be bad. This may be cured if the valid part of the award can be separated from the part which is invalid, but if severance cannot be achieved the whole award will be void.

Neither the ICE Conditions of Contract nor the new Arbitration Procedure lays down any requirements on how the award is to be made or executed. But, in the event of the parties having written some such provision into the arbitration agreement, the terms must be observed to the letter or the award will be bad.

## Publishing the award

The arbitrator may if he wishes take legal advice on the form and content of his award and may even employ a lawyer[2] to draft it for him. But he has no power to delegate the making of his award. All the decisions and directions contained within it must be the arbitrator's own. Failure to observe this rule may lead to the award's being set aside. However, where before the award the parties reach a settlement of the disputes, they will often ask the arbitrator to record the terms of the settlement in an "agreed award". In such cases the award will clearly not be of the arbitrator's own devising and he may safely leave the drafting to the parties, save that, before he executes it, the prudent arbitrator will check both form and content to make sure that it will be valid in law. Such an award should also state or recite that it is made "by consent".

The usual requirement is that the arbitrator shall "make and publish" his award. There is probably no distinction of any practical importance between these words. An award is generally considered to be "published" as soon as it has been "made" by being drawn up and executed by the arbitrator. Execution is achieved when the arbitrator signs a written award at its foot in the presence of a witness, who should also sign it to that effect. Once executed, the award is ready to be delivered and generally takes effect from the date of execution.

Once "made and published" the award must be "published to the parties". The arbitrator does this by notifying the parties that his award has been made and published and is ready to be delivered or "taken up". The usual practice is that the arbitrator will inform the parties that his award is ready and may be taken up on payment of his fee, thereby exercising his lien to withhold the award until he is paid.[3] Once payment in full has been received, the arbitrator will send the original of the award (by registered post, recorded delivery or other secure means of despatch) to the party who

---

[1] It seems, however, that he will not always be bound to decide all such issues: see *Northern Regional Health Authority* v. *Derek Crouch* [1984] Q.B. 644.

[2] He should not, of course, rely on the parties' own lawyers but should find one who is wholly unconnected with any of the parties.

[3] For the procedure to be followed where the parties consider the arbitrator's fee to be unreasonable, see p. 28, *post*.

pays him and a duly certified copy[1] to the other party.

Time for applying to the High Court for leave to appeal or for the award to be set aside runs from the date that the award is made and published to the parties, that is when the arbitrator gives notice to the parties that the award may be taken up.[2]

The arbitrator becomes *functus officio* with respect to the matters determined by his award from the moment that he executes it. He is, indeed, no longer an arbitrator with respect to such matters and has no power to open up, reconsider or vary anything that he has done unless his award is set aside by the High Court and he is ordered to prepare another award, or the original award is referred back to him by the Court for reconsideration.[3] The only exception to this is where the award contains some clerical mistake or error arising from an accidental slip or omission, in which case the arbitrator has power under s. 17 of the 1950 Act to correct his award.

## Content of the award

There are three kinds of award and one award may contain elements of one or more kinds as the terms of the reference and the parties' submissions require. The three kinds are as follows.

  (a) *Declaratory awards.* Such awards merely find facts or state conclusions on points of law (as, for example, on liability) without stating what action the parties shall take as a result. Declaratory awards can usually be identified by the use of the introductory words "I find . . ." (facts) or "I hold . . ." (on matters of law)—or, for convenience of drafting, "I find and hold . . .".

  (b) *Payment awards.* These are the kind most frequently encountered, where one party is ordered to pay to the other some specified amount of money. The order to pay will usually be prefaced with the words "I award and direct . . ." and, if the award is a final award, the amount to be paid may be followed[4] by the words ". . . in full and final settlement of all matters in issue in this Arbitration". Payment awards will often also contain some declaratory matter.

  (c) *Performance awards.* By s. 15 of the 1950 Act an arbitrator is given the same power as the High Court to order specific performance of any contract.[5] This means that a party can be ordered to demolish

---

[1] Some arbitrators prepare and execute three (or more) copies of the award, one for each of the parties and one for the arbitrator. Where such copies are prepared by photocopying or otherwise reproducing an "original" it is nevertheless a courtesy to send the original to the party who pays rather than to retain it in the arbitrator's own file. Where the copies are produced by word processor or automatic typewriter all copies are originals and this point no longer arises.

[2] R.S.C. Ord. 73, r. 5; *The Archipelorgos* [1979] Lloyd's Rep. 289; *Selous Street Properties* v. *Oronel Fabrics* (1984) 270 E.G. 643.

[3] Under the 1950 Act. Where an appeal is allowed under s. 1 of the 1979 Act the Court will itself amend the award and the award as varied takes effect automatically as if the arbitrator had himself made it in that form (s. 1(8)).

[4] But not always. A final award will be deemed to be so whether express words are used or not.

[5] But not contracts relating to land or any interest in land (s. 15 of the 1950 Act).

defective work and to replace it with sound materials and workman-
ship, or to complete unfinished work, or in general to do any other
action or thing apart from paying money to the other party.[1] The
introductory words will be the same as for a payment award.
However, the arbitrator should be slow to order specific performance
even where one party expressly asks him to do so unless the acts or
things to be done are "self-regulating" in that the quality of the result
to be achieved can be measured against some objective standard of
comparison without the need for inspection or supervision. The
problem here is that, once the award has been made, the arbitrator
has no further powers to intervene. The alternative of leaving
assessment of the result to others (such as ordering the work to be
carried out "to the Engineer's satisfaction") carries with it the risk
that fresh disputes may arise about the standard eventually achieved.
Thus, unless it is a simple matter such as replacing a defective pump
with a sound one of the same type, or (in the case of an interim
arbitration) ordering the Employer to give the Contractor access to
the site, or ordering the Contractor to proceed with the Works, the
prudent arbitrator will usually substitute[2] an award of damages, i.e.
a money payment to cover the estimated cost to the injured party of
putting the matter right himself.

All awards will usually include "recitals".[3] These are simply sentences
or paragraphs setting out the background to the arbitration, citing the
source of the arbitrator's powers and recording any Hearings or appear-
ances. Recitals cannot affect the operative part of the award but may be of
use in its interpretation.[4] However, they do answer some of the questions
which the Court will ask before granting an application to enforce the
award. The point where recitals end and the operative part begins will
usually be marked by formal words such as "Now I the said John Smith do
hereby make and publish this my Award . . .".[5]

## Costs

Having come to a decision on the matters at issue the arbitrator must[6]
deal in his award with the costs of the parties and with his own costs. The
latter are sometimes called the "costs of the award" and the former the
"costs of the reference", but costs in the reference are also often taken to
include the costs of the award. These matters may be included in the award
itself, which will then become a final award (whether or not it bears that or

---

[1] But an order for a named party to pay a third party is an order for specific performance and
not an award of damages.

[2] As in the High Court, specific performance is a remedy which is at the arbitrator's
discretion and cannot be claimed by any party as of right. It is always proper for the tribunal
to substitute an order for payment of damages if considered appropriate.

[3] If full recitals are included in the first of a series of interim awards they may be omitted in
subsequent awards.

[4] Should the operative part of an award be ambiguous it may sometimes be permissible to
look at the recitals to resolve the ambiguity, but not otherwise. An ambiguity which cannot
be resolved renders the award void.

[5] See Appendix VI for examples of appropriate wording.

[6] Unless requested by the parties to leave the matter to a later award.

some other title) if there remain no further issues to be determined. Alternatively, costs may be left for further argument and determination in a subsequent award, in which case the first award will be an interim award whether or not it is entitled "final".

The parties can make their own arrangements as to costs. But an agreement that any party shall pay his own costs whatever the result will be void unless it is part of an agreement to submit to arbitration a dispute which has already arisen.[1] In the absence of such arrangements[2] the arbitrator must deal with costs in his award and, if he fails to do so, the award may be remitted back to him to rectify the omission.[3]

The general rule is that costs should follow the event, that is, that the successful party should recover his costs from the other party who shall also pay his own and the arbitrator's costs. This is so even where the successful party recovers only part of the relief claimed. The reason for this is that the losing party could have settled the matter earlier and by not settling has obliged his opponent to resort to arbitration. However, in construction arbitrations both parties often put in a number of claims and both may succeed to some extent. In such cases there may be grounds for departing from the rule that "the winner takes all". Again, where in the absence of a counterclaim a claimant succeeds on one claim and fails on another on which substantial costs (or time spent at the Hearing) were incurred, it may be appropriate to make a partial award of costs or, in an extreme case, even to award no costs. But where the arbitrator is minded to depart from the general rule on costs he should give or be prepared to give reasons for so doing.[4]

## Sealed and open offers

In litigation there is a procedure[5] by which a defendant may pay into Court a sum of money which he considers to be sufficient to cover the amount of damages likely to be recovered by the plaintiff together with any interest thereon. The plaintiff is notified of the amount paid in and he may then accept the payment in settlement of his claim together with his costs. The action is thereupon at an end. If the plaintiff does not accept the amount paid in, the action proceeds and the money paid in is retained in an account (where it earns a standard rate of interest) until the action is determined. If the plaintiff obtains judgment for more than the amount paid in, the Court will make the usual order on costs and the amount paid in will usually be ordered to be paid over to the plaintiff in part payment of the judgment. But if judgment is for less than (or only equal to) the amount paid in then the plaintiff must usually pay both his own and the defendant's costs incurred from the date of payment in to the date of judgment. The reason for this is that if the plaintiff had accepted the amount paid in he would have been no worse off, and would have avoided the need for either party to incur costs beyond the date of payment in.

---

[1]  S. 18(3) of the 1950 Act.

[2]  See, for example, Rules 21.2 and 23.2 of the new Procedure.

[3]  S. 18(4) of the 1950 Act.

[4]  For a full discussion of this topic see Mustill & Boyd's *Commercial Arbitration*, p. 348.

[5]  See R.S.C. Ord. 22.

There is an analogous procedure, well known in arbitration,[1] and which will be supported by the Courts where the intention is clear.[2] The respondent[3] makes an offer to the claimant either as a "sealed offer" or as an "open offer" which, if accepted, brings the arbitration to an end. This offer and acceptance must also cover payment of the arbitrator's fees and expenses, since both parties are liable for them. A sealed offer is by custom placed in a sealed envelope and handed to the arbitrator before or during the Hearing with the request that he opens it after he has prepared his award and before he makes any order on costs. An open offer is sent only to the claimant or his Solicitors. Such an offer is usually made on condition that it shall not be shown to the arbitrator until he has made his award,[4] in which case the parties must ask him to defer argument on costs until the award has been made. Since he will not know whether an offer has been made, the arbitrator should agree to such a request unless there is good reason for refusing.

This procedure could be criticised on the ground that the existence of a sealed offer might affect the arbitrator's view of the parties' cases. This is most unlikely. Indeed, many arbitrators are keen to impress upon the parties the desirability of settling their disputes without a Hearing and award and are likely to assume that offers are being made, whether or not a sealed offer is produced.[5] One solution is for the parties to hand to the arbitrator an envelope which contains either a sealed offer, if there is one, or otherwise a sheet of plain paper.[6]

A similar problem may arise during discovery of documents, when one party seeks to introduce correspondence between the parties which the other claims is privileged as part of "without prejudice" negotiations. If the parties cannot themselves resolve the matter it may be put to the arbitrator, who may decide to inspect the documents in question before giving his decision on the point of privilege. If he then decides that they should be excluded he must ignore their contents. It is seldom suggested that, because he has seen privileged documents, the arbitrator will be biased.[7]

A more serious criticism of the sealed offer procedure is that, unlike payment into Court, the offeror is not compelled to deposit money to back up his offer. If the offer is accepted there is thus no guarantee that there are resources to pay the money. However, the accepting party would not then be in any better position were he to continue with the arbitration and then seek to enforce the award.

## Taxation of costs

The usual order is that A shall pay B's costs in the arbitration ". . . to be taxed if not agreed . . .". This means that, if the parties cannot agree the

---

[1] *Tramountana Armadora* v. *Atlantic Shipping* [1978] 2 A.E.R. 870.
[2] *Archital Luxfer* v. *Henry Boot* [1981] 1 Lloyd's Rep. 642.
[3] Or the claimant with respect to a counterclaim.
[4] See further Keating's *Building Contracts* (4th edn), p. 274.
[5] In any event, an offer to settle is neither an admission of liability nor necessarily a true assessment of the value of the claim.
[6] See *Tramountana Armadora* v. *Atlantic Shipping* [1978] 1 *op. cit.*
[7] See *F. C. Whitley* v. *Clwyd C. C.* [1983] 22 B.L.R. 48.

amount that A is to pay to B, the matter is to be referred to a Taxing Master of the High Court for review, with the object of reducing excessive amounts and removing improper items. Alternatively, s. 18(1) of the 1950 Act empowers the arbitrator himself to tax and settle the parties' costs.[1] It is unusual for an arbitrator to agree to do so but, where the parties are not legally represented or are represented by non-legal advocates, there is much to be said for the arbitrator's agreeing to tax the costs.[2] He has the advantage of having himself been involved in the activities giving rise to the costs to be taxed, and the taxation is almost certain to be quicker than if the costs are referred to the Taxing Master. Again, although the arbitrator will be entitled to charge a fee for this service, the expense of employing professional cost draughtsmen will be saved, as formal "schedules of costs" will not normally be needed.

Where the arbitrator agrees to tax costs he should first make an interim award[3] determining all matters at issue, including which party is to bear the costs of the reference. Taxation may then follow, during which he may at his discretion invite the parties to address him thereon, and a final award dealing only with taxation will then bring the reference to a close.

Section 18(1) of the 1950 Act also empowers the arbitrator to tax and settle his own costs (i.e. the costs of the award) and he will almost invariably do so. When he does he will state the fact in his award.[4] If the parties feel that his costs are unreasonably high s. 19(1) of the 1950 Act allows them to pay the fees demanded into Court and to obtain an order that the award be delivered to the applicant party and that the arbitrator's fees shall be taxed by the Taxing Master. Thus the arbitrator's lien on his award is converted by the Court's order into security for his costs pending adjudication before the Taxing Master. S. 19(4) entitles the arbitrator to appear before the Taxing Master when his fees are reviewed and it seems that, if his own taxation is upheld, he will be entitled to recover the costs of so doing. This right of review, however, is not available to a party who has agreed in writing to the fees demanded.[5]

## Interest

The arbitrator should normally award interest on the sums recovered. If interest is not to be awarded the arbitrator should give reasons for his decision. Interest so awarded may run up to the date of the award but no

---

[1] Unless the award otherwise directs, costs in arbitrations are taxable "in the High Court," i.e. at High Court rates and scales (s. 18(2)). Like the Court itself, an arbitrator may award costs to be paid on a "party and party" basis or on the higher "common fund" basis—but not, it would seem, on the highest, or "indemnity", basis.

[2] See, for example, the article by D. St J. Sutton in *Arbitration*, vol. 50, no. 1 (Aug., 1984) at p. 45, refuting the view of Mustill & Boyd (*Commercial Arbitration*, pp. 354–355).

[3] Taxation after a final award may be unenforceable against the unsuccessful party as the arbitrator, being *functus officio*, would seem to lack jurisdiction under s. 18 of the 1950 Act.

[4] For example ". . . I further direct that X shall pay the costs of this my Award which I hereby tax and settle in the sum of £ . . .". See also Appendix VI.

[5] Arbitration Act 1950, s. 19(2). It seems that the right of review is only lost if the agreement is for an ascertained sum. A party agreeing a rate per hour may still challenge the number of hours to be charged.

later, as the right to interest after that date is provided by s. 20 of the Arbitration Act 1950.[1]

The rate of interest up to the award and the date from which it should run are matters for the arbitrator's discretion. He should ordinarily award interest at a reasonable commercial rate; the Courts usually work on a rate related to the relevant base rate of the claimant's bank.[2] The date from which interest starts should be based on when the respondent ought to have paid the money, subject to any special matters which the arbitrator may consider to be relevant.[3]

Interest is sometimes claimed as part of the loss or cost incurred[4] by the claimant or by way of damages.[5] In such cases, discretionary interest is an alternative to the interest so claimed and should not be awarded for the period covered by such part of the latter as may be allowed.

Where interest is not claimable under the Contract or as damages, there was formerly no power available to arbitrators to award interest only, where the principal sum was paid before the award.[6] Now, however, such a power is available under the new s. 19A of the Arbitration Act 1950[7] which allows the award of simple interest on any sum which is the subject of the reference but which is paid before the award. In order to be the subject of the reference the sum must be outstanding when the proceedings are commenced.

## Counterclaim and set-off

Where there is a counterclaim the respondent is treated as a claimant with respect to the matters so pleaded. Thus, for example, the claimant may make a sealed offer to settle the counterclaim and the principles applicable to the award of interest are reversed, subject, however, to the question of set-off. A cross-claim which operates as a set-off may be an effective defence to the claim, for example, by preventing the claimant from obtaining or enforcing an award without taking into account (by deducting) the cross-claim. But if the claimant's claim fails, a mere set-off will fail with it, whereas the respondent can proceed on a counterclaim as if he were a claimant with respect thereto.

Generally, a counterclaim or cross-claim may be used as a set-off provided that it is sufficiently connected with the claimant's claim, as when it arises out of the same Contract or the same subject matter. In such a case it may be appropriate to make an award of the balance only, together with interest thereon.

As to costs, the right of set-off does not entitle the party with the larger claim to be awarded all the costs.[8] The arbitrator must deal with costs on

---

[1]  *Rocco Giuseppe* v. *Tradax Export* [1984] 1 W.L.R. 742.
[2]  For example, orders for 1% over the base rate are sometimes made.
[3]  For a further discussion and authorities see Mustill & Boyd, *op. cit.*, p. 345.
[4]  *Minter* v. *WHTSO* [1980] 13 B.L.R. 1.
[5]  *Wadsworth* v. *Lydall* [1981] 1 W.L.R. 598; but'see also *President of India* v. *La Pintada* [1985] A.C. 104; [1984] 3 W.L.R. 10.
[6]  *President of India* v. *La Pintada* (*op. cit.*); see also *Tehno Impex* v. *Van Weelde* [1981] 1 Q.B. 648.
[7]  Added by the Administration of Justice Act 1982.
[8]  *Archital Luxfer* v. *Henry Boot* [1981] 1 Lloyd's Rep. 642.

both claim and counterclaim although it may be convenient, having considered the costs separately, to make a global order. This may result in a fractional award of costs in favour of one party, which is intended fairly to reflect the overall result.[1]

**Reasons**

Until 1979 arbitrators in England rarely if every gave reasons with their awards because of the risk that the award would be set aside for error of fact or law "on the face".[2] Where reasons were issued, as in maritime arbitrations, it was often the practice to do so in a separate document upon the parties' undertaking not to use it in litigation or for any contentious purpose. Another device was to give reasons separately after the time limit for challenging the award had expired. These devices were occasionally used in construction arbitrations.

The power to set an award aside for error of fact or law appearing on its face was abolished by the Arbitration Act 1979 and there is now no reason why, in appropriate circumstances, the giving of reasons should not be encouraged.

It was made clear both in Parliament during the 1979 Bill's passage in the House of Lords[3] and by the Commercial Court Judges on many occasions since then that the giving of reasoned awards (or awards with reasons) should become the rule rather than the exception. That is not to say that reasons must now be given in all cases[4] and an arbitrator can only be ordered to give reasons under s. 1(5) of the 1979 Act where the arbitration involves, or is alleged to involve, a point of law. Nor will reasons usually be appropriate in a "quality" arbitration where the arbitrator is asked to inspect the Works and to decide whether or not they have been constructed properly, using his own knowledge of engineering. But in a complex engineering dispute an award without reasons all too often leads to a sense of frustration. The parties have no indication which of the individual claims succeeded or failed, or to what extent, or why, and they therefore have no means of knowing what went wrong with their venture or how to avoid making the same mistakes on future works. In most cases a short account of the basis for the arbitrator's decision will be of value to the parties and may assist in preventing similar disputes from reaching arbitration. In any event, the fear that the giving of reasons would encourage applications for leave to appeal does not seem to have been borne out.

**Drafting reasons**

Before deciding whether and, if so, how to give reasons the arbitrator should first enquire why reasons are wanted. There are in general three possible purposes. The first arises when the award is to be enforced ·in a foreign country under whose domestic law an award without reasons is not

---

[1] See Keating's *Building Contracts* (4th edn), p. 276. ·
[2] This was a power inherent in the High Court and was repealed by s. 1(1) of the 1979 Act.
[3] *Hansard*, vol. 398 (15th Feb., 1979), col. 1465.
[4] See, for example, Lord Diplock's speech (*Hansard*, vol. 398 (15th Feb., 1979)) at col. 1476.

enforceable. The second has already been mentioned, namely that the parties wish to know what went wrong with their venture so that the same mistakes can be avoided in future. And the third is to acquaint the High Court with the circumstances of a dispute and the basis on which the arbitrator reached his decision.

Reasons for the parties' own information may take any convenient form. They may form part of the award itself, in which case they count as part of the recitals.[1] But if more than a page or two of typescript is needed it will usually be preferable to produce reasons as a separate document, either annexed to the award or published separately. There is much to be said for the latter course as the parties' lawyers and accountants will be interested primarily in the award itself whereas their engineers will be mainly concerned with the reasons. Again, in drafting reasons the arbitrator is usually writing for members of his own profession or for persons familiar with civil engineering. No standard form need be followed, and one similar in style and layout to an ordinary engineering report should suffice. For the rest, the document should be as short and concise as the subject matter allows, and written in good, plain English.[2]

Reasons on a point of law for the Court are quite different. Experienced Judges have on a number of occasions stated that all that is needed is that reasons should be expressed in ordinary language such as the arbitrator is accustomed to use in his ordinary, non-arbitral practice. This may well be so in "consumer" arbitrations and in the vast number of comparatively simple references handled in the City of London. But things are otherwise in the heavy construction industry.[3] The difference lies in the complexity of even a small construction project and the fact that, although the parties and the arbitrator may be equally familiar with these complexities and with the jargon of their own trades or professions, the Judge for whom reasons are intended will almost certainly not be. Thus, while technical terms should be used where appropriate, they should be defined in ordinary non-technical terms where they first appear. Similarly, processes which are common knowledge within the construction industry must be described as to a layman and their practical consequences and effects spelt out. Legal jargon should be avoided unless the arbitrator is quite sure what it means, as the Judge *will* be an expert in these matters and may otherwise assume that the arbitrator is equally proficient.

As an appeal is possible only on a point of law, the arbitrator must set out in full the steps by which he reached his conclusions, citing relevant authorities when appropriate. He must also ensure that he includes findings of all the facts which the Court will need in its consideration of the points of law. In most cases a narrative form will be convenient. This should start with a short account of how the Contract between the parties was set up, followed by the events leading up to the disputes. The steps by which the

---

[1] See (for example) Form 18 in Appendix VI.
[2] See note 1 to Form 18, *ibid.*
[3] The 1979 Act was drafted primarily to deal with the problems facing arbitrators in the traditional markets and exchanges of the City of London and as such has been fairly successful. Unfortunately, in many ways it has exacerbated problems in construction arbitrations generally and in civil engineering arbitrations in particular.

arbitrator came to be seized of the reference should then be set down, followed by a concise summary of the issues and of the contentions of the parties. Where the facts have not been agreed or admitted, the arbitrator's formal findings of fact should be set out and his views on the application of relevant points of law should come next, leading finally to his decisions on the issues before him. Where the reasons are included in the body of the award, it may be useful to adopt formal language for the operative part of the award.

Whether pleadings or other documents should be annexed to the reasons (either included in the award or published separately) is a matter to be decided in the particular circumstances of each reference. There is no objection to the inclusion of appendices, but no document should be so annexed unless its absence would render the reasons incomplete or necessitate the inclusion elsewhere in the text of substantial quotations therefrom. However, the contracts from which the arbitration arose should *not* be annexed either to the reasons or to the award, as the Court can always require the appellant to produce them if need be. Similarly, it is both unnecessary and bad practice to attach to the award or reasons the agreed bundle of documents used at the Hearing, or any substantial part thereof. The Court has criticised this practice under the old "case-stated" procedure and will undoubtedly take the same view in appeals under the 1979 Act.

Finally, if the arbitrator sees no grounds for appeal there is no harm in his saying so and giving his reasons for holding that view as part of a reasoned award. The Court may well have an easier task in deciding whether or not to give leave to appeal if he does so.

### Refusing reasons

It is now common in construction arbitrations for both parties to ask the arbitrator to give reasons in or with his award, particularly where the parties are represented by lawyers. In some cases this may be because a later application to the Court for an order that reasons be given will fail unless such a request has been made to the arbitrator before the award is made.[1] Faced with a request for reasons, the arbitrator should ask the parties to state their purpose in making it.[2] If the purpose is for the parties' own information the arbitrator should normally agree to the request. But if reasons are wanted to support an application for leave to appeal the parties should be asked to state the points of law with which they wish the reasons to deal. If the parties then cannot or will not do so the arbitrator may refuse the request. In that event, he should state in his award that he has done so and why, but may give leave to apply for reasons after the award is made, provided that the applicant party can then specify the points of law with which he wishes the reasons to deal. The arbitrator may also ask the applicant to list the facts which he considers that the arbitrator should find, in addition to those already found as part of the award.

Finally, cases may arise in which the parties ask only for reasons for their own information but later decide that they wish to apply for leave to appeal.

---

[1]  S. 1(6)(a) of the 1979 Act.
[2]  Rule 18(2) of the new ICE Arbitration Procedure contains such a provision.

In these circumstances the reasons already given may not be adequate for the Court's purposes and fresh reasons on specific points of law would be desirable. It is therefore suggested that reasons for information purposes should normally be given in a separate document on the express understanding that neither party will use them for any litigious purpose[1] and that the arbitrator will consider sympathetically any subsequent application for reasons on specified points of law for use in Court.

## Enforcing the award

The fact that the arbitrator has made and published his award does not of itself compel compliance with its terms. If one party fails to comply, the other can secure performance of the award only by invoking the assistance of the Court.

The simplest and quickest way is for the party wishing to enforce the award to apply to the Court under s. 26 of the Arbitration Act 1950 for leave to enforce it as a judgment of the Court. If leave is granted, judgment is then entered in the terms of the award and the applicant may then take any steps available for execution of that judgment.[2] But the Court will not give leave to enforce the award in this way if there is any reason to doubt its validity or the applicant's right to proceed on it.

The alternative remedy is to sue on the award itself to recover judgment for the sum awarded or to obtain specific performance of a non-monetary award.[3] If the award is of a negative character an injunction may similarly be sought to restrain the other party from acting contrary to the award. Where the award is for a sum of money, summary judgment under R.S.C. Ord. 14 may be applied for. But in each case it is open to the other party to defend the action on the ground that the award should not be enforced. However, refusal of leave under s. 26 does not prevent a subsequent action on the award.

---

[1] Where separate reasons have been given on the understanding that no use shall be made of them in any action on the award, the Court could look at them only to satisfy itself that there had been no fraud or misconduct: *Atlantic Lines and Navigation Company Inc.* v. *Italmare SpA* [1985] 1 Lloyd's Rep. 597.

[2] See the *Supreme Court Practice*, Ord. 45–52.

[3] A declaratory award does not need to be enforced. If the other party acts contrary to the terms of the declaration this will either give the successful party a right of action on the *new* dispute so created or afford him a defence against any action brought by the other party in defiance of the terms of the declaration.

*Chapter 5*

# ARBITRATION AND THE COURTS

### Enforcing the arbitration agreement

An agreement to refer disputes to arbitration, although binding upon all the parties to it, cannot be enforced directly, nor will the Court compel a party to submit to arbitration by issuing a decree of specific performance.

Should one party refuse to proceed to arbitration the other party has two alternatives. He may seek to enforce the arbitration agreement in the Courts, or he can proceed with the arbitration. Of these, the second alternative is likely to be the more effective. Where the arbitration agreement is contained in Clause 66 of the ICE Conditions of Contract,[1] the party wishing to proceed may apply to the President of the Institution for an arbitrator to be appointed and then may ask the arbitrator to proceed *ex parte*. In such circumstances it would be prudent to ask the President to direct that the ICE Arbitration Procedure (1983) shall apply.

If one party chooses to ignore the agreement by commencing proceedings in the Courts, the other party (the defendant in the action) may apply to the Court for an order staying the proceedings under s. 4(1) of the Arbitration Act 1950.[2] Provided that the defendant is ready and willing to proceed with arbitration and has not himself taken any step in the action,[3] the Court has a discretion to stay the proceedings. There are no fixed rules governing the exercise of this discretion[4] but in general a stay will be granted unless the plaintiff can show good reason why the dispute should not be referred to arbitration.[5] And a stay may be ordered even when the arbitration cannot proceed forthwith.[6]

---

[1]  If the agreement is not that in Clause 66 (or Clause 67 of the FIDIC Conditions or Clause 18 of the FCEC "Blue Form") and contains no mechanism for appointing an arbitrator in default of agreement, the High Court has power under s. 10 of the 1950 Act to appoint an arbitrator on the application of any party to the arbitration agreement.

[2]  If the other party is content to proceed in the Courts, the arbitration agreement of course becomes irrelevant, save for the question whether a Judge can exercise the powers given by the agreement to an arbitrator, which is now doubtful: see *Northern Regional Health Authority* v. *Derek Crouch* [1984] Q.B. 644 (C.A.).

[3]  The defendant must first acknowledge service of the writ or summons initiating the proceedings, but this is not regarded as "taking a step" in the action. It may be prudent for the defendant to issue his summons under s. 4(1) at the same time as he acknowledges service.

[4]  See Keating's *Building Contracts* (4th edn), p. 242.

[5]  *Ibid.*, pp. 242–245.

[6]  A writ may issue as soon as a dispute arises but, under ICE Clause 66, it must first be referred to the Engineer for his decision and even then may be delayed further until the Works have been completed. See also *Russell on Arbitration* (20th edn), pp. 166–167. It is uncertain whether reference to the Engineer is to be regarded as a condition precedent to the right to sue.

Where the dispute involves a sufficient foreign element the Court has no jurisdiction to refuse a stay of proceedings.[1] An arbitration clause in a foreign contract is therefore to be regarded as mandatory unless the parties agree to take their dispute to Court.

## Concurrent actions

It may happen that proceedings are commenced in Court while an arbitration is in progress with regard to the same subject matter, or vice versa. It then becomes necessary to consider the positions of the two proceedings. In such a case the respective jurisdictions of the Courts and of the arbitrator are not regarded as mutually exclusive. The arbitrator cannot oust the Court by purporting to make an award in a matter where the Court is also seized of jurisdiction.[2] But the existence of a concurrent action does not prevent the parties from commencing or continuing with an arbitration, and an award made by agreement will bind the Court.[3] Similarly, the existence of arbitration proceedings does not prevent a party from invoking the jurisdiction of the Court, for example, to obtain summary judgment under R.S.C. Ord. 14.[4]

## Control by the Court

Despite some recent attempts by the Court of Appeal[5] to that end, it appears that the Courts have no general supervisory power over arbitration proceedings. The reasons for this are largely historical. Intervention by the Courts in what until then had been largely a common law procedure began in the early 19th century and, since the Arbitration Act 1889, the Court's powers have been exercisable only within limits prescribed by statute. While some extension to this principle must now be allowed (see below), the supervisory role of the Courts is in general limited to intervention during the currency of a reference or after an award has been made, and in either case only in particular circumstances.

The Court also has a supportive role to play. The enforcement of arbitration agreements[6] by virtue of s. 4(1) of the 1950 Act and the enforcement of awards under s. 26[7] have already been mentioned. Section 12 also empowers the Court to make various orders[8] on behalf of the arbitrator or the parties, and by virtue of s. 5 of the 1979 Act the Court can also extend the powers of the arbitrator himself.[9] Finally, the Court may determine any question of law which may arise in the course of a reference, subject to the conditions set out in s. 2 of the 1979 Act. This function is dealt with further below in the context of appeals.

---

[1] Arbitration Act 1975, s. 1.
[2] *Doleman & Sons* v. *Ossett Corp.* [1912] 3 K.B. 257.
[3] *Lloyd* v. *Wright* [1983] Q.B. 1065; 3 W.L.R. 223.
[4] *Travaux International SA* v. *Cerra Logullari TAS* [1981] 2 Lloyd's Rep. 169; *The Urstas Melors* [1981] Lloyd's Rep. 18.
[5] See *Bremer Vulkan Schiffbau* v. *South India Shipping* [1981] A.C. 909; *Andre et Cie* v. *Marine Transocean* [1981] Q.B. 694; *Paal Wilson & Co.* v. *Partenreederei* [1982] 1 A.C. 854; 3 W.L.R. 1149.
[6] See p. 35, *ante*.
[7] See p. 33, *ante*.
[8] See p. 14, *ante*.
[9] See p. 15, *ante*.

## Grounds for intervention

Applications for the Court's intervention in arbitration proceedings can arise either on grounds expressly set out in the Arbitration Acts or to a limited extent on grounds over which the Court exercises an inherent jurisdiction. Under statute, the broadest powers available are those contained in ss. 22 and 23 of the 1950 Act under which the Court may remit[1] an award for reconsideration by the arbitrator, or set the award aside[2] or remove the arbitrator from office.[3] This last remedy is available only on proof of an arbitrator's serious misconduct, and in practice an application to remit is invariably included as an alternative to removal. Should the Court find that the award cannot be allowed to stand but the arbitrator's conduct is not such as to justify his removal, the award may instead be remitted to him with appropriate directions.

There are also limited grounds on which the Court will remit an award when there has been no misconduct by the arbitrator.[4] These include the following: where new and material evidence[5] is discovered after an award has been made; where it can be shown that the arbitrator has misconceived or misstated the arguments addressed to him; where one of the parties can establish that he has not understood the nature of the case against him;[6] where there have been "procedural mishaps";[7] where the award contains a clerical error;[8] where the arbitrator has exceeded his jurisdiction;[9] or where costs have been awarded on the wrong principle.[10] And, until the 1979 Act, an award by way of case stated could be remitted if it contained insufficient findings of fact.[11] However, the Court has no general power to control arbitration proceedings by way of remission.

A further statutory remedy is available under s. 1 of the 1950 Act where, as an alternative to removing the arbitrator, the High Court or a Judge thereof may give leave to revoke his authority. This remedy is rarely granted[12] but may be applied, for example, where an arbitrator has had an interim award set aside and is proposing to continue with the reference.[12] Injunction proceedings are possible, for example, on the ground that a reference is invalid.[13] The Court may also grant a declaration as to the legal

---

[1] S. 22(1). But the Court has no power to remit an award on the ground that the Arbitrator has made a mistake unless he himself admits it, even where it is necessarily to be inferred that he has erred in law or has decided an issue on a point not canvassed before him—see *Atlantic Lines and Navigation Company Inc.* v. *Italmare SpA* [1985] 1 Lloyd's Rep. 597.

[2] S. 23(2).

[3] S. 23(1).

[4] See *Russell on Arbitration* (20th edn), pp. 422–430.

[5] This is analogous to the Court's power to order a new trial in similar circumstances, or to admit fresh evidence on appeal—see notes to R.S.C. Ord. 59, rr. 10, 11.

[6] Such cases will necessarily be rare on the facts.

[7] *Ismail* v. *Polish Ocean Lines* [1977] 2 Lloyd's Rep. 134 at p. 139; *GKN Centrax Gears Ltd.* v. *Matbro Ltd.* [1976] 2 Lloyd's Rep. 555.

[8] The arbitrator can himself correct such errors under s. 17 of the 1950 Act.

[9] If the part containing the excess is severable it may simply be ignored; if not, the award must be remitted for reconsideration.

[10] See p. 25, *ante*; also *Dineen* v. *Walpole* [1969] 1 Lloyd's Rep. 261.

[11] S. 21 of the 1950 Act, now repealed by s. 1(1) of the 1979 Act. But see p. 80 for the continued use of case stated as a common law procedure.

[12] *City Centre Properties* v. *Matthew Hall* [1969] 1 W.L.R. 772.

[13] See further *Northern Regional Health Authority* v. *Derek Crouch* [1984] Q.B. 644.

validity of the proceedings or of an award. The former power to grant relief for error on the face of the award has now been abolished by s. 1(1) of the 1979 Act.

The Court's inherent jurisdiction has given rise to much activity in connection with the striking out of "stale" claims. The Courts have always exercised this jurisdiction over litigation,[1] but attempts to persuade the Courts that arbitrators have a like jurisdiction have, so far, failed.[2] However, it would seem that the Courts have now accepted for themselves a jurisdiction to grant relief in respect of arbitration claims which are so stale as to make a fair hearing impossible.[3] The precise basis for such intervention awaits further clarification but the most likely justification is that the agreement to arbitrate has been brought to an end by repudiation, frustration or abandonment.

### Misconduct and removal

A party who is dissatisfied with the arbitrator, his award or the way in which the reference has been conducted may apply to the Court for relief. If the complaint is about the arbitrator (for example that he is not or may not be impartial) the complainant may apply to the High Court under s. 24(1) of the 1950 Act for leave to revoke the arbitrator's authority or for an injunction to restrain him or any other party from proceeding with the arbitration. This may arise where the arbitrator is not independent of all the parties involved or has himself an interest in the matters at issue. But not every such interest will disqualify him; the interest must be of such a nature that it is incompatible with the arbitrator's duty of impartiality between the parties.[4] Even where such an interest can be proved, the arbitrator will still not be disqualified if the interest complained of was known to the complainant party at the time that the appointment was made. But s. 24(1) of the Act provides that, where there is an agreement to submit *future* disputes to arbitration and the arbitrator is named or designated in the agreement, application under the section may be made even if the applicant party knew or should have known that the arbitrator, by reason of the interest complained of, might not be impartial.

The Court's power to set aside an award has already been mentioned.[5] In addition, despite the abolition[6] of the inherent power to set aside an award for error of fact or law on its face, the Court still retains power to set aside where it can be shown that the award was improperly procured, e.g. where signatures to the arbitration agreement were obtained by fraud, or the award was procured by perjury or by suppression of evidence. An award which has been set aside is a nullity and the parties are left in the same position as before the reference. But if the good parts of an award can be separated from the bad they may be allowed to stand.

---

[1]   *Allen* v. *McAlpine* [1968] 2 Q.B. 229.

[2]   *Crawford* v. *Prowting* [1973] Q.B. 1.

[3]   *Bremer Vulkan Schiffbau* v. *South India Shipping* [1981] A.C. 909; *Andre et Cie* v. *Marine Transocean* [1981] Q.B. 694; *Paal Wilson & Co.* v. *Partenreederei* [1982] 1 A.C. 854; 3 W.L.R. 1149.

[4]   *Kimberley* v. *Dick* [1871] L.R. 13 Eq. 1.

[5]   See p. 37, *ante*.

[6]   S. 1(1) of the 1979 Act.

There is no definition of misconduct and the Commercial Court Committee[1] has deplored its indiscriminate use to cover innocent mistakes of procedure as well as morally reprehensible or deliberate misdoings. Unfortunately, without amendment of the Arbitration Acts, arbitrators will continue to suffer the application of this opprobrious epithet.

Recent cases illustrate the type of conduct by the arbitrator which is likely to lead the Court to conclude that the arbitrator or his award cannot be accepted. Thus, misconduct was found in a case where the arbitrator made a cumulative series of procedural errors, none of which were very serious but which combined to reduce the arbitration to a state where there was no apparent prospect that justice would be done.[2] Again, an arbitrator took into consideration a document submitted by one party without permitting the other party to have a copy of it, and this was held to amount to misconduct.[3] Similarly, where an arbitrator, having heard submissions on a point of law from one party, made a decision in favour of that party without hearing the other, misconduct was held to have been committed.[4] An award has been set aside (and the arbitrator removed) where the respondent did not appear but the arbitrator relied on his own technical knowledge to reject part of the claimant's claim without disclosing his views to the claimant during the course of the proceedings.[5]

These cases emphasize that, in exercising control over arbitrations, the Courts are more concerned with the substance and the effect of any alleged misconduct rather than with the niceties of the arbitrator's behaviour. Thus the mere expression of opinion will not of itself constitute misconduct. On the other hand, if the arbitrator exhibits bias,[6] i.e. a state of mind whereby he does not have the same attitude of impartiality to both parties, this is likely to be held to be misconduct. Thus, where in an arbitration arising from a collision between a Norwegian ship and a Portuguese ship the arbitrator's remarks during the Hearing suggested that he held preconceived views about the honesty of witnesses of Portuguese nationality, he was held to have misconducted himself.[7] But the question of apparent bias can be difficult where there is a serious inequality in the standard of representation of the parties. If one has Counsel and the other appears in person it may be that in dealing with the latter's inexperience of legal process the arbitrator may seem to treat him more kindly than he does his opponent. Arbitrators must treat such cases with sensitivity. But if one party suspects bias he must raise an objection; otherwise, by proceeding with the arbitration without complaint, he may be deemed to have waived his objection.

## Fraud by a party

Under s. 24(2) of the Arbitration Act 1950 the High Court may order that an arbitration agreement shall cease to have effect and may give leave to

---

[1]  *Report on Arbitration*, Cmnd. 7284, HMSO, 1979, at p. 17, para. 67.
[2]  *Pratt* v. *Swanmore Builders* [1981] 15 B.L.R. 37; [1980] 2 Lloyd's Rep. 504.
[3]  *Maltin* v. *Donne* [1980] 15 B.L.R. 61.
[4]  *Modern Engineering* v. *Miskin* [1981] 15 B.L.R. 82; [1981] 1 Lloyd's Rep. 135.
[5]  *Fox* v. *Wellfair* [1981] 2 Lloyd's Rep. 514; 19 B.L.R. 52.
[6]  Bias can, of course, be inferred from interest—see p. 38, *ante*.
[7]  *Catalina* v. *Norma* [1938] 61 Lloyd's Rep. 360.

revoke the authority of any arbitrator or umpire appointed under the agreement. The principle behind this provision was based partly on the idea that a person accused of fraud ought to have the chance of clearing his name in public. Thus English lawyers were and still are reluctant to plead fraud in an arbitration, not only because an accusation impugning a person's honesty or integrity is not to be made lightly but more particularly because the party accused may apply to the Court for a stay of the arbitration proceedings.[1]

It may be that dishonesty will suffice to activate the Section. Thus if during arbitration proceedings it appears that some fraudulent or dishonest conduct is in issue and one party wishes to refer the matter to the Court, the arbitrator will normally adjourn the proceedings to allow the Court to dispose of that issue.

Since 1979 the High Court has been precluded from exercising its powers under the Section where the arbitration is not "domestic"[2] and the parties have entered into an exclusion agreement under s. 3(7) of the 1979 Act.[3]

## Appeals

The former right of appeal by way of case stated under the 1950 Act was abolished by s. 1(1) of the 1979 Act. Instead, an aggrieved party now has a strictly limited right of appeal to the High Court on any question of law (but not of fact) arising out of an award. In certain circumstances the High Court also has jurisdiction to determine any question of law arising in the course of a reference, thus perpetuating the consultative case procedure.

The right of appeal against an award is automatic where application to the Court is made with the consent of all parties to the reference.[4] Otherwise, the right is subject to the leave of the Court[5] which is not to be granted unless the Court considers that, having regard to all the circumstances, the determination of the question of law concerned could substantially affect the rights of one or more of the parties to the arbitration agreement. If it decides to give leave the Court may attach such conditions as it sees fit.[6]

In practice, it is not usually difficult to find points of law which can substantially affect the rights of the parties; there would be little point in an appeal if this were not so. The substantial hurdle which now lies in the path of any party who wishes to appeal on a point of law is in obtaining leave of the Court. This is now the subject of a substantial body of case law, at the summit of which lies the House of Lord's decision in *The Nema*.[7] In this case the House of Lords stated the grounds upon which leave should be given as follows.

(a) Where the question of law involves the construction of a "one-off" clause, leave should not normally be given unless it is apparent on a mere perusal of the reasoned award that the arbitrator is obviously wrong.

---

[1] The parties may, of course, accept the arbitrator's jurisdiction by not applying for a stay.
[2] As defined in s. 3(7) of the 1979 Act.
[3] See also Appendix I.
[4] S. 1(2) of the 1979 Act.
[5] S. 1(3) of the 1979 Act.
[6] S. 1(4) of the 1979 Act.
[7] *BTP Tioxide* v. *Pioneer Shipping Co.* [1981] 2 Lloyd's Rep. 239.

(b) Where the question is one of the construction of a contract in standard terms, rather less strict criteria are appropriate. If the decision would add significantly to the clarity and certainty of English commercial law it would be proper to give leave. But even here leave should not be given unless a strong *prima facie* case is made out that the arbitrator was wrong and, when the events to which the clause applies are "one-off" events, stricter criteria should be applied.

A wholly new philosophy is apparent from this approach, namely that the parties are required to accept the arbitrator's decision, right or wrong, unless the award embodies a point of law of wide application. This is reinforced by s. 1(7) of the Act which provides that no appeal shall lie to the Court of Appeal from the High Court's decision on an appeal from an award unless leave to do so is given by the Court or the Court of Appeal, and the question of law certified is by the High Court as one of general public importance or is one which for some other special reason should be considered by the Court of Appeal.

## The consultative case

Under s. 2 of the 1979 Act the scope for an application to the Court on a point of law during the course of the reference is much wider than in the case of an appeal from the award. An application may be made by any party to a reference, provided that all the other parties agree *or* that the arbitrator or umpire gives his consent. However, the arbitrator or umpire must have entered upon the reference, and he cannot himself apply directly to the Court, but only through one of the parties. The procedure is thus firmly in the hands of the parties.

Once the Court has jurisdiction under s. 2 of the 1979 Act on one point of law it can consider others which have not been formally submitted, provided that such other points are ancillary to the first point. As in the case of an appeal from an award under s. 1, there is no power to interfere with the arbitrator's findings of fact.

Where an application under s. 2 of the Act is made with the consent of all the parties to the reference the Court is bound to consider it. But if the application is by one party with the arbitrator's consent the Court will entertain it only if it might produce substantial savings in costs and (more important) if the question of law is one where leave to appeal would be likely to be given were the application to be made under s. 1.[1]

Section 2(3) of the Act provides that, as in the case of an appeal from the award, no appeal shall lie from the Court's decision to the Court of Appeal unless either the High Court or the Court of Appeal gives leave and it is certified by the High Court that the question of law to which the decision relates is one of general public importance or is one which for some other special reason should be considered by the Court of Appeal. It has been held that leave under s. 2(3) should only be granted on the same strict terms as now apply to the grant of leave to appeal under s. 1.[2]

---

[1] S. 2(2)(b), applying the provisions of s. 1(3)(b) of the 1979 Act.
[2] *Babanaft SA* v. *Avant Petroleum* [1982] 1 W.L.R. 871.

### Exclusion agreements

Where the 1979 Act applies to the arbitration agreement[1] it is open to the parties to enter into an "exclusion agreement" under s. 3 of the Act. In the case of a "domestic"[2] arbitration agreement this can be done only after a dispute has arisen and the arbitration has commenced.[3] An exclusion agreement can, however, validly be included in the *Notice to Refer*.[4]

An exclusion agreement must be in writing, but no particular form of words is prescribed. An agreement excluding the right of appeal under s. 1 will normally also exclude an application under s. 2 of the Act unless it is clear from the words used that the parties have otherwise agreed.[5]

In the case of non-domestic disputes the existence of an exclusion agreement will also prevent the High Court from intervening in the arbitration to deal with allegations of fraud. If the parties wish to preserve their right to have questions of fraud dealt with by the Court, therefore, they must include a statement to that effect in the exclusion agreement.[6] But exclusion agreements will have no effect on any of the other powers of the Court to intervene in or to control arbitration proceedings.[7]

---

[1]  It will not, in general, apply to oral agreements (which are governed by common law and not by statute) or to written agreements where the arbitration commenced before 1st August, 1979 (S.I. 750 of 1979), unless the parties agree in writing that it shall apply.

[2]  As defined in s. 3(7) of the Act. For the position with other kinds of arbitration agreement see Gibson-Jarvie & Hawker's *Guide to Commercial Arbitration under the 1979 Act*, p. 73. See also p. 147, *post*.

[3]  An arbitration is deemed to be commenced when a notice is served by a party to an arbitration agreement requiring the appointment of an arbitrator or requiring the other parties to submit a dispute to an arbitrator designated by the agreement (Limitation Act 1980, s. 34(3); see also s. 29(2) of the 1950 Act).

[4]  See Rule 1, p. 51, *post*.

[5]  S. 3(1) of the 1979 Act.

[6]  S. 3(3) of the 1979 Act.

[7]  For further discussion of the effect of ss. 3(1)–3(4) of the 1979 Act see Gibson-Jarvie & Hawker's *Guide to Commercial Arbitration under the 1979 Act*, pp. 25–29.

*Chapter 6*

# THE NEW ICE AND FCEC ARBITRATION CLAUSES

Since the ICE Arbitration Procedure (1983) was published in February, 1983 revisions have been issued to the ICE Conditions of Contract and to the FCEC Form of Sub-Contract. The latter appeared in September, 1984 and includes significant amendments to the arbitration Clause 18; the former was issued by the Conditions of Contract Standing Joint Committee[1] in March, 1985 and affects only Clauses 66 and 67 of the Conditions of Contract. All three new Clauses are set out in full in Appendix III.

### The new ICE Arbitration Clause

The revised text of Clause 66 is rearranged into six main Sub-Clauses. All reference to Scotland has been transferred to Clause 67.[2] But, while the marginal note *Interim Arbitration* has disappeared following the amalgamation of the old Clause 66(2) with the rest of the Clause, the concept is still very much alive.

For convenience, the new Sub-Clauses are commented on separately.

*Disputes to be referred to the Engineer*[3]

66(1)  If a dispute or difference of any kind whatsoever shall arise between the Employer and the Contractor in connection with or arising out of the Contract or the carrying out of the Works including any dispute as to any decision opinion instruction direction certificate or valuation of the Engineer (whether during the progress of the Works or after their completion and whether before or after the determination abandonment or breach of the Contract) it shall be referred in writing to and be settled by the Engineer who shall state his decision in writing and give notice of the same to the Employer and the Contractor.

The new Sub-Clause reproduces the first seven lines of the old Clause 66(1). The only change is that the new Sub-Clause expressly requires the reference to the Engineer to be in writing. No special form is stipulated, but for the avoidance of doubt it should be made clear that the reference is made under Clause 66(1) and not under any other Clause.[4]

---

[1]  Representing the bodies who promulgate the ICE Conditions of Contract, namely the Institution of Civil Engineers, the Association of Consulting Engineers and the Federation of Civil Engineering Contractors.

[2]  See p. 110, *post.*

[3]  This and subsequent marginal notes were included in an early draft of the new Clause but do not appear in the published version.

[4]  See p. 7, *ante.*

66(2)  Unless the Contract shall have already been determined or abandoned the Contractor shall in every case continue to proceed with the Works with all due diligence and the Contractor and Employer shall both give effect forthwith to every such decision of the Engineer unless and until the same shall be revised by an arbitrator as hereinafter provided. Such decisions shall be final and binding upon the Contractor and the Employer unless and until the dispute or difference has been referred to arbitration as hereinafter provided and an award made and published.

This covers lines 7–12 of the "old" Clause 66(1), the two main changes being that both the Employer and the Contractor are now expressly required to give immediate effect to the Engineer's decision, which itself is now to remain final and binding until replaced by an arbitrator's published award. Both are no doubt the intention of the original text, but the earlier wording appeared to leave it open to the Employer to ignore the decision and it could have been argued that the possibility of referral to arbitration deprived the decision of its binding force. Both these apparent ambiguities have now been corrected.

It should be noted that, if a dispute is referred to arbitration and is later settled, the terms of the settlement must now be recorded in the form of an award by agreement, as otherwise the Engineer's decision remains in force.

*Reference of a dispute to arbitration*

66(3)(a)  Where a Certificate of Completion of the whole of the Works has not been issued and
(i) either the Employer or the Contractor be dissatisfied with any such decision of the Engineer; or
(ii) the Engineer shall fail to give such decision for a period of one calendar month after such referral in writing
then either the Employer or the Contractor may within three calendar months after receiving notice of such decision or within three calendar months after the expiration of the said period of one month (as the case may be) refer the dispute or difference to the arbitration of a person to be agreed upon by the Parties by giving notice to the other Party.

66(3)(b)  Where a Certificate of Completion of the whole of the Works has been issued and
(i) either the Employer or the Contractor be dissatisfied with any such decision of the Engineer; or
(ii) the Engineer shall fail to give such decision for a period of three calendar months after such referral in writing
then either the Employer or the Contractor may within three calendar months after receiving notice of such decision or within three calendar months after the expiration of the said period of three months (as the case may be) refer the dispute or difference to the arbitration of a person to be agreed upon by the Parties by giving notice to the other Party.

Sub-Clause (3) as a whole replaces lines 12–18 of the "old" Clause 66(1). But under paragraphs (a) and (b) there is now a distinction drawn between the reference of a dispute before completion of the Works and after completion. In the latter case the earlier arrangement is preserved whereby the Engineer is given up to three months within which to make his decision. Before completion, however, this period for decision is reduced to one month. In either case, the old three-month period for reference to arbitration remains.

The reason for this change has not been made public, but it is obviously intended to speed up an interim reference. Before completion, the Engineer or his staff are still in close contact with the Works and should be able to arrive at a decision promptly, whereas after completion staff may well have dispersed to other projects and may have to be recalled to consider the dispute. The Engineer should not feel aggrieved at this restriction on his time for decision. If there are genuine reasons for taking longer than one month[1] to arrive at a decision (for example because further tests or other evidence is needed, or because urgent work elsewhere on the project takes priority) the Engineer may ask both Parties for an extension; should one Party unreasonably refuse such a request, the Engineer can make his decision within the prescribed period with a comment that more time ought to have been spent in considering it and identifying the Party who refused an extension. These facts can then be taken into account by any subsequent arbitrator and may result in the recalcitrant Party's being penalised in costs.

The only disadvantage of the new arrangements is that, for an interim reference, the Party wishing to refer a dispute to arbitration could be out of time within four months (rather than six) after his decision to proceed under Clause 66(1).

### Failure of agreement to appoint an arbitrator

66(4)(a)   If the Parties fail to appoint an arbitrator within one calendar month of either Party serving on the other Party a written Notice to Concur in the appointment of an arbitrator the dispute or difference shall be referred to a person to be appointed on the application of either Party by the President for the time being of the Institution of Civil Engineers.

66(4)(b)   If an arbitrator declines the appointment or after appointment is removed by order of a competent court or is incapable of acting or dies and the Parties do not within one calendar month of the vacancy arising fill the vacancy then either Party may apply to the President for the time being of the Institution of Civil Engineers to appoint another arbitrator to fill the vacancy.

66(4)(c)   In any case where the President for the time being of the Institution of Civil Engineers is not able to exercise the functions conferred on him by this Clause the said functions may be exercised on his behalf by a Vice-President for the time being of the said Institution.

This Sub-Clause incorporates lines 18–25 of the "old" Clause 66(1) and the provisions of the "old" Clause 66(3), rearranged into a more logical order. There is no change of substance.

### Procedure and powers

66(5)(a)   Any reference to arbitration shall be conducted in accordance with the Institution of Civil Engineers' Arbitration Procedure (1983) or any amendment or modification thereof being in force at the time of the appointment of the arbitrator. Such arbitrator shall have full power to open up review and revise any

---

[1]   Or, indeed, three months under Clause 66(3)(b).

decision opinion instruction direction certificate or valuation of the Engineer and neither Party shall be limited in the proceedings before such arbitrator to the evidence or arguments put before the Engineer for the purpose of obtaining his decision above referred to.

66(5)(b)    Any such reference to arbitration shall be deemed to be a submission to arbitration within the meaning of the Arbitration Act 1950 or any statutory re-enactment or amendment thereof for the time being in force. The Award of the arbitrator shall be binding on the Parties.

66(5)(c)    Any reference to arbitration may unless the Parties otherwise agree in writing proceed notwithstanding that the Works are not then complete or alleged to be complete.

This Sub-Clause deals with several important matters. Paragraph (a) now makes the ICE Arbitration Procedure (1983) mandatory (unless the Parties otherwise agree in writing) instead of the optional provision in lines 28–30 of the "old" Clause 66(1). The President's power to direct its use in the old text is therefore no longer required. As before, the new form empowers the arbitrator to "open up review and revise" any decision, opinion etc. of the Engineer, a power not available to the Courts.[1] Should the 1983 Procedure be amended, the version which is to apply is that extant at the time that the arbitrator is appointed.[2]

Paragraph (b) reproduces lines 25, 26, 27, 36 and 37 of the old form but the arbitrator's award is now to be binding upon the Parties instead of "final and binding". This amendment recognises that the provision is not intended to exclude an appeal under s. 1 of the Arbitration Act 1979.[3]

The main alteration introduced by the new Clause is the replacement of the former Clause 66(2) (interim arbitration) and the complementary provision in the penultimate sentence of the "old" Clause 66(1) and proviso (a) thereto. Instead of the previous limited right to proceed before completion of the Works there is now a general right to arbitrate any dispute whenever the claimant wishes to do so. It would be wrong to read into this paragraph an obligation to proceed in the absence of agreement to the contrary, primarily because the operative word is "may", but also because, under Sub-Clause (3), the only action necessary to preserve the right to challenge the Engineer's decision is service of the notice to refer, there being no obligation to continue with the reference at any particular time. Note that, to be effective, an agreement to defer the arbitration until after completion must be in writing.

Where a reference is to proceed before completion or alleged completion of the Works—save for a dispute under Clause 63 (Forfeiture)[4]—the arbitration will automatically become an interim arbitration under Rule 24 of the ICE Arbitration Procedure despite the fact that the expression no

---

[1]    See *Northern Regional Health Authority* v. *Derek Crouch* [1984] Q.B. 644.

[2]    There has been some criticism based on the view that the 1983 Procedure is so radically different from the 1973 version that it cannot properly be deemed to be an "amendment or modification" thereof. No problem arises where, under the "old" Clause 66, the Parties agree to adopt the Procedure, but the validity of a Presidential direction may be open to question.

[3]    No particular words are needed to create an exclusion agreement under s. 3 of the Act: see p. 42, *ante*.

[4]    Rule 24.1.

longer appears as a marginal note to Clause 66. The Parties, of course, remain free to agree whether Rule 24 or the provisions of the main Procedure shall apply. In view of the greatly enlarged scope of references which may now proceed before completion of the Works, there may well be interim references where the parties will not wish to use Rule 24, for example, because they foresee a need for the reference to continue after completion.

## *The Engineer as witness*

66(6)   No decision given by the Engineer in accordance with the foregoing provisions shall disqualify him from being called as a witness and giving evidence before the arbitrator on any matter whatsoever relevant to the dispute or difference so referred to the arbitrator as aforesaid.

This repeats what was formerly Clause 66(1)(b).

## *General comment*

A significant omission in the new Clause is any provision giving the Court jurisdiction in the event that a dispute, or part of it, is the subject of litigation. Such a provision is found in both the old and the new versions of the FCEC Arbitration Clause.[1] However, the position under the Main Contract will remain that the Courts may not accept jurisdiction to exercise the powers vested in the arbitrator unless given such powers by specific agreement.[2] Where the Parties are already in dispute, such agreement will seldom be possible.

## The new FCEC Arbitration Clause

The revision of the 1973 version of the FCEC Form of Sub-Contract was intended to deal with other matters, but the opportunity has been taken to update the arbitration clause as well in the light of developments in ICE arbitration. The new FCEC Form was issued some six months ahead of the new ICE Clause 66, but it is clear that amendments to the latter were taken into account.

## *Disputes between Contractor and Sub-Contractor*[3]

18(1)   If any dispute arises between the Contractor and the Sub-Contractor in connection with or arising out of this Sub-Contract or the carrying out of the Sub-Contract Works including any dispute as to any decision, opinion, instruction or direction of the Contractor and/or Engineer or any dispute as to payment under Clause 15 it shall, subject to the provisions of this clause, be referred to the arbitration and final decision of a person agreed between the parties, or failing such agreement, appointed upon the application of either of the parties by the President for the time being of the Institution of Civil Engineers and any such reference to arbitration may be conducted in accordance with the Institution of Civil Engineers' Arbitration Procedure 1983 or any amendment or modification thereof in force at the time of the appointment of the arbitrator.

The new version is in substance the same as the old Clause 18(1), but the

---

1   Clause 18(3) in each version—see below.
2   See *Northern Regional Health Authority* v. *Derek Crouch* [1984] Q.B. 644.
3   This and subsequent marginal notes do not appear in the published version.

opportunity has been taken to introduce much of the language of ICE Clause 66(1). Thus the category of disputes to be arbitrated is now to include "any decision opinion instruction or direction" of the Engineer. The reference to Clause 15 is to payment and certification. Similarly, the reference in the old form to disputes arising "in connection with the Sub-Contract" is now expanded in the ICE style to include the carrying out of the Sub-Contract Works. Reference has also been introduced to the ICE Arbitration Procedure (1983), but as an option rather than a mandatory requirement, because the new Form of Sub-Contract may, of course, be used in connection with a Main Contract whose provisions exclude the Procedure.

### Disputes under the Main Contract

> 18(2)   If any dispute arises in connection with the Main Contract and the Contractor is of the opinion that such dispute touches or concerns the Sub-Contract Works, then provided that an arbitrator has not already been agreed or appointed in pursuance of the preceding sub-clause, the Contractor may by notice in writing to the Sub-Contractor require that any such dispute under this Sub-Contract shall be dealt with jointly with the dispute under the Main Contract in accordance with the provisions of Clause 66 thereof. In connection with such joint dispute the Sub-Contractor shall be bound in like manner as the Contractor by any decision of the Engineer or any award by an arbitrator.

The first five lines repeat the "old" Clause 18(2) verbatim, but the remainder of the latter has now been discarded in favour of a much shorter provision aimed at joinder of the Main and Sub-Contract arbitrations. Instead of the rather complicated provisions relating to the powers of "the joint arbitrator" in the "old" version there is a simple provision that the Sub-Contract dispute shall be "dealt with jointly with the dispute under the Main Contract in accordance with the provisions of Clause 66 thereof". Thus all the provisions of the new Clause 66 are now to apply equally to both Main Contract and Sub-Contract disputes, including the reference to the Engineer for a decision under Clause 66(1) as a condition precedent to arbitration, and the differential time limits under Clauses 66(3)(a) and 66(3)(b). Similarly, any Engineer's decision under Clause 66(1) will bind Contractor and Sub-Contractor alike to the extent that the decision affects a Sub-Contract dispute, unless and until an arbitral award thereon has been made and published.[1]

Where the new FCEC Form of Sub-Contract is used with a Main Contract under which the old Clause 66 still applies, the effect of Clause 18(2) may differ somewhat from that described above. The main difference will probably be an inability to proceed with a Sub-Contract arbitration before substantial completion of the whole of the Works under the Main Contract (see "old" Clause 66(2)). This limitation may well be to the detriment of a Sub-Contractor whose work is finished early in the Main Contract. If so, it will nevertheless still be open to the Contractor and Sub-Contractor to agree to vary Clause 18(2) to allow the Sub-Contract arbitration to proceed early. But if the Contractor will not agree there will

---

[1]   Clause 66(2).

be little that the Sub-Contractor can do to expedite matters. However, this combination of forms will be a transitional phenomenon, and difficulty may be avoided by securing a suitable amendment to Clause 18(2) before the Sub-Contract is signed.

A significant difference between the old and the new forms of Clause 18(2) is the omission in the latter of any express provision for the Employer to approve a joint arbitration. But arbitration is founded in contract, and there is no privity of contract between Employer and Sub-Contractor. So in practice the Employer can prevent joint proceedings by refusing to allow the Sub-Contractor to participate in the Main Contract arbitration. However, where the same person is appointed arbitrator in both references, the arbitrator can request that the Sub-Contractor attends procedural meetings under the Main Contract arbitration[1] and (if the ICE Arbitration Procedure applies in both arbitrations) he can also order concurrent Hearings under Rule 7 if the Main Contractor agrees.[2]

This ability of the Employer to prevent joinder of arbitrations is a serious defect in the present system. The Commercial Court Committee recommended[3] that there should be a power of joinder in arbitration similar to that which already exists in respect of litigation, but Parliament chose not to include this feature in the 1979 Act. The recent Arbitration Ordinance of Hong Kong[4] includes such a power and it is to be hoped that this precedent will be followed in England and Wales in due course.[5] Meanwhile, its absence can be a fertile source of abuse leading to unnecessary delay and expense to the Sub-Contract parties.

### Abrogation of arbitration agreement

18(3) If at any time before an arbitrator has been agreed or appointed in pursuance of sub-clause (1) of this clause any dispute arising in connection with the Main Contract is made the subject of proceedings in any court between the Employer and the Contractor and the Contractor is of the opinion that such dispute touches or concerns the Sub-Contract Works, he may by notice in writing to the Sub-Contractor abrogate the provisions of sub-clause (1) of this clause and thereafter no dispute under this Sub-Contract shall be referable to arbitration without further submission by the Contractor and Sub-Contractor.

This is identical with the old Clause 18(3). Note that the Contractor *may* abrogate the arbitration clause but is under no obligation to do so. Thus, where liability turns on the same matters of law or fact in both Sub-Contract and Main Contract disputes but the quantum of any resulting claim is different (as where, for example, the Main Contract is fixed price

---

[1] Rule 12.1.

[2] An arbitrator appointed in both references may be able to apply to the High Court under s. 5 of the 1979 Act for powers of joinder, but it is as yet impossible to predict whether such power would or could be granted.

[3] *Report on Arbitration*, Cmnd. 7284, HMSO, 1978; see also Gibson-Jarvie & Hawker's *Guide to Commercial Arbitration under the 1979 Act*, p. 13.

[4] *Arbitration (Amendment) Ordinance 1982*, Ord. 10/82.

[5] Unfortunately, the recent Working Paper of the Commercial Court Committee's Sub-Committee on Arbitration (circulated for comment on 1st February, 1985) sees statutory provision for consolidation as impracticable, at least at present.

but the Sub-Contract price can be varied), it may be convenient to adjourn the Sub-Contract reference until the Courts have given judgment on the Main Contract dispute, and then to seek to apply the terms of that judgment to the matters at issue in the Sub-Contract reference. The Contractor would be wiser, however, to try to obtain the Sub-Contractor's agreement to being bound by the Court's judgment.

### Notice of Sub-Contract dispute

18(4) Notice of any dispute under this agreement shall be given by the Sub-Contractor to the Contractor in writing as soon as practicable after the event giving rise to the dispute. The Sub-Contractor shall be bound by the time limits imposed on the Contractor by Clause 66 of the Main Contract in respect of any decision given by the Engineer thereunder insofar as such decision affects the Sub-Contract Works.

This is a new Clause requiring timely notice in writing of any dispute under the Sub-Contract. No such provision was included in the "old" Clause 18 although, where a Sub-Contract dispute also affected the Main Contract, there was an implied duty to give timely notice of relevant facts in Clauses 3 and 10.[1] The need for the new Clause arises from the amendments to Sub-Clause 18(2) and, in particular, to the last sentence of that Sub-Clause.

---

[1] In particular, "old" Clause 3(4) (breach of Sub-Contract by Sub-Contractor) and "old" Clause 10(3) (Sub-Contractor's breach preventing recovery of money under the Main Contract); also "old" Clause 10(1) (Sub-Contractor to give return, notice etc.).

# COMMENTARY ON THE RULES

# Chapter 7

# APPOINTMENT AND POWERS

The next four chapters contain a commentary on the ICE Arbitration Procedure, the Rules being dealt with in numerical order. Each entry consists of a Rule or part of a Rule followed by notes and comment and is sometimes preceded by an introduction.

## PART A: REFERENCE AND APPOINTMENT

### Introduction

The first part of the Procedure sets out a largely mechanical process for obtaining an appointment. Parties to a dispute or their advisers are quite able to accomplish these steps without rules. But experience shows that serious and avoidable delays can occur at this stage, and the purpose of the Rules is thus to minimise such delay.

### Rule 1: Notice to Refer

1.1   A dispute or difference shall be deemed to arise when a claim or assertion made by one party is rejected by the other party and that rejection is not accepted. Subject only to Clause 66(1) of the *ICE Conditions of Contract* (if applicable) either party may then invoke arbitration by serving a *Notice to Refer* on the other party.

1.2   The Notice to Refer shall list the matters which the issuing party wishes to be referred to arbitration. Where Clause 66 of the ICE Conditions of Contract applies the Notice to Refer shall also state the date when the matters listed therein were referred to the Engineer for his decision under Clause 66(1) and the date on which the Engineer gave his decision thereon or that he has failed to do so.

*Scope of the Rule*

This Rule links the procedure under Clause 66 to the inception of an arbitration, when the question may arise—when is there an arbitrable dispute?

*When a dispute arises*

It is trite law that there must be a dispute before there can be a reference to arbitration. It is not enough that one party has asserted a claim. Until the other party has rejected it there is no dispute and thus nothing for an Arbitrator to decide. Mere failure to agree the claim is not enough. The other party may not be able to make up his own mind, or may prefer to postpone consideration of the claim until more facts are known, or until other claims can be considered at the same time. Only if such postponement becomes excessive may the Claimant infer rejection. Such an inference will not normally arise unless the Works have been completed, as only then can the final account be drafted.

Where there is no rejection of the claim itself, but merely a set-off, such a claim is not capable of arbitration, nor will the Courts grant a stay of proceedings to compel arbitration.[1]

### References to the Engineer

Under Clause 66(1) of the ICE Conditions, unless the parties otherwise agree, any dispute or difference must first be referred to the Engineer for a formal decision. Moreover, that decision is final and binding upon the parties unless the matter is referred to arbitration within three calendar months of the date of the decision. Once that three-month period has expired the right to arbitration on that matter (and, probably, to litigate thereon) is lost and no Arbitrator can have power to re-open an Engineer's decision which has thus become final and binding.[2]

If the Engineer fails to give his decision under Clause 66 within three calendar months of having been asked to do so, the matter may be referred to arbitration without his decision within a further three calendar months.[3] Once a valid reference to arbitration in default of a decision has been made, any later purported decision by the Engineer on that matter will be void and of no effect.

It should be noted that to satisfy Clause 66 there must be a reference to the Engineer under that Clause. The Engineer will give many and varied decisions during the course of the contract Works under many different provisions of the ICE Conditions. In so doing, he may well reject a claim by one or other of the parties. But if a party wishes to take that matter or decision to arbitration he must first refer it again asking for a decision under Clause 66. The Engineer is then bound to consider the matter afresh and to make a formal decision thereon. In so doing he may feel compelled to reverse his earlier opinion, in which case it may be the other party who then wishes to take the matter to arbitration.

Arbitration under Clause 66 is thus an appeal from the Engineer's formal decision. The Arbitrator is expressly empowered to open up and redetermine any decision, certificate or ruling of the Engineer.[4] He may also substitute his own engineering judgement for that of the Engineer. Where he elects to do so he is not necessarily saying that the Engineer was wrong, only that in the particular circumstances he considers a different solution to be more appropriate.

---

[1] See *Associated Bulk Carriers* v. *Koch* [1978] 2 A.E.R. 254.

[2] The Courts have power under s. 27 of the 1950 Act to extend the time within which any matter may be referred to arbitration.

[3] It is unclear whether the reference becomes time barred after the expiry of six months from the original request when the Engineer fails to give a decision. Arguably, there would be nothing to refer.

[4] This power is not available to a Judge hearing a dispute under the Contract unless the parties vest him with appropriate powers, e.g. by appointing an Official Referee as Arbitrator under s. 11 of the 1950 Act. See *Northern Regional Health Authority* v. *Derek Crouch* [1984] Q.B. 644.

*Notice to Refer*

This document *prima facie* defines the extent of the Arbitrator's jurisdiction. It should therefore contain a broad description of the matters to be referred so as not unduly to restrict any further or alternative contentions that the Claimant may wish to add. It should *not* be cluttered up with unnecessary detail, which is more appropriately dealt with in pleadings.[1]

Note that the Notice to Refer sets out only those disputes which the issuing party wishes to pursue. If his opponent wishes to pursue other claims[2] or disputes arising out of the same Contract, then unless the parties otherwise agree they must be referred to the Engineer for a decision under Clause 66 and a separate Notice to Refer must be given in respect thereof.[3]

## Rule 2: Appointment of sole Arbitrator by agreement

2.1  After serving the Notice to Refer either party may serve upon the other a *Notice to Concur* in the appointment of an Arbitrator listing therein the names and addresses of any persons he proposes as Arbitrator.

2.2  Within 14 days thereafter the other party shall

    (*a*) agree in writing to the appointment of one of the persons listed in the Notice to Concur

or  (*b*) propose a list of alternative persons.

2.3  Once agreement has been reached the issuing party shall write to the person so selected inviting him to accept the appointment enclosing a copy of the Notice to Refer and documentary evidence of the other party's agreement.

2.4  If the person so selected accepts the appointment he shall notify the issuing party in writing and send a copy to the other party. The date of posting or service as the case may be of this notification shall be deemed to be the date on which the Arbitrator's appointment is completed.

*Scope of the Rule*

This Rule is intended to formalize the process of appointment by agreement. If the parties can agree informally on a suitable Arbitrator Rules 2.1 and 2.2 can, of course, be omitted. In such cases a single letter of invitation may be sent signed by both parties, or one party may write enclosing a letter of concurrence from the other.

The ICE publishes a List of Arbitrators containing details of the qualifications, experience and fields of interest of persons considered by the Institution to be competent to preside over arbitrations under Clause 66 of the ICE Conditions. While most persons so listed are naturally corporate members of the Institution, members of other professions are also included.

*Completion of appointment*

The appointment is not completed until the Arbitrator either accepts it unconditionally or until any terms proposed by the Arbitrator have been agreed and settled. Thus the Arbitrator may ask the parties to agree his fees at this stage or alternatively to accept a formula by which they shall be

---

[1]  See Chapter 8.
[2]  i.e. claims by way of set-off which the issuing party may not as yet have rejected.
[3]  See also Rule 4.

calculated at the end of the reference.[1] Where the parties have not themselves so agreed, the Arbitrator may stipulate that the ICE Procedure shall apply to the arbitration,[2] as contemplated by Clause 66 of the ICE Conditions of Contract.

## Rule 3: Appointment of sole Arbitrator by the President

3.1 If within one calendar month from service of the Notice to Concur the parties fail to appoint an Arbitrator in accordance with Rule 2 either party may then apply to the President to appoint an Arbitrator. The parties may also agree to apply to the President without a notice to Concur.

3.2 Such application shall be in writing and shall include copies of the Notice to Refer, the Notice to Concur (if any) and any other relevant documents. The application shall be accompanied by the appropriate fee.

3.3 The Institution will send a copy of the application to the other party stating that the President intends to make the appointment on a specified date. Having first contacted an appropriate person and obtained his agreement the President will make the appointment on the specified date or such later date as may be appropriate which shall then be deemed to be the date on which the Arbitrator's appointment is completed. The Institution will notify both parties and the Arbitrator in writing as soon as possible thereafter.

*Scope of the Rule*

This Rule amplifies the procedure for a Presidential appointment as laid down in Clause 66 of the ICE Conditions of Contract.

It is preferable that the parties choose their own Arbitrator under Rule 2. There is no limit to the time that they may take in reaching agreement. However, it sometimes occurs that neither side will accept any person suggested by the other side, or one side persists in taking no action. In such a situation, provided that one calendar month has elapsed since the Notice to Refer was served, either party may ask the President of the ICE to appoint an Arbitrator. Alternatively, both parties may agree at the outset to leave it to the President to appoint.

Application for an appointment by the President should preferably be made using the documents designed for the purpose.[3] But an ordinary letter will suffice, provided that it contains all the information required in a formal Notice to Concur and is accompanied by any other necessary documents.

*Action by the President*

Before making the appointment the President[4] will inform the person selected of the nature of the dispute and the identity of the parties to ensure, as far as possible, that the nominee will be truly independent. Once the appointment has been made it cannot be revoked except by the Court or by agreement of both parties. Again, where each party has rejected all the names put forward by the other party, the President may still validly

---

[1] See Chapter 8.
[2] See Rule 26.1.
[3] See Appendix IV.
[4] Or the Institution's Arbitration Officer acting on his behalf.

appoint one of the persons so named. Such appointments are rare, but not unknown, and are most likely where the disputes involve a field of expertise where few are competent to sit in judgment. And, provided that the appointment has been made in good faith, the Courts may well be loath to remove an Arbitrator so appointed.

*Action by appointee*

It should be noted that there is no opportunity for a Presidentially appointed Arbitrator to stipulate that his fees be agreed in advance. He will usually (in his own interest) take an early opportunity of informing the parties what or how he intends to charge.[1] But if they object his appointment is not thereby nullified and the Arbitrator can and, indeed, must proceed with the reference. The parties' interests are not prejudiced thereby, as there always remains the right to challenge the Arbitrator's fees under s. 19 of the 1950[2] Act before taking up his Award.

The Arbitrator may stipulate that the ICE Arbitration Procedure shall apply to the arbitration and, if the parties do not accept this, they may terminate the appointment within 14 days under Rule 26.1 (below). However, Clause 66 gives the President power to direct that the ICE Procedure shall apply. In this case both parties and the Arbitrator are bound thereby unless all three agree otherwise. A Presidential direction was rarely, if ever, made under the 1973 Procedure. But such direction will be the rule in future unless the parties can advance very good reasons why the 1983 Procedure ought not to apply.[3]

## Rule 4: Notice of further disputes or differences

4.1 At any time before the Arbitrator's appointment is completed either party may put forward further disputes or differences to be referred to him. This shall be done by serving upon the other party an additional Notice to Refer in accordance with Rule 1.

4.2 Once his appointment is completed the Arbitrator shall have jurisdiction over any issue connected with and necessary to the determination of any dispute or difference already referred to him whether or not the connected issue has first been referred to the Engineer for his decision under Clause 66(1) of the ICE Conditions of Contract.

*Scope of the Rule*

These provisions cover the addition to the arbitration of disputes beyond those mentioned in the original Notice to Refer.

*New disputes*

Rule 4.1 deals with the addition of wholly new issues. It is self-evident that, until an Arbitrator has been appointed, it is open to either party to add

---

[1]  But he is not bound to do so.

[2]  By paying the disputed fees into Court, pending taxation.

[3]  Both the Institution's Arbitration Advisory Board and its Advisory Committee on Contract Administration and Law have advised that the President should direct that the Procedure shall apply in all cases, subject to his first considering any objections by the parties.

further disputes or differences to those to be referred. Each new dispute must have been referred to the Engineer under Clause 66(1) of the ICE Conditions of Contract (if it applies) and must be the subject of or included in a Notice to Refer in accordance with Rule 1.

Once the Arbitrator has been appointed, wholly new issues may be added only with his consent and, it would seem, with the concurrence of the other party. The first condition follows from the contract between the Arbitrator and the parties[1] which comes into existence at the moment of his appointment and cannot thereafter be varied without his consent. As to the second condition, the Arbitrator has been selected by reference to the subject matter of the original disputes and the parties cannot be assumed necessarily to have accepted him as being suitable to deal also with different disputes.

Should either party object to the addition of a wholly new dispute, application may be made to the President under Rule 3. If this is done, the existence of the first Arbitrator seized of one or more disputes under the same Contract may be one of the factors to be taken into consideration when making the fresh appointment.

### Connected disputes

Rule 4.2 is intended to deal with a different situation. When a dispute is first referred to arbitration the parties may think that they know what the real issues are but, as the case is prepared for Hearing, other aspects of the problem may arise. This may lead to the formulation of separate issues which, while relevant to the determination of the issues as originally envisaged, have not themselves been referred to the Engineer under Clause 66(1). Rule 4.2 therefore provides that such collateral or subsidiary issues may be dealt with without the delay which would ensue if the proceedings were adjourned to permit a Clause 66(1) reference. Whether or not such an additional issue is within the Rule is a matter to be decided by the Arbitrator.

Under the Rule the new issue must be both connected with and necessary to the determination of an existing dispute. Whether a connection exists may involve issues of fact or law.[2] Necessity is likely to be an issue of fact only. But even where the new issue is both connected and necessary, the Arbitrator might still take the view that it ought first to be considered by the Engineer, and he could on that ground refuse to deal with it until the Engineer's decision was known. However, the same result could be achieved by asking the Engineer to appear before him to give evidence.

## PART B: POWERS OF THE ARBITRATOR

### Introduction

Most of the powers set out in Part B of the ICE Procedure are either inherent in all Arbitrators by virtue of the common law or can be granted

---

[1] See Chapter 2.

[2] If the connection between "old" and "new" issues is factual the Arbitrator's decision is final and without appeal. If the connection is a matter of law, however (e.g. if it turns on a point of relevancy), the Courts may have power to intervene (see Chapter 5).

by the Court to the Arbitrator under s. 5 of the 1979 Act, or relate to functions that the Court itself can perform on behalf of the parties or the Arbitrator under s. 12 of the 1950 Act. Indeed, s. 12(1) of the 1950 Act itself confers very wide powers on the Arbitrator.[1] But, until now, most Arbitrators seem to have been loath to exercise them, in particular where non-legal Arbitrators have been confronted by Counsel seeking to persuade them to act or refrain from action for the benefit of their respective clients.

It is expected that, by codifying the more important powers of all three varieties into one set of Rules, the "lay" Arbitrator will be encouraged to wield them with confidence and despatch, so that engineering arbitration may regain the vigour and efficiency which in recent years it has lacked.

## Rule 5: Power to control the proceedings

5.1 The Arbitrator may exercise any or all of the powers set out or necessarily to be implied in this Procedure on such terms as he thinks fit. These terms may include orders as to costs, time for compliance and the consequences of non-compliance.

5.2 Powers under this Procedure shall be in addition to any other powers available to the Arbitrator.

*Scope of the Rule*

This Rule is mainly declaratory, as an introduction to the more detailed Rules which follow.

*"Such terms as he thinks fit"*

The power of an Arbitrator to impose terms is at the root of the current malaise affecting construction arbitration. While the Courts can call on the powers of the State to enforce their orders, an Arbitrator is much more limited. Under the ICE Procedure the Arbitrator will now have at his disposal important new powers including ordering the deposit of money (Rule 6.1(c)), proceeding to hear the parties and/or the issues in any order and at any time (Rules 8.1, 8.3 and 15.1) and debarring a party in default (Rule 11.4) or proceeding in his absence (Rule 15.4).

*"Other powers"*

The other powers include powers conferred by common law or by statute, or (in countries other than England and Wales) by the arbitration law of the country in which the arbitration is held, and any extra powers which the parties themselves may give to the Arbitrator (provided that such extra powers are not repugnant to the general law).

## Rule 6: Power to order protective measures

6.1 The Arbitrator shall have power
   (a) to give directions for the detention storage sale or disposal of the whole or any part of the subject matter of the dispute at the expense of one or both of the parties
   (b) to give directions for the preservation of any document or thing which is or may become evidence in the arbitration

---

[1] See Chapter 3.

     (*c*)  to order the deposit of money or other security to secure the whole or any part of the amount(s) in dispute

     (*d*)  to make an order for security for costs in favour of one or more of the parties

and  (*e*)  to order his own costs to be secured.

6.2  Money ordered to be paid under this Rule shall be paid without delay into a separate bank account in the name of a stakeholder to be appointed by and subject to the directions of the Arbitrator.

### *Scope and origin of the Rule*

The powers set out under Rules 6.1(a), 6.1(b) and 6.1(d) are adapted from powers otherwise exercisable by the High Court on application by one of the parties to an arbitration.[1] That under Rule 6.1(c) is analogous to the power of the High Court to order money to be "paid into Court" as a condition of granting some other relief, for example, one which would otherwise prejudice the other party. Such power should be exercised sparingly—see, for example, Rule 14.2 (below). An example of the exercise of such a power by the Court might be where the Respondent applies for a last-minute adjournment to raise a new defence. He may be granted such an adjournment only on condition that the sum in issue or part of it is placed on deposit with a stakeholder. Note that the power is *not* intended to be used against a Respondent whose only fault is lack of means.

In such a case, however, the Claimant may be able to obtain protection when proceeding against a foreign Respondent. The Courts have recently developed a device known as a "Mareva injunction"[2] whereby the assets in this country of a non-resident party may be secured to prevent dissipation or removal pending the outcome of the case. No Arbitrator can make such an order and it will be for the party seeking such relief to apply to the Court in the usual way.

### *Security for costs*

The ground upon which security for costs may be ordered (Rule 6.1(d)) is that the Claimant (or the Respondent when bringing a counterclaim) may, if unsuccessful, be unable to pay his opponent's costs.[3] It would be a ground for *not* ordering such security if the parties have adopted the Short Procedure under Part F of these Rules, under which there is normally no power to award costs to the successful party.

## Rule 7: Power to order concurrent Hearings

7.1  Where disputes or differences have arisen under two or more contracts each concerned wholly or mainly with the same subject matter and the resulting arbitrations have been referred to the same Arbitrator he may with the agreement of all the parties concerned or upon the application of one of the parties being a party to all the contracts involved order that the whole or any part of the matters at issue shall be heard together upon such terms or conditions as the Arbitrator thinks fit.

---

[1]  Arbitration Act 1950, s. 12(6).

[2]  See *Mareva* v. *International Bulk Carriers* [1975] 2 Lloyd's Rep. 509.

[3]  See Companies Act 1948, s. 447 and *Parkinson* v. *Triplan* [1973].

7.2 Where an order for concurrent Hearings has been made under Rule 7.1 the Arbitrator shall nevertheless make and publish separate Awards unless the parties otherwise agree but the Arbitrator may if he thinks fit prepare one combined set of Reasons to cover all the Awards.

*Scope of the Rule*

This Rule is directed at disputes involving both the Main Contract and one or more Sub-Contracts. Joinder of arbitrations, although strongly advocated by the Commercial Courts Committee,[1] was not included in the 1979 Act, nor is there anything in arbitration analogous to third-party proceedings in the High Court. However, there can be no objection to the adoption of a procedure which avoids or minimises duplication of Hearings and the attendant risk of different Awards on the same subject matter. This Rule provides such a procedure.

Even where all parties are in agreement the Arbitrator's consent is still needed because it is for him alone to decide how best to dispose of the issues before him. The point does not arise where all parties agree to concurrent Hearings *before* the Arbitrator is appointed, as he will then be bound by that agreement. However, this would produce a single arbitration with more than two parties rather than a combination of separate two-party arbitrations, and Rule 7 would not then apply.

The Arbitrator apart, the application of Rule 7 depends upon the party who is common to all the Contracts. Unless that party agrees, the Arbitrator cannot order combined Hearings.

## Rule 8: Powers at the Hearing

8.1 The Arbitrator may hear the parties their representatives and/or witnesses at any time or place and may adjourn the arbitration for any period on the application of any party or as he thinks fit.

8.2 Any party may be represented by any person including in the case of a company or other legal entity a director officer employee or beneficiary of such company or entity. In particular, a person shall not be prevented from representing a party because he is or may be also a witness in the proceedings. Nothing shall prevent a party from being represented by different persons at different times.

8.3 Nothing in these Rules or in any other rule custom or practice shall prevent the Arbitrator from starting to hear the arbitration once his appointment is completed or at any time thereafter.

8.4 Any meeting with or summons before the Arbitrator at which both parties are represented shall if the Arbitrator so directs be treated as part of the hearing of the arbitration.

*Scope and object of the Rule*

These provisions codify existing powers, the full import of which, however, is not always appreciated. It must be remembered that, unlike a Court action, an arbitration does not need to be "set down" for trial, nor is there need for a formal opening. Moreover, while in an action before the Court it is the parties who must take the initiative, in arbitration the

---

[1] *Report on Arbitration*, Cmnd. 7284, HMSO, 1978, by analogy with R.S.C. Ord. 4, r. 10.

Arbitrator has—if not a duty—a positive discretion to ensure so far as may be possible that progress in the reference is maintained.[1]

One of the objects of the new Procedure is to achieve a large measure of flexibility. Often, by the time the Arbitrator has been appointed, the parties have already prepared and considered more-or-less formal claims and counterclaims. In such a case there is no reason why the Arbitrator should not proceed at once to a Hearing. For this purpose, therefore, any meeting attended by both parties or their representatives may suffice as part of the Hearing provided that the ordinary rules of natural justice are observed, and Rules 8.3 and 8.4 expressly provide that this shall be so.

*Representation*

Rule 8.2 makes it clear that a party may be represented in any way that he thinks fit before the Arbitrator. Common sense indicates that some matters are best handled by managers or technical experts, others by Solicitors and still others by Counsel. Moreover, there is no exclusive right of audience before an Arbitrator and the same person may well be able to discharge different functions at different stages of an arbitration. And if a party sees fit to change advocates part-way through a Hearing (for example), he is unlikely to prejudice anyone but himself. In the unlikely event of a purely tactical switch intended to discountenance the other side, the Arbitrator has ample power to rectify matters by ordering an adjournment with such order for costs as may be appropriate.

Rule 8.2 removes any possible doubt that a person may be disqualified from acting as advocate before the Arbitrator by any convention, custom or rule of law. Thus, while a Barrister or Solicitor appearing before the Courts may not usually give evidence in the same proceedings, any such disability before the Arbitrator is expressly removed by the Rule. But the Rule is aimed primarily at engineers, quantity surveyors and others who are necessarily witnesses in a case, but who may also be required (or wish) to conduct the case or part of the case as advocates.

## Rule 9: Power to appoint assessors or to seek outside advice

9.1 The Arbitrator may appoint a legal technical or other assessor to assist him in the conduct of the arbitration. The Arbitrator shall direct when such assessor is to attend hearings of the arbitration.

9.2 The Arbitrator may seek legal technical or other advice on any matter arising out of or in connection with the proceedings.

9.3 Further and/or alternatively the Arbitrator may rely upon his own knowledge and expertise to such extent as he thinks fit.

*Scope of the Rule*

The Arbitrator will usually have been chosen because of his expertise in the subject matter of the dispute. But issues involving other fields of knowledge often arise in arbitration. This Rule allows the Arbitrator of his own motion to obtain advice and, if he deems it necessary, to appoint an

---

[1] *Per* Lord Diplock in *Bremer Vulkan* v. *South India Shipping* [1981] A.C. 909, at pp. 983–984.

assessor to sit with him and to hear the evidence and arguments put forward by the parties.

The Arbitrator may make his own choice of adviser or assessor, although he should take account of any views thereon which the parties may put forward. Unless both parties otherwise agree, it will be for the Arbitrator to pay the fees and expenses of the adviser or assessor that he appoints.[1]

While he is entitled to take into consideration the views of his adviser or assessor, it is a fundamental principle that the Arbitrator must make his own decision on the issues before him.

*Arbitrator's knowledge*

It is axiomatic that a technical Arbitrator will rely on his own expertise. But he is entitled to do so only to interpret or augment the evidence adduced by the parties. He is *not* entitled to supply evidence from his own experience which the parties have not seen fit to put before him, and if he does so he may commit misconduct.[2] Nevertheless, while relying on his own expertise, he should ensure that any view which he forms which differs from those canvassed at the Hearing is made known to the parties before he makes his Award, and the parties should then be given an opportunity of dealing with it.

Such considerations are even more important where the Arbitrator has actual knowledge which is relevant to the issues. The parties must always be told of this and must be given an opportunity both of addressing the Arbitrator on the matter and of adducing further evidence if they so wish.[3]

---

[1] The Arbitrator's terms of appointment should therefore be wide enough to enable him to recover such payment from the parties.

[2] See Chapter 5.

[3] See *Fox* v. *Wellfair* [1981] 2 Lloyd's Rep. 514; 19 B.L.R. 52.

# Chapter 8

# PROCEDURE

*PART C: PROCEDURE BEFORE THE HEARING*

## Rule 10: The preliminary meeting

10.1   As soon as possible after accepting the appointment the Arbitrator shall summon the parties to a preliminary meeting for the purpose of giving such directions about the procedure to be adopted in the arbitration as he considers necessary.

10.2   At the preliminary meeting the parties and the Arbitrator shall consider whether and to what extent

  (*a*)  Part F (Short Procedure) or Part G (Special Procedure for Experts) of these Rules shall apply
  (*b*)  the arbitration may proceed on documents only
  (*c*)  progress may be facilitated and costs saved by determining some of the issues in advance of the main Hearing
  (*d*)  the parties should enter into an exclusion agreement (if they have not already done so) in accordance with s. 3 of the Arbitration Act 1979 (where the Act applies to the arbitration)

and in general shall consider such other steps as may minimise delay and expedite the determination of the real issues between the parties.

10.3   If the parties so wish they may themselves agree directions and submit them to the Arbitrator for his approval. In so doing the parties shall state whether or not they wish Part F or Part G of these Rules to apply. The Arbitrator may then approve the directions as submitted or (having first consulted the parties) may vary them or substitute his own as he thinks fit.

*Scope of the Rule*

This Rule governs the important preliminary step of holding a meeting to consider directions. Note that, after appointment of the Arbitrator and adoption of this Procedure, the form of the arbitration still remains to be directed or agreed.

It is mandatory for the Arbitrator to summon a meeting, although the parties are not bound to attend and may agree their own directions, subject to Rule 10.3.

*Purpose of the meeting*

Once he has been appointed the Arbitrator should be concerned to ensure that no time is wasted in getting the arbitration under way. The simplest means of achieving this is to meet the parties or their representatives face to face. Yet there is often considerable reluctance to hold such a meeting at the start of the reference. In some cases this may be due to a laudable desire to save costs. But, where lawyers are involved, it may also reflect the influence of High Court practice where fixed procedures and standardised timetables apply. Thus in the High Court it is left to the parties themselves to progress the action unless and until one of them elects to issue a Summons to invoke the Court's assistance. In arbitration there are no fixed timetables to be applied. Thus, the importance of holding a preliminary meeting as soon as possible cannot be overemphasized.

The formal purpose of a preliminary meeting is to decide upon the procedure most suited to the speedy and efficient determination of the matters at issue. All too frequently, much time and money is wasted in attempting to agree directions in correspondence. Yet real progress is seldom achieved until there is a meeting with the Arbitrator. It follows that the preliminary meeting should take place as soon as possible. It is most desirable that any advocates or representatives whom the parties may wish to employ should come to the meeting properly briefed about the disputes, and able adequately to inform the Arbitrator about them. This is not to say that attempts should never be made to agree directions in advance. But experience indicates that a better result is almost always achieved if the procedures to be adopted have been discussed face to face.

### Consideration of Special Procedures

If Part F (Short Procedure) or Part G (Special Procedure for Experts) is to be adopted it is desirable that this should be decided at the outset. This can lead to difficulty where one or both parties are contemplating representation by Counsel. The parties or their representatives may be reluctant to commit themselves to unfamiliar procedures which will restrict the involvement of advocates. But in appropriate cases the Arbitrator should urge the parties to agree to expedited procedures. Once accepted, advocates will in practice find little difficulty in adapting themselves to the new procedures, and the parties will benefit from savings in time and cost.

### Rule 10.2—"Whether and to what extent"

The parties may agree to apply part only of the special procedures. For example, the Short Procedure might be adopted subject to reserving the right to cross-examine one particular witness, who may be crucial to the case. Where this is done the parties should also consider the question of costs.[1]

### Rule 10.2(b)—"Documents only"

The parties are free to adopt any procedure that they may wish, without resorting to the special procedures available. They would be well advised, however, to work out their intentions in detail, for which purpose they may use the special procedures as a guide or check list.

### Rule 10.2(c)—"Determining some of the issues in advance"

See Rule 15.1 for the powers of the Arbitrator as to the order in which he will hear the issues and/or the parties.

---

[1] See Rules 21.1 and 23.2.

*Rule 10.3*

Circumstances may be such as to favour agreement of directions without a preliminary meeting, for instance, when the Arbitrator and the parties are in different countries or the amounts of money at issue are small. The procedure in Rule 10.3 may then be applied. But the Arbitrator retains a discretion to vary the directions, and he may still ask for a preliminary meeting if he feels that it is necessary. Consultation with the parties may be by letter, telephone or other appropriate means.

## Rule 11: Pleadings and discovery

11.1 The Arbitrator may order the parties to deliver pleadings or statements of their cases in any form he thinks appropriate. The Arbitrator may order any party to answer the other party's case and to give reasons for any disagreement.

11.2 The Arbitrator may order any party to deliver in advance of formal discovery copies of any documents in his possession custody or power which relate either generally or specifically to matters raised in any pleading statement or answer.

11.3 Any pleading statement or answer shall contain sufficient detail for the other party to know the case he has to answer. If sufficient detail is not provided the Arbitrator may of his own motion or at the request of the other party order further and better particulars to be delivered.

11.4 If a party fails to comply with any order made under this Rule the Arbitrator shall have power to debar that party from relying on the matters in respect of which he is in default and the Arbitrator may proceed with the arbitration and make his Award accordingly. Provided that the Arbitrator shall first give notice to the party in default that he intends to proceed under this Rule.

*Scope of the Rule*

The Arbitrator has power, outside the Procedure, to order pleadings and discovery. This Rule seeks to ensure that he does not simply follow High Court practice (in which these matters are subject to fixed rules), and gives him express power to decide the appropriate form for pleadings and, in effect, to order discovery by stages.

*Pleadings and discovery*

In litigation, the purpose of formal pleadings is to define the issues which are really in dispute between the parties and to discard anything not relevant. A proper pleading should set out the matters in which the party is aggrieved, the facts upon which he intends to rely and the remedies that he seeks. The documentary evidence to support the claims is not normally included, being the subject of a separate and subsequent procedure known as "discovery". In giving discovery the parties exchange lists of all relevant documents in their possession, custody or power. Each party then inspects the other's documents and an agreed bundle is assembled therefrom.

This formal procedure may also be followed in arbitration. Indeed, in very heavy and complicated matters it may well be the best procedure available. It is also the procedure with which professional lawyers are most familiar and the one for which, consciously or unconsciously, they will naturally tend to press. However, in the majority of engineering disputes both parties are usually in possession of most of the relevant documents and, having already prepared their submissions to the Engineer under Clause 66(1) of the ICE Conditions, they will be well aware of the nature of the dispute.

Rule 11.1 therefore permits the use of simple statements of case in lieu of formal pleadings. Rule 11.2 allows the Arbitrator to order delivery of documents in advance of formal discovery, so that documents may be disclosed before pleadings, or pleadings may be ordered to be served with documents annexed.

### Form of pleadings

Informal statements of case can be in any convenient form. In engineering disputes it may often suffice to deliver copies of the parties' original submissions to the Engineer together with such further material as the party may wish to put to the Arbitrator. Indeed, an acceptable format for a pleading could well be a purely formal "front sheet" with the original submission to the Engineer attached thereto.[1] But, whatever format is adopted, it should always be remembered that the Arbitrator is himself expert in the matters at issue, unlike a Judge who is allowed to know little more than the law. Much that must be included in pleadings for an action in Court can with advantage be omitted in arbitration. Thus, for example, the Arbitrator will be well acquainted with the ICE Conditions of Contract and there is no need to transcribe a multitude of Clauses into the pleadings. Again, "terms of art" and technical words with special meanings may be used without necessarily defining them when drafting for an expert Arbitrator, and technical explanations and arguments can be curtailed. In any event, if the claims have already been prepared in engineering terms, nothing will be gained (and much may be lost) in merely recasting them in legal parlance. Finally, it is often helpful to include a brief summary of existing documents, whether or not these are attached to the pleading.

Similarly, all that may be required from the Respondent by way of defence may be a brief statement of the reasons why the existing claim has been rejected. A defence, whatever its form, must deal with every claim put forward by the Claimant. However, having dealt with the main issues, it may suffice to cover other matters not expressly pleaded to in the defence by including a general denial.[2]

### Formal discovery

Formal discovery is not dealt with in the Procedure. The parties may insist on full formal discovery if they wish,[3] but this is a long and expensive process which also tends to prolong any Hearing by generating large numbers of documents, some of doubtful relevance. If partial discovery under Rule 11.2 is thought to be insufficient the parties may seek to obtain the necessary documents by selective requests, as an alternative to wholesale discovery.

---

[1]  See Appendix V for a selection of "model forms".
[2]  See Appendix V.
[3]  See s. 12(6) of the 1950 Act and R.S.C. Ord. 25.

*Further and better particulars*

One of the least helpful contributions by lawyers, in the eyes of many Arbitrators, is the excessive requesting and giving of further and better particulars. While it is difficult to limit the practice, Rule 11.3 offers the Arbitrator an opportunity to control the supply of particulars. Where such requests are justified, costs may sometimes be saved by requesting and giving particulars by letter rather than in formal subsidiary pleadings.

*Default of a party*

Rule 11.4 gives the Arbitrator express power, having first given due notice of his intention, to debar any party from relying on a matter in respect of which he has failed to comply with an order of the Arbitrator. Without such a power, a defaulting party may often ignore interlocutory orders with impunity. Experience in the High Court shows that any order which threatens debarring (colloquially referred to as an "unless" order) almost invariably produces some measure of compliance within the time limit set. There is no reason to suppose that similar orders by an Arbitrator will not meet with equal success. In a proper case the Court will not hesitate to use its debarring power, and Arbitrators should be prepared to follow suit where milder measures are likely to fail.

## Rule 12: Procedural meetings

12.1   The Arbitrator may at any time call such procedural meetings as he deems necessary to identify or clarify the issues to be decided and the procedures to be adopted. For this purpose the Arbitrator may request particular persons to attend on behalf of the parties.

12.2   Either party may at any time apply to the Arbitrator for leave to appear before him on any interlocutory matter. The Arbitrator may call a procedural meeting for the purpose or deal with the application in correspondence or otherwise as he thinks fit.

12.3   At any procedural meeting or otherwise the Arbitrator may give such directions as he thinks fit for the proper conduct of the arbitration. Whether or not formal pleadings have been ordered under Rule 11 such directions may include an order that either or both parties shall prepare in writing and shall serve upon the other party and the Arbitrator any or all of the following

> (a)  a summary of that party's case
> (b)  a summary of that party's evidence
> (c)  a statement or summary of the issues between the parties
> (d)  a list and/or a summary of the documents relied upon
> (e)  a statement or summary of any other matters likely to assist the resolution of the disputes or differences between the parties.

*Scope of the Rule*

This Rule seeks to place the initiative in calling procedural meetings firmly in the Arbitrator's hands so that he may consider and review the progress of the reference.

Parties are often reluctant to attend meetings in which they see no particular advantage for themselves. This may stem from a possibly deep-seated conviction that an arbitration should be conducted by the parties' lawyers. To counteract this, Rule 12.1 encourages the Arbitrator to adopt a positive role. Conversely, where the Arbitrator is asked to hold a meeting for some comparatively trivial purpose (such as granting an extension of time), Rule 12.2 allows him to deal with this in a summary manner.

### *"The Arbitrator may request"*

The Arbitrator cannot enforce the attendance of any particular person as contemplated by Rule 12.1. But the parties are usually anxious to appear to be helpful and will try to ensure that the person requested does attend. Thus, for example, the appearance of the Engineer at an early meeting may well do much to dispel misunderstanding, to the benefit of both parties.

### *Summaries and statements*

The summaries listed in Rule 12.3 are often of assistance in assimilating the issues, the evidence and the parties' contentions. Such documents are often prepared by the parties during a Hearing, and there is no good reason why they should not be prepared in advance at the Arbitrator's direction. A prime object of such a procedure would be to ensure that everyone concerned, the Arbitrator as well as the parties, is well versed in the issues at the start of the Hearing so that undue time is not taken up before the real issues are reached.

## Rule 13: Preparation for the Hearing

13.1   In addition to his powers under Rules 11 and 12 the Arbitrator shall also have power
> (*a*) to order that the parties shall agree facts as facts and figures as figures where possible
>
> (*b*) to order the parties to prepare an agreed bundle of all documents relevant to the arbitration. The agreed bundle shall thereby be deemed to have been entered in evidence without further proof and without being read out at the Hearing. Provided always that either party may at the Hearing challenge the admissibility of any document in the agreed bundle.
>
> (*c*) to order that any experts whose reports have been exchanged before the Hearing shall be examined by the Arbitrator in the presence of the parties or their legal representatives and not by the parties or their legal representatives themselves. Where such an order is made either party may put questions whether by way of cross-examination or re-examination to any party's expert after all experts have been examined by the Arbitrator provided that the party so doing shall first give notice of the nature of the questions he wishes to put.

13.2   Before the Hearing the Arbitrator may and shall if so requested by the parties read the documents to be used at the Hearing. For this or any other purpose the Arbitrator may require all such documents to be delivered to him at such time and place as he may specify.

### *Scope of the Rule*

This Rule deals with orders which may be made in respect of various categories of evidence. The object is to streamline procedure at the Hearing, to cut out wasted effort and to save time and costs.

*Facts and figures*

In many cases the bulk of the facts concerning the Works will not be at issue. Both parties will be well aware of what happened on site and, even when they are not, a simple comparison of their respective site records will usually reveal a wide measure of concurrence. Again, the Engineer's Representative will have measured[1] the Works with the assistance or at least in the presence of the Contractor's Agent each month for the regular Interim Valuation and dayworks records can and, indeed, should have been agreed on the spot and signed by both sides as a true record of fact without prejudice to liability.[2] Thus both parties will usually know *what* happened on site, the dispute being about *why* it happened or who is to pay for it.

Again, once claims have been submitted by the Contractor and investigated by the Engineer, there will usually be a fair volume of facts and figures which both sides will utilise during negotiations. For example, quantity may be accepted where quality is not, or opinions may differ as to which of several differing rates shall apply to certain items of work where the validity of the rates themselves is not challenged. Clearly, a large volume of facts and figures can usually be agreed as such without prejudice to disputes about their application. This helps to limit the proceedings before the Arbitrator to what really matters.

Rule 13.1(a) therefore empowers the Arbitrator to order the parties to agree facts as facts and figures as figures where possible. The Rule cannot itself secure any result and the Arbitrator may well consider it more to the point to enquire what steps have been taken to reduce areas of disagreement, particularly as to figures. If the parties ignore or appear to resist such enquiries an order of this kind may persuade them to reconsider their attitude. If not, they are thereby put on notice that, if it appears to the Arbitrator that one side has prolonged the proceedings unnecessarily, he is likely to be penalised in costs.

It may happen that the parties themselves are willing to agree facts and figures but their advisers are not. This has been known where advisers are brought in from outside, or in "public sector" projects where a "paymaster" authority (not itself a party to the Contract) refuses to allow agreement before the formal Hearing. In such cases a preremptory order under Rule 13.1(a) may break the deadlock.

*Documentary evidence*

In disputes of any substance the parties or their advisers invariably prepare an "agreed bundle" from the documents disclosed by each side. Technically, the production and admission of documents does not make them evidence in the arbitration.[3] The effect of Rule 13.1(b) is therefore that the bundle of documents, once agreed, will become evidence, subject to the right subsequently to challenge any particular document. The popular belief that documents do not become evidence until they are read out at the Hearing is wrong, and the Arbitrator may properly refuse to

---

[1]  ICE Conditions of Contract, Clause 56(3).
[2]  See *ibid.*, Clause 52(3).
[3]  17 *Halsbury's Laws*, para. 136.

allow time at the Hearing to be taken up by the reading of documents "into the record".

The fact that a document is admitted as evidence does not mean that what the document contains is admitted. Other parties may challenge the correctness of the contents by cross-examining the author (if available) or adducing their own evidence in refutation. Where the contents of a document are challenged but the author cannot be called to prove its truth, notice under the Civil Evidence Acts[1] may be given. This gives the tribunal a discretion to admit the document as evidence of its contents. In construction disputes it is common for documents such as site diaries, dayworks records, drawings and the like to be accepted as evidence of their content without formal Civil Evidence Acts notices. The Arbitrator should, however, take due note of the circumstances when considering their credibility.

### The agreed bundle

It is common for the parties to include in the agreed bundle a copy of every document which could conceivably refer to the Contract or to the carrying out of the Works. This practice is unnecessary, very wasteful, and can impede the conduct of the Hearing through the sheer weight of paper. While the lists of documents exchanged by the parties must be complete, it is vital during subsequent inspection that only those documents which are relevant to the matters at issue are included in the agreed bundle.

Such careful examination of what is inevitably a great mound of documents is a slow and tedious task. It is too often left to an assistant who knows little of the issues and less about engineering and who will include everything least he omits something vital. It cannot be overemphasized that inspection must always be done by persons well acquainted with their party's case, and with appropriate expert advice if they are not themselves qualified in engineering. The aim should be to assemble the smallest possible bundle containing only documents that are essential to the parties' cases. Should any document be omitted which is later found to be necessary it can readily be introduced, preferably before the Hearing but if necessary at any time up to the making of the Award. Provided that its omission was an oversight and the other party is allowed time to consider it, no harm will result.

### Experts under Rule 13.1(c)

Rule 13.1(c) deals with evidence of opinion produced by the parties' experts.[2] As with an action before the Courts, a civil engineering arbitration is subject to the Civil Evidence Act 1972[3] and to Rules of Court on the conditions upon which expert evidence may be given.[4] Such Rules require a party wishing to call expert evidence to obtain leave, which is usually given on terms requiring disclosure of the substance of any expert's

---

[1]   See Civil Evidence Act 1968, s. 10(3) and R.S.C. Ord. 38, rr. 20–34.
[2]   And see Rules 16 and 22.
[3]   S. 5(2).
[4]   S. 2(4).

report.[1] The same rules apply in Arbitration, subject to such modifications as may be appropriate,[2] and subject to any other agreement.

Rule 13.1(c) represents a compromise between High Court procedure and the special procedure for experts in Part G of these Rules. The initial examination of all the experts is conducted by the Arbitrator, following which the parties may themselves ask further questions of their own and of opposing experts.

This "inquisitorial" approach is well within the Arbitrator's inherent powers at common law. It will often save time compared with the traditional "adversarial" system of formal examination, cross-examination and re-examination by the parties' advocates, not least because all the participants in the initial examination by the Arbitrator will talk the same professional language. Further time will be saved by exchanging experts' reports in advance, each witness then being free to concentrate upon the more important aspects of his evidence.

Notice is required of the nature of the questions to be put by the parties or their representatives after examination by the Arbitrator. Such notice need not be formal and may consist simply of telling the Arbitrator the point which it is desired to bring out. This requirement need not be oppressive but is included to discourage duplication.

Finally, it should be noted that, unlike the special procedure in Part G, Rule 13.1(c) does not require the consent of the parties.

*Reading the documents*

Rule 13.2 incorporates the growing and useful practice of having the tribunal read the documents in advance so that time is not wasted at the Hearing.[3] Where this is adopted, advocates must expect their opening to be truncated and should be prepared to go directly to the matters at issue.

## Rule 14: Summary Awards

14.1    The Arbitrator may at any time make a *Summary Award* and for this purpose shall have power to award payment by one party to another of a sum representing a reasonable proportion of the final nett amount which in his opinion that party is likely to be ordered to pay after determination of all the issues in the arbitration and after taking into account any defence or counterclaim upon which the other party may be entitled to rely.

14.2    The Arbitrator shall have power to order the party against whom a Summary Award is made to pay part or all of the sum awarded to a stakeholder. In default of compliance with such an order the Arbitrator may order payment of the whole sum in the Summary Award to the other party.

14.3    The Arbitrator shall have power to order payment of costs in relation to a Summary Award including power to order that such costs shall be paid forthwith.

14.4    A Summary Award shall be final and binding upon the parties unless and until it is varied by any subsequent Award made and published by the same Arbitrator or by any other arbitrator having jurisdiction over the matters in

---

[1]    R.S.C. Ord. 38, rr. 36 and 38.
[2]    Civil Evidence Act 1968, s. 10(3).
[3]    Cf. practice note (Court of Appeal: new procedure) [1982] 1 W.L.R. 1312.

dispute. Any such subsequent Award may order repayment of monies paid in accordance with the Summary Award.

## Scope and purpose of the Rule

The Supreme Court Rules permit the Court to give summary judgment in cases where there is no real defence to the plaintiff's claim, or to a substantial part of his claim. The procedure is covered by R.S.C. Ord. 14 and Ord. 29, part 2,[1] and enables the Court to reduce the matters at issue to those which are really in dispute.

No similar procedure is available in arbitration. There is power to make an *Interim Award* under s. 14 of the Arbitration Act 1950. But an Interim Award will be final as to the matters thereby determined,[2] so that the degree of proof required is the same as for a Final Award.

Rule 14[3] of the ICE Procedure has therefore been drafted by analogy with the Supreme Court Rules to provide a means of achieving the same procedural objective. The term *Summary Award* is original and is to be applied solely to an Award made under this Rule.

## Application for a Summary Award

As in the case of the High Court procedure, the Arbitrator must act on appropriate admissible evidence before making a Summary Award, but no form is laid down by the Rule. Normally, the party wishing to apply for a Summary Award will apply for directions, which may be done at the preliminary meeting, or under Rule 12.2, or otherwise. In many cases it may be appropriate for the Arbitrator to follow High Court practice and to direct that affidavits in support of and in opposition to the application shall be served in advance of the date for hearing the application.

The Rule will be of use where there is a sum owing to which there is no, or no serious, defence, for example, where earlier certificates not themselves at issue remain unpaid. In such circumstances there may be pressure on an impecunious Claimant to abandon or modify his claim lest payment against the earlier certificates be further delayed. Again, where the disputed claim is small in comparison with such arrears, the amount apparently at issue in the arbitration may be inflated, leading to a hardening of the parties' attitudes.

Rule 14 is wide enough to allow an Award where no specific sum can be identified as owing, but where it appears from the evidence that the creditor is bound in the end to obtain *some* award. However, the power will not be exercisable where liability is genuinely in issue, or where there is a set-off[4] which might extinguish the claim.

## Payment to stakeholder

The power in Rule 14.2 to order payment to a stakeholder is equivalent to the Court's power to order money to be paid into court. Clearly, the Arbitrator cannot receive the money himself (whether or not he has a

---

[1]   See *Supreme Court Practice*, vol. 1.

[2]   See *Fidelitas Shipping Co.* v. *Exportchleb* [1966] 1 Q.B. 630.

[3]   The numbering of the ICE Rule is fortunate, if not wholly coincidental.

[4]   See *Hanak* v. *Green* [1958] 2 Q.B. 9; see also p. 29, *ante*.

separate "clients' account") and should designate some outside banker or finance house for the purpose. He should be careful to stipulate that the money is to be held to his own order, and that it should bear interest at a proper rate. However, should an order under Rule 14.2 be resisted by the party ordered to pay, this would present difficulties of specific performance. The Rule therefore gives the Arbitrator a power, in default, to order payment directly to the successful applicant, who can then enforce the order if necessary.

*Variation by subsequent Award*

Rule 14.4 provides that a Summary Award is final and binding upon the parties and anyone claiming through them with respect to the matters determined thereby unless and until varied by some subsequent Award by the same Arbitrator or by any other Arbitrator having jurisdiction over the matters in dispute. The latter situation would arise if the Summary Award was made in pursuance of an interim arbitration under Clause 66(2) of the ICE Conditions of Contract about one aspect of the Works and the parties later entered into arbitration after completion of the Works over the Final Account before some other Arbitrator.

## PART D: PROCEDURE AT THE HEARING

## Rule 15: The Hearing

15.1   At or before the Hearing and after hearing representations on behalf of each party the Arbitrator shall determine the order in which the parties shall present their cases and/or the order in which the issues shall be heard and determined.

15.2   The Arbitrator may order any submission or speech by or on behalf of any party to be put into writing and delivered to him and to the other party. A party so ordered shall be entitled if he so wishes to enlarge upon or vary any such submission orally.

15.3   The Arbitrator may on the application of either party or of his own motion hear and determine any issue or issues separately.

15.4   If a party fails to appear at the Hearing and provided that the absent party has had notice of the Hearing or the Arbitrator is satisfied that all reasonable steps have been taken to notify him of the Hearing the Arbitrator may proceed with the Hearing in his absence. The Arbitrator shall nevertheless take all reasonable steps to ensure that the real issues between the parties are determined justly and fairly.

*Scope of the Rule*

This Rule deals with the manner and order in which a case is presented to and decided by the Arbitrator. It permits, in several important respects, substantial departures from the usual mode of presentation following High Court practice.

*Separate issues*

Rules 15.1 and 15.3 deal with the order in which the issues are to be heard. The Arbitrator is given power to determine the order in which particular issues shall be dealt with and, if appropriate, to hear and determine issues separately. Thus of his own motion he may decide to hear and determine all or some of the issues of liability before dealing with quantum. In such cases the parties are often able to agree quantum once liability is established by an Interim Award, thereby saving the cost of a Hearing on quantum. It should be noted that one or even both parties may take a different view from that of the Arbitrator on how the issues should be dealt with. But, while the Arbitrator should always consult the parties first, questions of procedure are entirely within his discretion, and his decision thereon is final.

### Order of parties

In addition to these general powers to control the procedure, the Arbitrator also has power to determine the order in which the two parties (or more if there are to be concurrent Hearings[1] under Rule 7) shall present their cases. This is a substantial departure from High Court practice where the plaintiff always has the right to begin unless the burden of proof of all the issues is on the defendant. The right to begin is thought by many professional advocates to be a substantial advantage since it usually carries with it the right to make the last closing speech (the so-called right to the "last word"). However, such considerations will have little weight or importance in a civil engineering arbitration. The important point about these powers is that the Arbitrator may, and often will, depart from the "usual" order of procedure and direct that the Hearing shall deal first with those matters which he deems to be of greatest importance; and further that any such matter shall be opened by whichever party the Arbitrator deems most appropriate.

### Written addresses

Rule 15.2 deals with the important matter of speeches or submissions. There is a growing practice in the High Court in cases heard before Official Referees for speeches and submissions, whether on factual or on legal issues, to be put into writing. This has a number of obvious advantages, not least in that if copies are given to the tribunal the labour of note taking is alleviated and accuracy improved. However, there is at present no means of regulating this process, even to the extent of knowing in advance whether a speech will be delivered orally or by reading from a script. This Rule allows the Arbitrator to make orders as to these matters, including an order that any such document shall be delivered to the other party. Possible injustice is avoided by the proviso which allows oral enlargement or variation of the delivered document at the Hearing. Rule 16 contains parallel provisions for putting evidence into writing.

Once speeches or submissions are rendered into writing, the practice of having them subsequently read aloud becomes unnecessary. In many cases it will be more appropriate for the Arbitrator to read and consider these documents in private (together, if necessary, with the agreed bundle of documentary evidence) and then to use the Hearing as an opportunity to ask questions arising out of the written material. This procedure will be

---

[1] See p. 58, *ante.*

especially valuable where parties appear in person or are represented by non-legal advocates who may lack the experience and flexibility of regular Counsel. Written speeches have the further advantage that they can be checked for mistakes and "polished" before exchange, avoiding the risk of an inadvertent slip. The scope for misunderstanding by the opposing side or by the Arbitrator is also greatly reduced.

*Absence of party*

Rule 15.4 deals with the failure of a party to attend the Hearing. Unless the parties otherwise agree, all Arbitrators have a common law power to proceed *ex parte* in such circumstances. But this area of law is still uncertain and strewn with traps for the unwary. The Rule seeks to overcome this by laying down how the Arbitrator is to proceed. He remains bound to hear and determine the dispute(s) referred to him.[1] Once the disputes have been determined, he becomes *functus officio*; he cannot re-open the matters if the absent party subsequently wishes to appear. The Rule gives the Arbitrator express power to proceed with the Hearing in such circumstances. This may have the practical effect of striking out a defence (or a claim)[2] if the absent party persists in his refusal to attend. The proviso that the Arbitrator is to ensure that the real issues are determined justly and fairly would normally require him to take into account any claim or defence that the absent party may have and which is disclosed by the pleadings or other documents. It does not, however, require (and could not empower) the Arbitrator to substitute his own evidence for that which might have been adduced by the absent party.[3] He is neither bound nor entitled to do other than to determine the issues on the basis of whatever evidence is available before him, including any formal admissions by the party or parties who do appear.

## Rule 16: Evidence

16.1 The Arbitrator may order a party to submit in advance of the Hearing a list of the witnesses he intends to call. That party shall not thereby be bound to call any witness so listed and may add to the list so submitted at any time.

16.2 No expert evidence shall be admissible except by leave of the Arbitrator. Leave may be given on such terms and conditions as the Arbitrator thinks fit. Unless the Arbitrator otherwise orders such terms shall be deemed to include a requirement that a report from each expert containing the substance of the evidence to be given shall be served upon the other party within a reasonable time before the Hearing.

16.3 The Arbitrator may order disclosure or exchange of proofs of evidence relating to factual issues. The Arbitrator may also order any party to prepare and disclose in advance a list of points or questions to be put in cross-examination of any witness.

16.4 Where a list of questions is disclosed whether pursuant to an order of the Arbitrator or otherwise the party making disclosure shall not be bound to put any

---

[1] But see *Northern Regional Health Authority* v. *Derek Crouch* [1984] 2 W.L.R. 676 (C.A.).

[2] An Arbitrator cannnot strike out unless given express power to do so. See, for example, *Bremer Vulkan* v. *South India Shipping* [1981] A.C. 909 *per* Lord Roskill at p. 942. See also s. 5 of the Arbitration Act 1979.

[3] *Fox* v. *Wellfair* [1981] 2 Lloyd's Rep. 514; 19 B.L.R. 52.

question therein to the witness unless the Arbitrator so orders. Where the party making disclosure puts a question not so listed in cross-examination the Arbitrator may disallow the costs thereby occasioned.

16.5 The Arbitrator may order that any proof of evidence which has been disclosed shall stand as the evidence in chief of the deponent provided that the other party has been or will be given an opportunity to cross-examine the deponent thereon. The Arbitrator may also at any time before such cross-examination order the deponent or some other identified person to deliver written answers to questions arising out of the proof of evidence.

16.6 The Arbitrator may himself put questions to any witness and/or require the parties to conduct enquiries tests or investigations. Subject to his agreement the parties may ask the Arbitrator to conduct or arrange for any enquiry test or investigation.

### Scope of the Rule

This Rule gives the Arbitrator powers to regulate the way in which evidence is placed before him. Much of the evidence in a civil engineering arbitration will be of a specialist or technical nature. The Arbitrator will usually be expert in such matters and may therefore be better placed than the parties' own advocates to know what is important to the issues before him and what, though relevant, is merely peripheral. This will be so even when the parties' advisers are themselves expert in the subject matter. They may be too close to the issues to be able to be objective. Again, parties often feel obliged to press matters because they cannot be sure that they are not relevant. This Rule therefore allows the Arbitrator to take positive steps to keep the evidence to matters which are relevant.

### Witnesses

Rule 16.1 allows the Arbitrator to require a list of witnesses from each party. Such lists will not bind the parties but are intended to make the parties "show their hand" at an early stage in the proceedings and to discourage the common practice of not calling relevant but potentially damaging witnesses (which will sometimes include the Engineer).

### Exchange of proofs

Rule 16.2 deals with the evidence of experts and is complementary to Rule 13.1(c). The comments to that Rule apply equally here.[1]

The disclosure or exchange of proofs of factual (as distinct from expert) evidence is an increasingly common practice which can shorten substantially the time spent at the Hearing. Rule 16.3 gives the Arbitrator power to order such disclosure (i.e. to the Arbitrator and to the other parties) or to order exchange of proofs between the parties themselves (but without being revealed to the Arbitrator). Where a proof is disclosed, whether pursuant to the Arbitrator's order or otherwise, the Arbitrator may under Rule 16.5 order that the proof shall stand as the evidence in chief of that witness without requiring him to be called. However, this is subject to the right of any other party to cross-examine that witness.

---

[1] See p. 70, *ante.*

*Cross-examination*

Cross-examination is dealt with in Rules 16.3, 16.4 and 16.5. Experience has shown that considerable time can be absorbed at the Hearing and heavy costs incurred in relatively routine cross-examination which does little to assist in the proper determination of the issues. There is a popular misconception among advocates that every opposing witness must be thoroughly cross-examined. If a given witness's oral evidence is at variance with the contemporaneous record (for example, the site diaries), little will usually be gained by taking the witness through it and cross-examining on every discrepancy. It will usually suffice (and may well have far greater impact with the Arbitrator) to point out the discrepancies and to leave it to the opposing side to try to explain them in re-examination. These three rules, therefore, allow the Arbitrator to circumvent unproductive cross-examination by

(a) ordering the disclosure of points or questions to be put in cross-examination (Rule 16.3);

(b) ordering the delivery of written answers to any such questions (Rule 16.5); and in any event

(c) effectively limiting cross-examination to any disclosed list of questions (Rule 16.4).

A persistent advocate will usually be able to insist on cross-examining beyond these limits. But his client may be penalised in costs if, at the end of the day, such action is seen to have been unnecessary.

*Conducting tests*

Rule 16.6 deals with the important question of tests or other investigations. In the High Court there is power to order "... any sample to be taken ... or any experiment to be tried ...".[1] But this is exercisable only on the application of one of the parties, and is rarely used. This Rule gives the Arbitrator power himself to require tests to be carried out and, if the parties so wish, the power (but not the duty) to arrange for or to conduct tests himself. Where the parties have each instructed their own experts such further tests may be inappropriate; the Special Procedure for Experts (Part G) is available for the speedy determination of factual disputes in such circumstances. However, this Rule offers the parties in effect a further and possibly cheaper alternative of asking the Arbitrator to take on the role of the expert.[2]

Where the Arbitrator himself conducts any such test or enquiry it is fundamentally important that he should make full disclosure of all relevant matters so that the parties (in particular a party adversely affected) have an adequate opportunity of dealing with them.[3] It may well be appropriate in such circumstances for the Arbitrator to prepare a written report setting out all relevant observations and results. But such a report must not contain findings which could constitute an Award, since the parties must first be

---

[1] R.S.C. Ord. 29, r. 3(1).

[2] This situation is, of course, familiar in commodity arbitrations, where it is known as the "look–sniff" procedure.

[3] *Fox* v. *Wellfair* [1981] 2 Com L.R. 140 C.A.; 19 B.L.R. 52.

given a chance of dealing with the report and addressing the Arbitrator upon it if they so desire.

## PART E: AFTER THE HEARING

### Rule 17: The Award

17.1   Upon the closing of the Hearing (if any) and after having considered all the evidence and submissions the Arbitrator will prepare and publish his Award.

17.2   When the Arbitrator has made and published his Award (including a Summary Award under Rule 14) he will so inform the parties in writing and shall specify how and where it may be taken up upon due payment of his fee.

*Scope of the Rule*

This Rule is a declaration of the usual practice on making and publishing the Award. No particular form is required for an Award, but it is usual for it to be in writing, and to be signed, witnessed and dated. The particular requirements of a valid Award are set out in Chapter 4.

*The Arbitrator's fees*

The Arbitrator has a lien on his Award for the payment of his fees. Where the party wishing to take up the Award has agreed to the Arbitrator's scale of fees he must pay the whole sum due and the Arbitrator will then deliver the original of his Award to the party taking it up and a copy to the other party. Should the party wishing to take up the Award not have agreed to the Arbitrator's scale of fees he may as an alternative pay the full amount demanded into Court and apply for an order under s. 19 of the Arbitration Act 1950 that the Arbitrator deliver his Award and for his fee to be taxed in the High Court. The amount allowed by the Taxing Master will be paid to the Arbitrator and the balance (if any) returned to the party who paid it in.[1] The Arbitrator is entitled to appear and be heard on any s. 19 taxation.[2]

The Award will usually direct which party is to pay the Arbitrator's fees with a provision that, if this is not the one taking up the Award, the other party will reimburse the first one forthwith. This can lead to an anomaly where the party taking up the Award has agreed to or is content with the Arbitrator's fees but the other party is not, and it is the latter who is directed by the Award to pay the Arbitrator's fees. It would seem that in this situation the latter party has lost his right to have the fees taxed under s. 19. There is no simple solution, but the problem was discussed in the *Rolimpex* case.[3]

### Rule 18: Reasons

18.1   Whether requested by any party to do so or not the Arbitrator may at his discretion state his Reasons for all or any part of his Award. Such Reasons may

---

[1]   S. 19(1).

[2]   S. 19(4).

[3]   *Rolimpex Centrala Handlu Zagranicznego* v. *Haji E. Dossa & Sons Ltd.* [1971] 1 Lloyd's Rep. 380.

form part of the Award itself or may be contained in a separate document.

18.2    A party asking for Reasons shall state the purpose for his request. If the purpose is to use them for an appeal (whether under S. 1 of the Arbitration Act 1979 or otherwise) the requesting party shall also specify the points of law with which he wishes the Reasons to deal. In that event the Arbitrator shall give the other party an opportunity to specify additional points of law to be dealt with.

18.3    Reasons prepared as a separate document may be delivered with the Award or later as the Arbitrator thinks fit.

18.4    Where the Arbitrator decides not to state his Reasons he shall nevertheless keep such notes as will enable him to prepare Reasons later if so ordered by the High Court.

*Background to the Rule*

The changes wrought by the 1979 Act with respect to the giving of reasons with arbitral awards have already been discussed in Chapter 4. Section 1(5) of the Act empowers the Court to order an Arbitrator to give reasons for his Award if the Award itself is silent or, if reasons are given, they are thought to be insufficient. However, an s.1(5) order will not be made unless one of the parties gave the Arbitrator notice before the Award was made that reasons would be required, or unless there was some special reason why such notice was not given.[1]

*Giving reasons*

An Arbitrator is not bound to give reasons at all, unless ordered to do so by the High Court. On the other hand, it is the Arbitrator who drafts the Award and there is nothing to prevent his giving reasons therein should he think it appropriate. Rule 18.1 therefore confirms his discretion to state reasons, whether or not any party has sought them.[2]

Where reasons are requested in connection with an intended appeal, Rule 18.2 provides that the party asking for reasons shall specify the points of law with which he wishes the reasons to deal. If he refuses to do so the Arbitrator may refuse to state his reasons; he should also in his Award state that he has refused the request and why he has done so. An appeal to the Court can lie only on a point of law and the appellant must specify the points of law he wishes to raise when applying for leave. There is thus no injustice in requiring the applicant to tell the Arbitrator the points of law he intends to raise. On the contrary, the Arbitrator is thereby able to ensure that the Court is provided with all the reasons and findings of fact necessary to the proper consideration of the appeal. Not only will this save the Court's time and minimise the parties' costs but it may also avoid the need for a later order for further reasons under s. 1(5). Conversely, an applicant who does not know the points upon which he will appeal, or who cannot make up his mind, should be discouraged from "fishing" should the Award not be to his liking.

However, before the Award is made a party may be fairly certain that the Arbitrator will find against him but at that stage may be genuinely unable to

---

[1]    S. 1(6).
[2]    It follows that he can state his reasons even if both parties expressly ask him to refrain from doing so. But the occasion for such action will be rare indeed.

identify any points of law on which leave to appeal might be sought. If so, he should tell the Arbitrator of his dilemma. The Arbitrator may then reserve his decision on the giving of reasons until the Award has been made and published or, alternatively, he may refuse the request but grant leave to reapply within a specified time following publication of the Award. But such occasions should be rare and, in general, unspecific requests for reasons should be resisted.[1]

Finally, Rule 18.4 records the undoubted duty of an Arbitrator to be prepared to deliver reasons if so ordered by the Court, where he decides not to give reasons in or with his Award. The same applies where he gives reasons restricted to non-contentious use, whether or not the parties agree to accept that restriction.

### Form of reasons

Rules 18.1 and 18.3 provide that reasons may form part of the Award or be contained in a separate document delivered either with the Award or later. Thus, for example, where a dispute about methods of working must be resolved quickly to minimise standing time on site an Award can be issued with a minimum of delay and the reasons can follow at leisure.

The drafting of reasons has already been discussed in Chapter 4.[2]

### Difficult points of law

If the Arbitrator is in real doubt about the correct view of a point of law he should, if possible, persuade the parties to co-operate in an application to the Court to determine the question of law under s. 2 of the 1979 Act. The parties can agree to go to the Court under s. 2 whether the Arbitrator agrees or not, but the Arbitrator can do so only if at least one party also agrees. If none will agree, the Arbitrator may seek legal advice.[3] If that does not resolve his difficulty it is submitted that, despite the repeal of the old "case-stated" procedure[4] by the 1979 Act, it is still open to an Arbitrator to make an Award which has the effect of an Award by way of case stated. To achieve this the Award should state the point of law and then give alternative Awards depending on the possible answers to the point of law. There should also be a direction that, if application for leave to appeal under s. 1 of the 1979 Act is not made within 21 days[5] of the date of the Award, or if such application is refused, one of the alternative Awards shall thereupon become final and binding upon the parties.

Such an Award should, it is submitted, be treated as a compelling ground for giving leave to appeal. But the Court's decision whether to give leave must still take into account whether the point is "one off" in nature or of wider application. The Arbitrator should therefore consider this factor also when contemplating an Award in this form.

---

[1]  To give reasons which cover adequately every possible point of law which might arise in a civil engineering arbitration will usually involve considerable and wholly disproportionate time and cost.

[2]  See p. 30.

[3]  Rule 9(2).

[4]  Under s. 21 of the 1950 Act, since repealed by s. 1(1) of the 1979 Act. See also Appendix 3 to Mustill & Boyd's *Commercial Arbitration*.

[5]  The time allowed under R.S.C. Ord. 73, r. 5(2).

# Rule 19: Appeals

19.1  If any party applies to the High Court for leave to appeal against any Award or decision or for an order staying the arbitration proceedings or for any other purpose that party shall forthwith notify the Arbitrator of the application.

19.2  Once any Award or decision has been made and published the Abitrator shall be under no obligation to make any statement in connection therewith other than in compliance with an order of the High Court under S. 1(5) of the Arbitration Act 1979.

*Purpose of the Rule*

If any party seeks leave to appeal there is no formal requirement for notice thereof to be served on the Arbitrator, other than in cases of alleged misconduct.[1] Rule 19.1 therefore requires that the Arbitrator be notified of any application to the Court which might affect him. If his conduct is to be criticised the Court will usually be prepared to receive evidence from the Arbitrator by way of affidavit.[2]

The effect of Rule 19.2 is to discourage any of the parties to the arbitration from involving the Arbitrator in any subsequent proceedings. For instance, a Main Contractor who has an Award made against him may wish to enforce that Award against a Sub-Contractor.[3] But the Arbitrator may, if he thinks fit, give assistance to the parties in any subsequent proceedings.

---

[1]  *Port Sudan Cotton Co.* v. *Chettiar* [1977] 1 Lloyd's Rep. 166.

[2]  See *Fox* v. *Wellfair* [1981] 2 Com L.R. 140 C.A.; 19 B.L.R. 52.

[3]  If either party attempted to compel the attendance of the Arbitrator as a witness by subpoena, his remedy would be an application to set aside the subpoena—see R.S.C. Ord. 38, rr. 14–19/11.

# Chapter 9

# SPECIAL PROCEDURES

*PART F: SHORT PROCEDURE*

## Introduction

This part of the Procedure, like the following part dealing with the evidence of experts (Part G), is intended to provide the parties with an opportunity of obtaining a binding decision on the merits quickly and at minimal cost. It is not uncommon for the parties themselves to devise some *ad hoc* system for this purpose, thereby avoiding what are often (if erroneously) seen as the complexities of "formal" arbitration. But such attempts can be disastrous if the losing party is able to challenge the validity of the proceedings. To avoid such difficulties, this Short Procedure and the following Special Procedure for Experts are offered as a ready-made system of summary arbitration. The parties remain at liberty to agree their own rules or any amendment to these Rules.

The Short Procedure will be most appropriate in cases where the dispute is comparatively well defined. In particular, it will be of use where the issues have already been thoroughly ventilated before proceeding to arbitration, for instance, as part of a preliminary reference to the Engineer for a decision under Clause 66(1) of the ICE Conditions of Contract. In such a case, the necessary documents for submission to the Arbitrator may already be available and the Arbitrator can, as it were, take up the matter at the point already reached by the parties in negotiation. Examples of suitable cases might include disputes on whether certain work is extra to Contract; or whether some certificate has been properly given or withheld; or the effect of the terms of the Contract on an otherwise undisputed factual situation. Another example arose where an Arbitrator's jurisdiction was challenged. At his suggestion, the parties gave him a separate appointment to resolve the matter and the Short Procedure was used to minimise the delay to the "main" arbitration.[1]

The Short Procedure may also be used (with or without Rule 21.1—see below) to dispose of one or more of a number of issues within a larger, conventionally conducted arbitration. This use of the Short Procedure is analogous to the former High Court practice of transferring questions or issues of fact to an Official Referee either for trial or for enquiry and

---

[1] No Arbitrator can determine the extent of his own jurisdiction, which is normally a matter for the Courts. But the parties can themselves validly refer the issue of jurisdiction to arbitration, either by appointing another Arbitrator for that purpose or by expressly agreeing to extend the first Arbitrator's terms of appointment.

report.[1] The main arbitration may then stand adjourned or may continue in parallel on other issues. In due course the results obtained under the Short Procedure are "fed back" into the main arbitration for incorporation in the Final Award or may be made the subject of a separate Interim Award.

## Rule 20: Short Procedure

20.1   Where the parties so agree (either of their own motion or at the invitation of the Arbitrator) the arbitration shall be conducted in accordance with the following *Short Procedure.*

20.2   Each party shall set out his case in the form of a file containing
>    (*a*) a statement as to the orders or awards he seeks
>    (*b*) a statement of his reasons for being entitled to such orders or awards

and   (*c*) copies of any documents on which he relies (including statements) identifying the origin and date of each document

and shall deliver copies of the said file to the other party and to the Arbitrator in such manner and within such time as the Arbitrator may direct.

20.3   After reading the parties' cases the Arbitrator may view the site or the Works and may require either or both parties to submit further documents or information in writing.

20.4   Within one calendar month of completing the foregoing steps the Arbitrator shall fix a day when he shall meet the parties for the purpose of
>    (*a*) receiving any oral submissions which either party may wish to make

and/or   (*b*) the Arbitrator's putting questions to the parties their representatives or witnesses.

For this purpose the Arbitrator shall give notice of any particular person he wishes to question but no person shall be bound to appear before him.

20.5   Within one calendar month following the conclusion of the meeting under Rule 20.4 or such further period as the Arbitrator may reasonably require the Arbitrator shall make and publish his Award.

### *Application*

Rule 20.1 provides that the Short Procedure may be used only if the parties agree, although the Arbitrator may himself raise the question and express a view on its suitability. Thus no party can be compelled to submit to the Short Procedure if he prefers a "full" arbitration.[2] If one party objects only to certain features of the Short Procedure it is open to him to agree an amended version with his opponent, subject to agreement by the Arbitrator.

### *Statements of case*

Where the Short Procedure is adopted, Rule 20.2 requires each party simultaneously[3] to prepare a file containing a statement of his case with all necessary supporting documentary evidence. This takes the place of conventional pleadings and may be in any form which is clear, convenient

---

[1]   See *Official Referees' Business* by His Honour Edgar Fay QC, Sweet & Maxwell, 1983, and R.S.C. Ord. 36. A similar procedure survives in the County Courts for referring issues to an Arbitrator appointed by the Court.

[2]   But see Part H, *post.*

[3]   Unless otherwise ordered. Simultaneous delivery of the files should in principle halve the time needed to complete this part of the procedure.

and (preferably) short. The statement need not be formal; the only essentials are that it shall state what the party seeks and why he thinks he is entitled to it.

There will not normally be any need to resort to lawyers to draft the various statements, although legal advice on their content may be sought. Nor is there any express provision for replies. However, having read the files and, if necessary, having visited the site of the Works,[1] the Arbitrator may invite or order replies to be exchanged under Rule 20.3. He may also seek such other information or documents as he may deem necessary. Should one party wish to submit a reply to his opponent's file he may do so only if the Arbitrator gives leave, in which case the other party must be given an opportunity to do likewise. In such cases care is needed to prevent the development of a succession of ripostes. If replies are to be exchanged, these too should be delivered simultaneously.

*Oral Hearing*

In many arbitrations under the Short Procedure a decision "on documents only" will be the mutual wish of the parties and of the Arbitrator. However, Rule 20.4 requires the Arbitrator to allow the parties to present their cases to him at an oral Hearing if they so desire and he should always obtain the parties' express agreement to waive an oral Hearing unless this has already been given.[2]

It should, however, be noted that while Rule 20.4 preserves the parties' right to an oral presentation of their case it does not give them the right to place oral evidence before the Arbitrator, although they remain free to adduce an unlimited amount of written evidence. A more important point is that there is no right of cross-examination. All these provisions are designed to ensure that time and costs are saved, while preserving the essential requirements of natural justice.

Nevertheless, in more complex cases the Arbitrator will often need to seek amplification of the documents submitted under Rules 20.2 and 20.3. Accordingly, Rule 20.4 empowers the Arbitrator to insist on a Hearing, whether the parties wish it or not, if he considers it right to do so, either as the most economical way of obtaining further evidence, or to test documentary evidence by cross-examining deponents, or even to ensure that justice is seen to be done.

Occasionally, the parties may be persuaded in general of the advantages to be gained by adopting the Short Procedure but be loath to agree to Rule 20.4. Thus, if one party thinks it to be to his advantage to attack his opponent's case rather than to rely on establishing his own, or where he wishes to challenge the credibility of his opponent's witnesses, this Rule may seem inappropriate. Again, where the parties retain professional advocates, the latter will find little scope for the exercise of their craft

---

[1] In making any such visit, the Arbitrator must either be alone or must be attended by representatives of all parties. In the latter event, it is preferable if the representatives are "all of a kind"—i.e. all Engineers or all lawyers.

[2] The prudent Arbitrator will make sure that the *fact* of any such agreement is duly recorded on the face of his Award.

under this Rule. But if one party does object either to the Short Procedure as a whole or to the inclusion of Rule 20.4 and, at the resulting "full" arbitration, the Arbitrator concludes that the objection has caused unnecessary delay or expense, that view may well find expression in the Arbitrator's order for costs.

Where the parties do agree to dispense with an oral Hearing, the single calendar month allowed by Rule 20.5 for the Arbitrator to make and publish his Award will presumably run from the date of the agreement to waive a Hearing or from the date on which the steps set out in Rules 20.2 and 20.3 are completed, whichever is the later. The provisions of Part E of the ICE Procedure (Award, reasons and appeals) will then apply in the usual way.

### Rule 21: Other matters

21.1   Unless the parties otherwise agree the Arbitrator shall have no power to award costs to either party and the Arbitrator's own fees and charges shall be paid in equal shares by the parties. Where one party has agreed to the Arbitrator's fees the other party by agreeing to this Short Procedure shall be deemed to have agreed likewise to the Arbitrator's fees.

21.2   Either party may at any time before the Arbitrator has made and published his Award under this Short Procedure require by written notice served on the Arbitrator and the other party that the arbitration shall cease to be conducted in accordance with this Short Procedure. Save only for Rule 21.3 the Short Procedure shall thereupon no longer apply or bind the parties but any evidence already laid before the Arbitrator shall be admissible in further proceedings as if it had been submitted as part of those proceedings and without further proof.

21.3   The party giving written notice under Rule 21.2 shall thereupon in any event become liable to pay

      (*a*)  the whole of the Arbitrator's fees and charges incurred up to the date of such notice

and   (*b*)  a sum to be assessed by the Arbitrator as reasonable compensation for the costs (including any legal costs) incurred by the other party up to the date of such notice.

Payment in full of such charges shall be a condition precedent to that party's proceeding further in the arbitration unless the Arbitrator otherwise directs. Provided that non-payment of the said charges shall not prevent the other party from proceeding in the arbitration.

*Costs*

Rule 21.1 provides that each party shall pay half of the Arbitrator's costs and the whole of his own costs in any event. Each therefore knows from the start the order of costs to which he is committed. Each party may seek as much (or as little) legal or other advice as he wishes at his own expense and is free from the burden of having to meet punitive costs from the other side should his claims be unsuccessful. Such provision should assist the parties to proceed with despatch, and with the minimum of administrative restraint. The last sentence of Rule 21.1 frees the Arbitrator from dispute about the level of his fees[1] and creates no injustice as it only applies if the Short

---

[1]   Other than under s. 19 of the 1950 Act.

Procedure is agreed by all parties.[1]

It must be remembered that s. 18(3) of the Arbitration Act 1950 provides that any provision in an arbitration agreement which requires the parties to pay their own costs in any event shall be void. However, the same subsection contains a proviso that such a provision in an agreement to refer an *existing* dispute to arbitration shall remain valid. Thus, provided that the parties' agreement to adopt the Short Procedure is made after the dispute has arisen (which will normally be the case), Rule 21.1 will apply to the resolution of that dispute. There could be an exception where an Arbitrator is appointed under Rules 2 or 3 *before* a dispute has arisen or been referred to the Engineer under Clause 66(1),[2] if the parties agree at the outset to apply Part F. Such difficulty would be overcome, it is thought, by confirming agreement to Rule 21.1 each time a dispute is referred to the appointed Arbitrator.

*Rescission of agreement*

Circumstances may occur where an arbitration originally thought by all concerned to be suitable for determination under the Short Procedure subsequently appears less appropriate. Rule 21.2 therefore allows any party to rescind his original agreement to the Short Procedure and to revert to conventional procedure at any time before the Award is made. The Rule provides that any evidence which has already been adduced before the Arbitrator shall be admissible in subsequent proceedings without further proof, thereby saving both time and costs and avoiding unnecessary repetition. There is, however, a stiff sanction in costs. By Rule 21.3, a party who changes his mind must as a condition of proceeding further pay the whole of the Arbitrator's costs to that point together with the whole of his opponent's costs up to the date of the Rule 21.2 notice whatever the eventual outcome may be. It therefore behoves a party contemplating a Rule 21.2 notice to think carefully before acting, as in appropriate circumstances the Arbitrator may see fit to allow an alternative application for limited cross-examination or some other variation of the Short Procedure if he deems it desirable.

## PART G: SPECIAL PROCEDURE FOR EXPERTS

### Introduction

Like the Short Procedure (Part F), this Special Procedure is intended to provide the parties with a means of obtaining a binding decision quickly and at minimal cost, in this case on matters which depend on evidence of opinion given by experts. Parties often wish to augment the Arbitrator's own expertise in the subject matter of the dispute by retaining their own experts as witnesses. The conventional processing of such evidence by formal examination in chief, followed by cross-examination and re-examination can be tedious, and matters familiar to expert witness and

---

[1]  See comment under Rule 20.1, above.

[2]  For example, if a "Contract Arbitrator" is appointed at tender or tender acceptance stage.

Arbitrator alike are often examined needlessly and at length.

Both witness and Arbitrator will be well able to distinguish between matters which are vital and those merely incidental to the main issues. Common sense therefore indicates that substantial savings in time and cost and improvements in clarity should be achievable by dispensing with the advocate as intermediary. It has been the experience of many Engineers and Arbitrators that useful savings can be made by holding more-or-less informal meetings between Arbitrator and experts without the assistance of professional advocates. This Special Procedure accordingly formalises this mode of conducting the reference and lays down guide-lines on how the investigation should proceed.

The Special Procedure will be particularly appropriate where there is a purely technical issue on which the parties' experts genuinely disagree—such as whether admittedly defective work is capable of economic repair or the true cause of some failure. The essential requirement is, of course, that the differences between the experts' views should be sufficiently ventilated and explored for the Arbitrator to achieve a firm grasp of the opposing opinions.

It is appropriate to note here that, while expert witnesses are commonly referred to as "independent", they are still retained and paid by one party. They should therefore be regarded, at least in part, as members of their Client's team of advocates. While, like Counsel, the expert must never mislead the tribunal even by omission, it is quite proper for him to exclude matters from his proof of evidence which are, or are thought to be, prejudicial to his Client's case provided that the proof as a whole is not thereby rendered misleading. Of course, the expert should warn his Client of matters prejudicial to his case when giving advice in preparation for litigation or arbitration. But that advice, whether written or oral, is privileged and need not be divulged to the tribunal or the other side. However, if the point should arise in cross-examination, the expert must give his honest view.

## Rule 22: Special Procedure for Experts

22.1 Where the parties so agree (either of their own motion or at the invitation of the Arbitrator) the hearing and determination of any issues of fact which depend upon the evidence of experts shall be conducted in accordance with the following *Special Procedure*.

22.2 Each party shall set out his case on such issues in the form of a file containing

    (*a*) a statement of the factual findings he seeks

    (*b*) a report or statement from and signed by each expert upon whom that party relies

and  (*c*) copies of any other documents referred to in each expert's report or statement or on which the party relies identifying the origin and date of each document

and shall deliver copies of the said file to the other party and to the Arbitrator in such manner and within such time as the Arbitrator may direct.

22.3 After reading the parties' cases the Arbitrator may view the site or the Works and may require either or both parties to submit further documents or information in writing.

22.4    Thereafter the Arbitrator shall fix a day when he shall meet the experts whose reports or statements have been submitted. At the meeting each expert may address the Arbitrator and put questions to any other expert representing the other party. The Arbitrator shall so direct the meeting as to ensure that each expert has an adequate opportunity to explain his opinion and to comment upon any opposing opinion. No other person shall be entitled to address the Arbitrator or question any expert unless the parties and the Arbitrator so agree.

22.5    Thereafter the Arbitrator may make and publish an Award setting out with such details or particulars as may be necessary his decision upon the issues dealt with.

## Outline of the Rule

Comparison of Rule 22 with Rule 20 will show that the Special Procedure for Experts follows the same form as the Short Procedure, save that in the Special Procedure the meeting between Arbitrator and experts assumes much greater importance and constitutes a complete Hearing, albeit conducted without professional advocates. Thus Rule 22.1 provides that the Special Procedure may be used only if the parties agree,[1] although the Arbitrator may himself raise the question and express a view on its suitability. Rule 22.2 provides that each party shall simultaneously prepare a file containing a statement of the factual findings he seeks, reports or statements from each of his expert witnesses, and all the supporting documentary evidence which is necessary. As in the Short Procedure, this takes the place of conventional pleadings and may be in any form which is clear, convenient and concise. There is no express provision for replies although the Arbitrator may order these to be exchanged under Rule 22.3. This Sub-Rule also allows the Arbitrator to visit the site or to seek such further information or documentation as he may deem necessary. Unlike the Short Procedure, there is no provision for reverting to conventional procedures analogous to that in Rules 21.2 and 21.3.

## Meeting the experts

Rule 22.4 provides for an oral Hearing in the form of a meeting between opposing experts with the Arbitrator as Chairman. The parties may have anyone they wish present at this meeting but the role of lawyers or other advocates will normally be restricted to taking notes and giving private advice to their respective Client's experts. Thus, for example, a Solicitor may suggest questions which his Client's expert may wish to put to the opponent's expert but may not himself intervene to question an expert or to address the Arbitrator unless all the parties and the Arbitrator agree.

It will be seen that at this meeting the Arbitrator is acting "inquisitorially" instead of following the "adversarial" procedure traditional in English Courts. By agreeing to the Special Procedure the parties accept that the Arbitrator may so act. But even without such agreement it is arguable that Arbitrators in England have inherent power to act inquisitorially, unless the parties otherwise agree. Certainly, the Courts are now much

---

[1]    But see Part H, *post*.

more amenable to the use of such procedures.[1] International developments also suggest a trend towards inquisitorial procedure.[2]

As all experts' reports or statements have been exchanged before the meeting, no witness need give evidence in chief as such. The intention is that each expert in turn should introduce his report with a few comments by way of explanation or emphasis. He will then be questioned directly by the other experts, under the overall chairmanship of the Arbitrator, who will also probe and question as he thinks fit. This discussion will continue until the Arbitrator is satisfied that all useful evidence and opinion has been elicited. At that point he will draw the meeting to a close and proceed to prepare, make and publish an Award in accordance with Rule 22.5 setting out such particulars as may be necessary to assist the parties with the remainder of the reference.

### Rule 23: Costs

23.1 The Arbitrator may in his Award make orders as to the payment of any costs relating to the foregoing matters including his own fees and charges in connection therewith.

23.2 Unless the parties otherwise agree and so notify the Arbitrator neither party shall be entitled to any costs in respect of legal representation assistance or other legal work relating to the hearing and determination of factual issues by this Special Procedure.

*Costs*

Unlike the Short Procedure, Rule 23.1 of the Special Procedure empowers the Arbitrator to make such orders as to costs as he thinks fit relating to the handling of the evidence of experts. However, Rule 23.2 provides that each party must meet the full cost of his own side's legal representation (if any), assistance or other legal work in any event. This follows logically from the concept of the Special Procedure, which seeks to concentrate on the experts to the exclusion of lawyers. If the parties agree otherwise they must inform the Arbitrator before the end of the meeting. Once an Award on costs has been made, it may be too late for the Arbitrator to amend his order.

The costs of applying the Special Procedure can be reduced to a minimum, or even avoided, to the extent that the parties' experts can themselves settle their differences. The Special Procedure is designed to encourage such settlement by bringing the experts together and promoting inter-expert discussion. If the parties can arrange for their experts to meet at an early stage to discuss the matters in issue, so much the better. Such policies should be the general rule in all construction arbitrations.

---

[1] See, for example, the note of Sir Michael Mustill's address to the 1982 Annual Conference of the Chartered Institute of Arbitrators—*Arbitration*, vol. 48, no. 4 (May, 1983) at p. 293.

[2] For example, the current initiative by the United Nations Commission on International Trade and Law (UNCITRAL) aimed at the formulation of a "model law of arbitration".

# Chapter 10

# INTERIM ARBITRATION AND OTHER MATTERS

## PART H: INTERIM ARBITRATION

### Introduction

Within the ICE Conditions of Contract the term "Interim Arbitration" appears once only, as a marginal note to Clause 66(2). As it is nowhere expressly defined, all that can be said is that Interim Arbitration denotes a reference which may proceed "notwithstanding that the Works shall not then be or be alleged to be complete". This contrasts with other arbitrations under Clause 66, where "... no steps shall be taken ... until after the completion or alleged completion of the Works ...".[1] No other distinction is drawn anywhere in the Conditions between Interim Arbitration and any other arbitrations, nor did the 1973 version of the ICE Arbitration Procedure make special provision for any one category of arbitration.

Clause 66(2) of the ICE Conditions allows arbitration before completion[2] on any dispute or difference for

(a) any matter arising under Clause 12 of the Conditions of Contract (adverse physical conditions or artificial obstructions);

(b) the withholding by the Engineer of any certificate (usually for payment, but not limited thereto[3]);

(c) the withholding of any portion of the retention money under Clause 60 to which the Contractor claims to be entitled; or

(d) the exercise of the Engineer's power to give a certificate under Clause 63(1) (entitling the Employer to expel the Contractor from the Site and the Works).

Save for (d), which is in a different category, a prime requirement in all such disputes is for a speedy decision. Under Clause 12, for example, the decision may well have a fundamental effect on the further conduct of the Works, their design or the Contractor's working methods, while monthly certificates and payment of retention money are vital to the Contractor's cash flow and the profitability of the Contract as a whole. Yet all too frequently such interim references are allowed to drag on indefinitely, often

---

[1] Unless the Employer and Contractor otherwise agree in writing (Clause 66(1), line 39).

[2] That is, actual or alleged "substantial completion" within the meaning of Clause 48. By Clause 48(3), this can be achieved in respect of part of the Works before completion of the whole of the Works. See also Chapter 6 for the position under the new Clause 66.

[3] *A. E. Farr* v. *Minister of Transport* [1960] 1 W.L.R. 956; but see also *Costain International* v. *A.G. of Hong Kong* [1983] 23 B.L.R. 48.

continuing long after the Works have been completed, thereby frustrating the whole purpose of Clause 66(2).

Undoubtedly, one of the main obstacles to speedy Interim Arbitration has been the absence of any suitable interim procedure. The result has been that, whether by intent or inadvertence, parties have allowed such references to become bogged down in the interlocutory complexities inherent in conventional procedures. It is not uncommon for a dilatory Interim Arbitration to be overtaken by a "regular" Clause 66(1) arbitration arising on the final account, giving rise to the problem of whom to appoint as the "regular" Arbitrator. If different Arbitrators are appointed in the two references, both may be hearing evidence and argument about the same, or connected, facts and issues, with the accompanying risk of inconsistent Awards.

On the other hand, if the parties wish to extend the jurisdiction of the first Arbitrator to cover the issues in the second arbitration, a number of equally difficult problems may arise. First, the Arbitrator may not want to have his jurisdiction extended, particularly if he is already part way through the first reference. Secondly, while the first Arbitrator may be well qualified to deal with the interim issues, he may not be the best man for the "regular" issues; an Arbitrator chosen for a Clause 12 claim may lack the skills needed to cope with a final account, and vice versa. Whatever expedient is chosen, there will be waste and duplication of effort, and the result is almost certainly to be slow, expensive and inherently disappointing to the parties.

The purpose of Part H is therefore to create a procedure which will allow the Arbitrator to determine the issues swiftly and, normally, well before completion of the Works. Interim Arbitration tends to bring together most of the difficulties currently afflicting engineering arbitration. The new interim procedure therefore has to make use of all the available procedural devices for achieving a workable solution. Coincidentally, it also offers a means whereby those who seek an independent view during the currency of a Contract where Engineer and Contractor cannot agree may achieve a form of conciliation.

Where the new (1985) version of Clause 66 applies,[1] the restriction of the term "Interim Arbitration" to those references falling within the old (1973) Clause 66(2) is lifted and the procedure under Rule 24 is available for any arbitration, provided only that it starts before substantial completion of the whole of the Works.

## Rule 24: Interim Arbitration

24.1 Where the Arbitrator is appointed and the arbitration is to proceed before completion or alleged completion of the Works then save in the case of a dispute arising under Clause 63 of the ICE Conditions of Contract the following provisions shall apply in addition to the foregoing Rules and the arbitration shall be called an Interim Arbitration.

---

[1] See Chapter 6 and Appendix III.

*Effect of the Rule*

Except in the case of a Clause 63 dispute, every arbitration under Clause 66(2) must be conducted in accordance with the new Interim Arbitration procedure unless all parties otherwise agree. A party wishing to utilise the benefits of the new system cannot, therefore, be prevented from doing so by a reluctant opponent. A party wishing to delay a decision for his own purposes cannot insist that conventional procedures, with all their potential for prevarication and delay, shall be followed. Where there are genuine reasons for postponing a final decision on certain issues Rules 24.5 and 24.6 provide the Arbitrator with ample scope to accommodate such matters without impairing the efficiency of the new system as a whole.

Since drafting for this new procedure was put in hand, the fear has been expressed that it would deprive the parties of the right to choose their own procedure. Such criticism is misconceived. If the parties wish to follow conventional procedures ample opportunity exists to make such a requirement, either at tender stage or when referring specific disputes or differences to arbitration, or when appointing the Arbitrator. Where the new procedure applies, the parties will have declined all such opportunities to exclude it. It is anticipated, however, that experience of the procedure in use will allay fears that any party is thereby deprived of his rights. The speedy determination of Interim Arbitrations should encourage certainty in, and minimise subsequent disruption to, the smooth administration of the Contract, to the benefit of Employer and Contractor alike.

*Disputes not included*

Disputes under Clause 63 are excluded from the new Interim Arbitration procedure. Although such a reference may proceed while a new Contractor is continuing with the Works, the issues (being concerned with the validity of a forfeiture) will not normally be suitable for determination in a summary manner. But there is nothing to prevent the parties in such a situation from agreeing to use the Part H procedure if that is what they wish. Indeed, any dispute whatever, whether it falls within the scope of Clause 66(2) or not, may be resolved in accordance with the Part H procedure if the parties so agree.

---

24.2 In conducting an Interim Arbitration the Arbitrator shall apply the powers at his disposal with a view to making his Award or Awards as quickly as possible and thereby allowing or facilitating the timely completion of the Works.

24.3 Should an Interim Arbitration not be completed before the Works or the relevant parts thereof are complete the Arbitrator shall within 14 days of the date of such completion make and publish his Award findings of fact or Interim Decision pursuant to Rule 24.5 hereunder on the basis of evidence given and submissions made up to that date together with such further evidence and submissions as he may in his discretion agree to receive during the said 14 days. Provided that before the expiry of the said 14 days the parties may otherwise agree and so notify the Arbitrator.

24.4 For the purpose only of Rule 24.3 the Arbitrator shall decide finally whether and if so when the Works or the relevant parts thereof are complete.

*Time for making the Award*

The essence of the Interim Arbitration procedure is that the Arbitrator must strive towards making his Award as soon as possible in the interests of both parties and in any event before substantial completion of the Works or of that part of the Works relevant to the issues before him. This is duly spelt out in Rule 24.2. But much of the delay in regular arbitrations stems not from excessive length of Hearings but from a general lack of urgency and priority. Parties who embark on an Interim Arbitration must be prepared to adopt a different approach.

However, disputes may arise late in the contract period or, despite the best efforts of all concerned, progress with the reference may be slow. In such cases the reference may still be running when the Works or the relevant parts thereof are nearing substantial completion. The purpose of Rule 24.3 is therefore to ensure and, if necessary, to enforce the speedy progress and conclusion of an interim reference.

Rule 24.3 requires the Arbitrator to make his Award or otherwise to terminate the interim proceedings within 14 days of such substantial completion. In doing so he is empowered by the Rule to reach his decision on the basis of such evidence and submissions as are tendered to him up to the date of substantial completion. But, as such evidence and submissions may be incomplete, he can agree to receive further such material within the 14-day period.

Thereafter, the parties may offer further evidence or request leave to make further submissions. But the Arbitrator has an absolute discretion under the Rule as to whether he will accept them. Conversely, the Arbitrator may invite such additional evidence or submissions, but under Rule 24.3 he cannot compel the parties to comply. Indeed, the Rule is designed with the prime objective of winding up the Interim Arbitration within the stipulated 14 days. If this engenders a risk of a less than satisfactory result, the Arbitrator will tend to use the less draconian of the alternatives available to him under Rule 24.5. There is, however, an alternative course open to the parties. They may agree to extend the 14-day period provided that that agreement is communicated to the Arbitrator before the 14-day period expires. In that case the Arbitrator will usually agree to receive further evidence or submissions, or both. But the Arbitrator cannot himself extend the 14-day period, however inconvenient he may find that to be.[1]

Where the Arbitrator fails to make an Award within the applicable time limit he could become liable for costs thrown away, should the reference be treated as aborted. He should normally be able to avoid such liability by making a late Award, so as to give the parties the opportunity of accepting it and avoiding the waste of costs. However, the Arbitrator should ensure that both parties so agree before delivering the Award, otherwise it is likely that the losing party will take the point that the Award is invalid, and the costs will be thrown away.

---

[1] Should the Arbitrator fail to make his Award within the prescribed 14 days, the parties may either agree an extension of time or treat the arbitration as aborted and refer the issues to regular arbitration under Clause 66(1) before another Arbitrator. In the latter event, evidence submitted under the aborted reference will normally need to be proved again.

*Date of completion*

Rule 24.4 is necessary to circumvent any dispute about the fact of substantial completion which would prevent the parties from knowing when the 14-day period under Rule 24.3 should start. The Arbitrator's power is confined, in effect, to establishing when the 14-day period starts to run. If the date of substantial completion is otherwise a real issue he must determine this separately, whether under the Interim Procedure or in another arbitration brought under Clause 66(1). A decision under Rule 24.4 need not be expressed as an Award or finding of fact; a simple order or a ruling as part of an Order for Directions will suffice.

---

24.5   In an Interim Arbitration the Arbitrator may make and publish any or all of the following
    (*a*) a Final Award or an Interim Award on the matters at issue therein
    (*b*) findings of fact
    (*c*) a Summary Award in accordance with Rule 14
    (*d*) an Interim Decision as defined in Rule 24.6.
An Award under (*a*) above or a finding under (*b*) above shall be final and binding upon the parties in any subsequent proceedings. Anything not expressly identified as falling under either of headings (*a*) (*b*) or (*c*) above shall be deemed to be an Interim Decision under heading (*d*). Save as aforesaid the Arbitrator shall not make an Interim Decision without first notifying the parties that he intends to do so.

24.6   An *Interim Decision* shall be final and binding upon the parties and upon the Engineer (if any) until such time as the Works have been completed or any Award or decision under Rule 24.3 has been given. Thereafter the Interim Decision may be re-opened by another Arbitrator appointed under these Rules and where such other Arbitrator was also the Arbitrator appointed to conduct the Interim Arbitration he shall not be bound by his earlier Interim Decision.

*Options available to the Arbitrator*

To create the greatest degree of flexibility, Rule 24.5 provides the Arbitrator with a far wider range of options than is usually available. From these options he will select the formula which he considers most appropriate to the resolution of the matters before him. These are as follows.

*A Final Award or an Interim Award.*[1] Final Awards or Interim Awards are the options normally available, which finally determine the issues with which they deal. The issues cannot thereafter be re-opened or the Award challenged other than on the grounds available following a regular arbitration. An Award under Rule 24.5(a) will be appropriate where a full reference has been conducted, with or without the special procedures under Part F or Part G.[2] It follows that, where an Interim Arbitration is to be terminated in accordance with Rule 24.3, an Award under this head should be made only when there are no grounds for adducing further evidence and the parties have had all reasonable opportunity to make appropriate submissions.

---

[1]   S. 14 of the Arbitration Act 1950.
[2]   See below under Rule 24.7.

*Findings of fact.* The finding of fact option has, in law, the effect of an Award. It is therefore final and binding upon the parties to the reference and any persons claiming through them. The Arbitrator is also *functus officio* with respect to the facts found and neither he nor any subsequent Arbitrator nor the High Court has jurisdiction thereafter to re-open those facts. Findings under Rule 24.5(b) are of particular value in resolving disputes of fact "on the spot", thereby recording those facts for all time and relieving future tribunals of the task of considering such matters again. This may be a substantial advantage in subsequent disputes, where the evidence would otherwise have to be heard, often years after the event.[1] Again, should the Arbitrator feel that he is unable to make an Award on liability he can instead make findings of relevant facts. These may be coupled with findings on quantum or of the rates to be applied to the facts found, should a later tribunal confirm liability. This ability to "freeze" relevant information and to take it out of issue before subsequent tribunals should go far to eliminate the perennial problems created for construction Arbitrators by "stale" evidence. But if the Arbitrator feels unable even to make a final finding of fact he can instead make an Interim Decision under Rule 24.5(d).

*A Summary Award.* Rule 24.5(c) secures for the Interim Arbitration all the advantages and flexibility of summary judgment under Rule 14.[2] As noted under that Rule, a Summary Award is an award of money representing a reasonable proportion of the final nett amount which the Arbitrator thinks is likely to be awarded. It is final and binding unless and until varied by any subsequent Award.[3]

*An Interim Decision.* The Interim Decision is an entirely new concept and is defined in Rule 24.6. It allows a decision to be given which is binding during the construction of the Works, so that everyone concerned can get on with the project. For this reason it has to bind the Engineer, who is *not* a party either to the Contract or to the Interim Arbitration, as well as the parties. The arbitration will, of course, usually be by way of appeal from the Engineer's own decision on the matters at issue. Once the Works are substantially complete an Interim Decision can, if necessary, be reviewed by a subsequent Arbitrator.

Where the subsequent Arbitrator happens also to have been the Interim Arbitrator he will not be bound in his new appointment by his Interim Decision. Thus the decision is analogous to an Engineer's decision under the first leg of Clause 66(1) in that it may be re-opened and referred to arbitration once the Works are substantially complete. It is also analogous to a Summary Award in that, once made, it is immediately final and binding

---

[1] As a typical civil engineering project will take several years to complete and "regular" Clause 66(1) arbitration will normally not start until the Contractor's final account has been submitted and considered, a year or more after substantial completion, most oral evidence will be "stale"—a condition aggravated because the witness will doubtless have been engaged on at least one and often more similar projects in the interval and be honestly unable to distinguish the events of one project from another.

[2] *Ante*, p. 71.

[3] Rule 14.4.

upon parties and Engineer alike and remains so unless and until varied by some subsequent Award.

The Interim Arbitrator's decision may incorporate any or all of the foregoing options. For example, if he feels unable to conclude any part of the dispute he may nevertheless award a sum of money to be paid by way of a Summary Award and make such final findings of fact as he feels able to. Alternatively, he may allow the whole of the issues to be re-opened later by confining himself to making Interim Decisions. The parties will usually leave him in no doubt about what form they would prefer his decisions to take. Where the parties are to that extent agreed, the Arbitrator should seriously consider how far it would be proper for him to acquiesce. But the parties have no power to dictate to the Arbitrator the form of his decisions, and they have no remedy[1] if they dislike his choice of option.

### Unidentified decision

For the avoidance of doubt, Rule 24.5 provides that any decision of the Arbitrator not expressly identified as falling under either of Rules 24.5(a) (Final or Interim Award), 24.5(b) (finding of fact) or 24.5(c) (Summary Award) shall be deemed to be an Interim Decision under Rule 24.5(d). This is logical, as an Interim Decision is reversible after substantial completion of the Works and is therefore the least harmful of the available options. However, if the Arbitrator *intends* to make an Interim Decision he must first notify the parties of that intention. Such notice need not be given at the Hearing but may be given at any time before the making of the Award, Finding or Decision provided that the parties are given a reasonable opportunity to respond to the notice, for example by asking for a stronger option to be applied.

---

24.7   The Arbitrator in an Interim Arbitration shall have power to direct that Part F (Short Procedure) and/or Part G (Special Procedure for Experts) shall apply to the Interim Arbitration.

### Use of special procedures

In a regular arbitration neither the Short Procedure (Part F) nor the Special Procedure for Experts (Part G) can normally be brought into play unless the parties agree. In an Interim Arbitration, however, Rule 24.7 empowers the Arbitrator to impose either or both of these procedures upon the parties, thus nullifying the effect of both Rules 20.1[2] and 22.1.[3] The purpose is to expedite the proceedings and to assist the Arbitrator in the discharge of his express duty under Rule 24.2. As is pointed out under Rule 24.1,[4] no injustice should ensue from the use of this Rule as the parties will have foregone several chances to amend the Procedure before the Arbitrator considers the use of Rule 24.7.

---

[1]   Other than the right to seek leave to appeal under s. 1 of the Arbitration Act 1979 or to seek relief in the event of misconduct by the Arbitrator.

[2]   See p. 84, *ante.*

[3]   See p. 88, *ante.*

[4]   See p. 92, *ante.*

Unless the parties themselves otherwise agree, it will often be appropriate to use one or both of the special procedures. Where the Interim Arbitrator is minded to direct their use he should be chary of directing otherwise at the request of one party unless cogent reasons are adduced. It is further suggested that the Arbitrator may properly persist with a Rule 24.7 direction in an appropriate case even where the parties are agreed in their opposition. Of course, if the parties are sufficiently adamant and remain unanimous, they may agree to replace the Arbitrator. But most parties, and even their legal advisers, are more likely to respect and co–operate with an Arbitrator who is prepared to take a positive line and to hold to it.

## PART J: MISCELLANEOUS

### Rule 25: Definitions

25.1   In these Rules the following definitions shall apply.
   (*a*) 'Arbitrator' includes a tribunal of two or more Arbitrators or an Umpire.
   (*b*) 'Institution' means The Institution of Civil Engineers.
   (*c*) 'ICE Conditions of Contract' means the Conditions of Contract for use in connection with Works of Civil Engineering Construction published jointly by the Institution, the Association of Consulting Engineers and the Federation of Civil Engineering Contractors.
   (*d*) 'Other party' includes the plural unless the context otherwise requires.
   (*e*) 'President' means the President for the time being of the Institution or any Vice-President acting on his behalf.
   (*f*) 'Procedure' means The Institution of Civil Engineers' Arbitration Procedure (1983) unless the context otherwise requires.
   (*g*) 'Award', 'Final Award' and 'Interim Award' have the meanings given to those terms in or in connection with the Arbitration Acts 1950 to 1979. 'Summary Award' means an Award made under Rule 14 hereof.
   (*h*) 'Interim Arbitration' means an arbitration in accordance with Part H of these Rules. 'Interim Decision' means a decision as defined in Rule 24.6 hereof.

*Scope of the Rule*

The definitions given are declaratory and are included for the avoidance of doubt. In addition to these definitions, the Practice employs terms from the ICE Conditions of Contract, which are defined in Clause 1(1) thereof.

The Rules are drafted on the basis that there will be a sole Arbitrator appointed. The Rules can, however, be used equally where there is more than one Arbitrator or where two Arbitrators are appointed with provision for them to appoint an Umpire. Additional considerations which may affect such appointments are discussed in Chapter 2.

### Rule 26: Application of the ICE Procedure

26.1   This Procedure shall apply to the conduct of the arbitration if
   (*a*) the parties at any time so agree
   (*b*) the President when making an appointment so directs
or   (*c*) the Arbitrator so stipulates at the time of his appointment.

Provided that where this Procedure applies by virtue of the Arbitrator's stipulation under (*c*) above the parties may within 14 days of that appointment agree otherwise in which event the Arbitrator's appointment shall terminate and the parties shall pay his reasonable charges in equal shares.

26.2   This Procedure shall not apply to arbitrations under the law of Scotland for which a separate *ICE Arbitration Procedure (Scotland)* is available.

26.3   Where an arbitration is governed by the law of a country other than England and Wales this Procedure shall apply to the extent that the applicable law permits.

## Use of the Procedure

The Procedure may be adopted, either in whole or in part, in any arbitration, whether under Clause 66 of the ICE Conditions or not, and at any stage during the proceedings. Thus, for example, it can be used for certain issues only, or the special procedures can be applied to the taking of certain parts of the evidence, without thereby necessarily applying to the proceedings as a whole.

While drafted mainly for use in Clause 66 arbitrations, the Procedure is equally applicable to arbitrations under Clause 18 of the "Blue Form" of Sub-Contract[1] and to arbitrations under Clause 67 of the FIDIC Conditions.[2] Outside civil engineering it may also be found useful for arbitrations under the JCT Conditions,[3] the "Green Form"[4] of Sub-Contract and under many of the more specialised construction forms. It may also be used in "administered" arbitrations with the agreement of the administering authority.

Rule 26.1(b) repeats the discretion given to the President in Clause 66 of the ICE Conditions, when appointing an Arbitrator, to direct that the arbitration be conducted in accordance with this Procedure. Such a direction will not infringe the parties' rights under the general law as it is open to the parties to agree to depart from the Procedure despite the President's direction under the proviso to Rule 26.1.

## Requirement by the Arbitrator

Rule 26.1(c) will apply only where the Arbitrator is appointed by the President (or, exceptionally, some other appointing authority). This is because in all other cases the parties will have been in communication with the prospective appointee before his appointment and will normally have been informed of his views in advance. But on a Presidential appointment under Rule 3 the Arbitrator is appointed *before* he makes contact with the parties. The situation can therefore arise where the parties do not wish the Procedure to apply but the Arbitrator is only willing to act if it does apply.[5] Although it is unlikely, this could happen if one of the parties (or their advisers) has such a reputation that the Arbitrator considers that it is

---

[1]   See p. 142, *post.*
[2]   See p. 139, *post.*
[3]   See p. 141, *post.*
[4]   A matching form of Sub-Contract designed for use with the JCT Conditions.
[5]   This assumes that, for some reason, the President has not directed that the Procedure shall apply: see p. 55, *ante.*

necessary to be armed with the stronger powers available under the Procedure. In that event, the Arbitrator may stipulate that the Procedure shall apply and the parties then have 14 days in which to reject the stipulation and to revoke the appointment. In practice, negotiation may well ensue, with the parties offering some compromise rather than be left without an Arbitrator.

To some extent the Rule does offer a reluctant Respondent scope for procrastination, but only if he can persuade the Claimant to join him in revoking the Arbitrator's appointment. In such a situation the Arbitrator could agree to waive his stipulation and to rely instead on applying to the Court for additional powers under s. 5 of the 1979 Act should this later become necessary.

*Variant Procedures*

The ICE Arbitration Procedure (Scotland) is discussed in detail in Chapters 11 and 12. Application of the England and Wales version to Northern Ireland and the Irish Republic is discussed in Chapter 13.

*Training Arbitrators*

The powers and discretions given by this Procedure are such that the Arbitrator must be capable of exercising them in a proper and a judicial manner. This presupposes that he will have received adequate training and will have acquired experience before being appointed. It has been suggested that, in adopting such a Procedure, the Institution impliedly accepted a commitment to maintain a pool of suitable and competent Arbitrators.

Fortunately, the Institution was one of the first of the professional bodies to recognise this need. In recent years it has formulated a system of specialised study leading to examinations in civil engineering law and arbitration. This has enabled it to build up a respected body of Chartered Engineers and others capable of handling references under the ICE Conditions of Contract. Their names appear in an official list published by the Institution, from which the parties may select their own Arbitrator and to which the President refers when making an appointment. Candidates for inclusion in the list must first be of standing in their own profession and must also demonstrate a sufficient knowledge of general law and the law and practice of arbitration, with particular reference to civil engineering. Finally, each candidate is interviewed to ensure that, as far as possible, he is capable of acting in a judicial manner.

## Rule 27: Exclusion of liability

27.1 Neither the Institution nor its servants or agents nor the President shall be liable to any party for any act omission or misconduct in connection with any appointment made or any arbitration conducted under this Procedure.

*Scope of the Rule*

This Rule protects the Institution, its officers and servants from suit at the hands of a party that is dissatisfied with an arbitration conducted in accordance with this Procedure, or with an Arbitrator appointed by the President. Despite recent developments in the law relating to tortious liability, it is thought that the chances of success in such an action even without this Rule would be minimal, provided (as is usual) that the President chose the Arbitrator from the ICE List or from some panel of equal standing.

# SCOTLAND

*Chapter 11*

# ARBITRATION IN SCOTLAND

## Introduction

In this chapter the main features of Scots arbitration law and practice are briefly discussed. The text is aimed chiefly at non-Scottish practitioners who find themselves operating in Scotland, but it may also serve as an introduction to the subject for Scottish Engineers who have limited experience of arbitration. For further information, reference may be made to M. E. L. Weir's *Arbitration in Scotland*.[1]

Arbitration throughout the United Kingdom generally has its sources in the common law. For England and Wales, Northern Ireland and Eire, statute law is now the main source of procedure. In Scotland, however, arbitration is still almost wholly a matter of common law.

Recent statutes in England and Wales[2] do not apply to Scotland, where only minor aspects of the arbitral process have been affected by legislation. The only statutes[3] covering domestic Scottish arbitrations are the Act of Regulation 1695 concerning the "reduction" (or setting aside) of an award for corruption; the Arbitration (Scotland) Act 1894 which permits parties to agree to submit future disputes to a person not named in the Contract; the Administration of Justice (Scotland) Act 1972 which enables the parties to submit points of law to the Court of Session for the opinion of that Court, while leaving them free to agree not to do so; and the Law Reform (Miscellaneous Provisions) (Scotland) Act 1980 which allows Judges of the Court of Session to accept appointments as Arbiters. There is nothing equivalent to the English Arbitration Act 1950 and an Arbiter has no inherent power at common law to award damages, to order specific performance ("specific implement" in Scotland) or to administer oaths unless the parties so provide in their Deed of Submission.

The attitude of the Courts to arbitration in Scotland is very different from that in England and Wales. The supervisory role of the English Courts has no parallel in Scotland. Similarly, while in England and Wales the Court has discretionary power to stay court proceedings brought in breach of an arbitration agreement, in Scotland the Courts must give effect to the parties' agreement to arbitrate.

This different approach to arbitration in Scotland is illustrated by the words of Lord Dunedin in *Sanderson & Sons* v. *Armour & Co. Ltd.*[4]

---

[1] M. E. L. Weir, *A Synopsis of the Law and Practice of Arbitration in Scotland*, Department of Building, Heriot-Watt University, 2nd edn, Jan., 1980.
[2] Part I of the Arbitration Act 1950 and the Arbitration Acts of 1975 and 1979; see Appendix I.
[3] See Appendix II.
[4] [1922] S.C. (H.L.) 117.

"The English common law doctrine—eventually swept away by the Arbitration Act of 1889—that a contract to oust the jurisdiction of the Courts was against public policy and invalid, never obtained in Scotland. In the same way, the right which in England pertains to the Court under that Act to apply or not to apply the arbitration clause in its discretion never was the right of the Court in Scotland. If the parties have contracted to arbitrate, to arbitration they must go."

## Case stated

In England and Wales an Arbitrator can decide questions of law as well as questions of fact, but his decisions on questions of law may be subject to review by the Courts. In Scotland, prior to 1972, there was no right of appeal to the Courts either in fact or in law and, in particular, no Scottish equivalent to the English "case-stated" procedure then in force. This was the background to the leading case of *James Miller & Partners Ltd.* v. *Whitworth Street Estates (Manchester) Ltd.*[1] in which the House of Lords held that the law governing procedure in an arbitration between the parties was Scots law as distinct from the proper law of the Contract under which it arose, and that accordingly the Arbiter had no power to make an award[2] in the form of a Special Case.

Two years later, the Special Case procedure was introduced into Scotland by s. 3 of the Administration of Justice (Scotland) Act 1972.[3] However, the parties to an arbitration agreement could still contract out of the Act's provisions by including in their agreement a stipulation to that end. Under the new Act, as in England and Wales until 1979, the Arbiter may, if requested to do so by a party to the arbitration, state a case to the Court of Session for its decision on a question of law. If the Arbiter refuses to state a case an aggrieved party may apply to the Court of Session for an order directing the Arbiter to state a case.[4] Nevertheless, it is understood that, so far, no case has yet been fully contested under this new procedure.

## Appointing the Arbiter

Until 1894 the Courts in Scotland would enforce a Decree Arbitral only if the Arbiter had been named in the arbitration agreement. Thus the parties had to agree in advance to appoint a named Arbiter; it would not suffice to agree that the Arbiter would be the holder of a particular office, or that he should be named by a third party. Again, where there was a reference to two Arbiters (one appointed by each side), the Arbiters had no power to appoint an Oversman, with the result that if the Arbiters could not agree the whole arbitration came to a standstill.

However, the Arbitration (Scotland) Act 1894[5] rectified this situation by providing that an agreement to refer to arbitration should not be invalid or ineffectual by reason of the Arbiter's not being named, or being described as the holder for the time being of any office or appointment, or

---

[1] [1970] A.C. 583.

[2] Or Decree Arbitral—see p. 108, *post*.

[3] See Appendix II.

[4] But such an order is not appropriate once the Arbiter has made a final Decree Arbitral—see *Fairlie Yacht Slip Ltd.* v. *Lumsden* [1977] S.L.T. (Notes) 41.

[5] See Appendix II.

where he was to be named by another person. Provision was also made for the appointment of Oversmen, and the Court was empowered to appoint in default of appointment by the parties. To this extent, therefore, Scots law is now broadly comparable with the law of England and Wales. In addition, provision has recently been made whereby a Judge of the Court of Session may accept an appointment as Arbiter or Oversman in a dispute of a commercial nature.[1]

## The submission[2]

A submission is a contract or agreement between any number of parties to have their differences referred to the final determination of an Arbiter or Arbiters, and for such determination to be final and binding. In Scotland the submission to arbitration need not be in writing, but it is obviously wise that it should be. It is usual—but not essential—for it to be in the form of a Deed of Submission prepared at the commencement of the arbitration. The principal functions of this document are to appoint the arbitral tribunal, to describe the issues to be decided and to confer any desired powers or to define any limitations on the tribunal.

A Deed of Submission is often referred to as an "ordinary" submission, namely one whose terms are wholly concerned with the disputes to be referred to arbitration.[3] Traditionally, there is also an alternative form of submission known as an "ancillary" submission,[4] which arises where the agreement to refer is already incorporated in a contract between the parties which is also concerned with other matters. It is considered that the ICE Arbitration Clause, the Notice to Refer and the ICE Arbitration Procedure together constitute such a submission.

Where an ancillary submission is already in existence it is not necessary for the parties to agree an ordinary submission. However, if the matters in dispute are to be limited to certain items or the Arbiter's power or jurisdiction is to be limited in some way, the parties may choose to have an ordinary submission, in which case the ordinary submission will supersede the ancillary submission in respect of those matters. But failure to agree on the terms of a Deed of Submission can cause considerable delay and, if the parties insist on proceeding in that manner, the Arbiter will be powerless to act until the Deed has been properly executed.

The duration of a submission is generally subject to agreement between the parties and can therefore be extended by them from time to time, again by agreement. Alternatively, the parties can give the Arbiter power to extend the duration, which is then known as "prorogation". But if the submission is silent it will only remain valid for a year and a day.[5] Where the Arbiter grants prorogation he must do so in writing; his power is

---

[1]  S. 17 of the Law Reform (Miscellaneous Provisions) (Scotland) Act 1980 (see Appendix II). Compare the similar provision in England and Wales under s. 4 of the Administration of Justice Act 1970.

[2]  See M. E. L. Weir's *Arbitration in Scotland*, p. 27.

[3]  An ordinary submission, of course, need not be in the form of a Deed.

[4]  Or "submission ancillary".

[5]  See M. E. L. Weir's *Arbitration in Scotland*, p. 33.

discretionary but its use is an act of jurisdiction and, as such, must be exercised in a judicial manner.

## The Arbiter's Clerk

Except in small or very informal arbitrations it is the normal Scottish practice that, after appointment, the Arbiter will appoint a lawyer to act as his Clerk and legal adviser. As with the Arbiter himself, the Clerk is subject to disqualification should he have any interest in the parties or in the matter in dispute. But, as in England, an interest which is disclosed to the parties may be waived by them. As well as being the Arbiter's legal adviser the Clerk provides nearly all of the secretarial and administrative services required throughout the whole of the reference, in contrast with the practice in England, where the Arbitrator will usually provide these services himself.

Once the Clerk is appointed, the parties are notified, and they will then communicate through the Clerk to the Arbiter on all matters in the arbitration. Throughout the whole of the reference the Arbiter will make and his Clerk will transmit to the parties a series of Interlocutors[1] which are generally equivalent to the Orders for Direction which the Arbitrator makes in other parts of the United Kingdom.

## Preliminary procedure[1]

The Arbiter may decide to hold a Preliminary Meeting soon after appointment, but in Scotland it is usual practice to dispense with a meeting and to conduct the preliminary stages of the arbitration by a series of Interlocutors. All questions about time limits for lodgment of claims, answers, counterclaims and the like are matters for the Arbiter's discretion.

Apart from small and very informal arbitrations, most Arbiters adopt procedures which follow fairly closely those of the Scottish Courts. Thus the Statement of Claim customarily opens with "recitals" comprising a short introduction listing the remedies sought, with or without a narrative, followed by a "condescendence" or statement of facts and concluding with "Pleas-in-Law". The Respondent's defence ("Answers") follows the same pattern and may include a counterclaim which the Claimant will answer in the same manner. It is usual for the Arbiter to issue an Interlocutor stipulating the time within which the parties must prepare and serve the foregoing documents, after which they are assembled into one document covering all the pleadings and known as the "Open Record".[2]

A period is then allowed (usually by a further Interlocutor) for "adjustment", during which each party may amend his pleadings in the light of his adversary's statements. This system is peculiar to Scotland but can be likened to the procedure for obtaining further and better particulars which obtains elsewhere in the United Kingdom. When this period (which is relatively short) has expired, the Open Record combined with the adjustments becomes the "Closed Record", which is then printed and sent to the Arbiter's Clerk for retention.

---

[1] See M. E. L. Weir's *Arbitration in Scotland*, pp. 51–52.
[2] Pronounced re<u>cord</u>.

The Closed Record thus sets out all the issues of fact and of law which the Arbiter is required to determine. No further amendment to the Closed Record is allowed without the Arbiter's leave, which will not be given lightly. Experience shows that it is a most convenient document for everyone concerned in the arbitration, and its use could well prove beneficial elsewhere in the United Kingdom.

At this stage it may often be desirable to settle the Pleas-in-Law in advance of the main Hearing. This is achieved by means of a "Legal Debate", which is a preliminary Hearing at which the parties will usually be represented by Counsel or Solicitors, and following which the Arbiter will deliver a Part Decree Arbitral or a further Interlocutor as may be appropriate. Not infrequently, this will result in the parties' being able themselves to settle any remaining issues, but it will usually be necessary to follow the Debate with a full Hearing to establish the facts. Occasionally, however, it may be expedient to reverse the above order and to proceed with "Proof before Answer" to establish the facts in preparation for a subsequent Hearing to deal with the Pleas-in-Law. If appropriate, Proof before Answer can be on documents only, but a Debate on documents without a Hearing, although permissible, would be rare.

## Documents

As with all court cases and arbitrations it is necessary to assemble the documentary evidence. In Scotland, this process is known as "recovery"[1] and is the subject of yet a further Interlocutor by the Arbiter whereby the parties are required to produce all the necessary evidence to support their case together with such additional evidence as may be requested by the other party. Any issues which arise in recovery are dealt with by the Arbiter's Clerk and, should either party fail to provide the documents ordered, the Arbiter and his Clerk can apply to the Courts for a diligence[2] to compel their production.

## The Hearing

Following the Closed Record and recovery of documents the Arbiter makes a further Interlocutor stating the venue, date and time for the parties to be heard. Procedure at the Hearing follows closely that of the Scottish Courts and is generally similar to the procedures in other parts of the United Kingdom.

At the Hearing the function of the Arbiter's Clerk is broadly comparable with that of a Clerk to the Court, or the Judge's Associate in the English Queen's Bench Division. He will marshall the various persons attending the Hearing, ensure that the documentary evidence, reference books and the like are available as needed, and attend to such other matters as will assist the smooth running of the proceedings. He will also advise (in private) the Arbiter on matters of law and procedure, keep a note[3] of the evidence

---

[1] See the glossary at the end of this chapter; the equivalent term in England and Wales is "discovery".

[2] See the glossary at the end of this chapter.

[3] The Arbiter will, of course, also keep his own note; later comparison with the Clerk's notes will provide a useful check on accuracy.

and submission and draft such Interlocutors and other papers as may be required.

### Decrees Arbitral

An arbitration Award in Scotland is known as a "Decree Arbitral". It is a document prepared by the Arbiter which gives decisions on all matters referred to him in the Closed Record. In general, there is no set pattern in the way that the document is written and there is no attempt to standardize Awards in the same way as has developed in England and Wales. There is, however, one difference in that, before making his Decree Arbitral, the Arbiter may communicate with the parties via his Clerk and issue a note of his proposed findings.[1] Where this procedure is followed, it is open to the parties to appear again before the Arbiter to make further representations to him on the substance of his proposed findings. Where this procedure is not adopted, however, the Arbiter will finalise the content of his Decree Arbitral for his Clerk to despatch to the parties. Nevertheless, it is usual to delay issuing the Decree Arbitral until the expenses of the arbitration[2] have been paid.

As is the rule elsewhere in the United Kingdom, the Decree Arbitral must deal with all matters at issue in the reference and must not go beyond them. There are times when the Arbiter will give reasons for or with his Decree Arbitral, but he need not do so and cannot be compelled to do so by the Courts. A Part Decree Arbitral is one which decides some only of the matters at issue, leaving others to be determined by further Part Decrees or the final Decree Arbitral; it is thus the Scottish equivalent of an English Interim Award.

There is, however, in Scotland a further type of Award known as a "Decree Arbitral *ad interim*". This differs from the other kinds of decree in that it can be amended[3] by a subsequent Decree Arbitral. It is, in a sense, broadly analogous to an Interim Certificate under the ICE Conditions of Contract. While such a Decree is final unless and until amended, it is virtually unknown in the rest of the United Kingdom. However, the Summary Award created by Rule 14[4] of the England and Wales version of the ICE Arbitration Procedure is intended to serve the same purpose and to that extent is a new and, so far, the only non-Scottish equivalent of the Decree Arbitral *ad interim*.

### Expenses

A Scottish Decree Arbitral should deal not only with the matters in dispute, as shown in the Closed Record, but also with costs—known in Scotland as "expenses". If the matter of expenses is not specifically provided for in the Deed of Submission,[5] expenses will be entirely in the Arbiter's discretion. As in England and Wales, the general rule is that

---

[1] It seems that in Scotland the Arbiter has no formal lien on his Decree Arbitral to secure payment of his expenses.

[2] Equivalent to the English "costs of the Award".

[3] It is not clear whether a Decree Arbitral *ad interim* can be *reversed* by a later Decree.

[4] See p. 71, *ante*.

[5] For example, by an agreement that each party shall bear his own expenses.

expenses are paid by the unsuccessful party, but the Arbiter may depart from this rule as he sees fit.

Again, as in England and Wales, the expenses are divided into two parts. The first covers the fees of the Arbiter and his Clerk, together with their outlays and administrative expenses. The second is known in Scotland as the parties' expenses, including the fees of Solicitors and Counsel, the expenses of witnesses and other proper outgoings. The general rule is that the losing party pays all the expenses, but the Arbiter can vary this as he sees fit. The allocation of expenses will often be the subject of a small Hearing after the terms of the Decree Arbitral are known, or it may be dealt with in separate addresses to the Arbiter by the parties at the close of the main Hearing.

If a dispute should arise as to the amounts of the expenses, as distinct from their allocation, this can be referred to the Auditor of the Court of Session or, alternatively, to the Clerk of a Sheriff Court. There is no general power in the Arbiter to tax and settle costs similar to that under s. 18 of the English Arbitration Act 1950, but the parties may include such a power in the terms of the submission if they wish.

## Enforcement[1]

Decrees Arbitral of all kinds can be enforced in Scotland by action in the Courts, the resulting order being known as a "decree conform". However, the usual procedure is for the parties to agree in the arbitration agreement to the registration of the Decree Arbitral in the Books of Council and Session for "preservation and execution". Should a party thereafter fail to comply with the terms of the Decree Arbitral, enforcement can then be obtained through the Courts by summary diligence.

## Appeals

Apart from the recent introduction of a special case procedure under s. 3 of the Administration of Justice (Scotland) Act 1972,[2] which seems in practice to have been very little used, the Scottish Courts will in general not intervene where the parties have agreed to refer their disputes to arbitration. A Decree Arbitral can be challenged,[3] but only on the ground of some defect in the submission itself or of misconduct by the Arbiter or his Clerk.[4] Corruption or bribery[5] will constitute misconduct, and other faults by the Arbiter such as exceeding his jurisdiction, improper procedure or some serious defect in the Decree Arbitral itself may suffice. As to the latter, the terms of the Decree Arbitral should be clear and in accordance both with the Closed Record and with whatever Deed of Submission is applicable. Finally, where a Decree Arbitral is deemed to be defective only in part, enforcement of the "good" part may be obtainable if severance is feasible.[6]

---

[1]  See M. E. L. Weir's *Arbitration in Scotland*, ch. VIII.
[2]  See Appendix II. See also p. 103, *ante*.
[3]  M. E. L. Weir's *Arbitration in Scotland*, p. 68 *et seq*.
[4]  *Ibid.*, pp. 77–78; also p. 72.
[5]  *Ibid.*, pp. 70–71; see also the Articles of Regulation 1695 (Appendix II).
[6]  *Ibid.*, p. 75.

### The new Clause 67

Revised versions of Clauses 66 and 67 for use with the ICE Conditions of Contract, fifth edition, were issued in March, 1985. The new Clause 66 is dealt with in Chapter 10. Clause 67, in the revised text, is expanded into two Sub-Clauses, the effects of which are as follows.

> 67(1)   If the Works are situated in Scotland the Contract shall in all respects be construed and operate as a Scottish contract and shall be interpreted in accordance with Scots Law and the provisions of this Clause shall apply.

This is the old Clause 67 applying Scots law to the Contract, together with linking words to the new Sub-Clause (2).

> 67(2)   In the application of Clause 66 the word "arbiter" shall be substituted for the word "arbitrator". Any reference to the Arbitration Act 1950 shall be deleted and for any reference to the Institution of Civil Engineers' Arbitration Procedure (1983) there shall be substituted a reference to the Institution of Civil Engineers' Arbitration Procedure (Scotland) (1983).

This Sub-Clause adapts Clause 66 for use in Scotland by deleting the term "arbitrator" and the reference to the ICE Arbitration Procedure[1] and substituting the Scottish equivalents. Reference to the Arbitration Act 1950[2] is also deleted without substitution, as there is no equivalent Scottish statute.

The former reference in Clause 66(1) to the Arbitration (Scotland) Act 1894 has been omitted, as adoption of the ICE Procedure provides a ready means of securing the appointment of an Arbiter and, in any event, the new Clause 66(4) empowers the Institution's President to appoint if the parties fail to do so. The statutory provisions empowering the Court to appoint are thus in most cases superfluous.

## GLOSSARY OF RELEVANT SCOTTISH LEGAL TERMS

*Adjustment* is the alteration of written pleadings to meet the facts stated or allegations made by the other party or parties.

*Amendment, Minute of,* is a document setting out an amendment to a pleading.

*Ancillary submission* means an arbitration clause incorporated in a contract between the parties concerning other matters.

*Answer* is a response or reply by one party to a pleading or minute lodged by the other.

*Arbiter* means Arbitrator.

*Auditor of Court* is an official of the Court of Session who conducts judicial audits of the parties' costs in civil actions. His English equivalent is a High Court Taxing Master.

*Citation* is a summons.

*Cited* means summoned to appear in Court.

*Closed Record* is an open Record plus all the adjustments.

---

[1]   Clause 66(5)(a).
[2]   Clause 66(5)(b).

*Commission for taking proof* means an authorization by the Court for some qualified person to take the evidence of witnesses. It is linked with a diligence which enables witnesses to be cited and documents to be produced.

*Condescendence* is a detailed statement of fact on which a party relies. Together with Pleas–in–Law, it forms part of that party's pleading.

*Debate* means a preliminary Hearing to determine matters of law.

*Decree Arbitral* means Award.

*Decree Arbitral ad interim* means an interim Award which can be re-opened. It is equivalent to a Summary Award under Rule 14 of the ICE Procedure (England and Wales) but is not otherwise known outside Scotland.

*Decree conform* is the means by which the Court enforces a valid Award which has not been registered in the Books of Council and Session.

*Deed of Submission* is an ordinary submission in formal terms stating the disputes to be referred and specifying the Arbiter's powers.

*Diet* means hearing; it also means the date of a hearing.

*Diligence* is a procedure by which a Decree Arbitral is enforced, or writings are recovered from an opponent, or the evidence of witnesses is obtained. There is no exact English equivalent, but similar results will be obtained by writ of execution, order for discovery and *subpoena ad testificandum* respectively.

*Expenses* means costs, often referred to as "fees and outlays".

*Ex proprio motu* means "of his own accord".

*Incompetent* means that the conclusions of an action conflict with an applicable rule of law.

*Interlocutor* means any order or decision of the Court or the Arbiter which does not finally dispose of the case.

*Irrelevant* means "not pertinent"—as when it can be said that, were the alleged facts proved, the remedy sought would not be granted.

*Motion* means any application to the Court or the Arbiter.

*Open Record* is a document incorporating all the pleadings before final adjustment, at which stage it becomes a Closed Record.

*Ordinary submission* is an agreement to refer disputes to arbitration which is not part of some other contract. It may, and normally will, take the form of a Deed of Submission.

*Part Decree Arbitral* is equivalent to an English Interim Award. It cannot be re-opened but decides only some of the matters at issue.

*Pleas–in–Law* means a party's statement of his alleged legal right to the remedy sought. Together with the condescendence, it forms part of that party's pleading.

*Precognition* is a written statement of the evidence a witness can give. It differs from an English proof of evidence in that the witness is not bound to give his evidence exactly as set out therein. The term also covers experts' reports.

*Preservation and execution:* see *registration for preservation and execution.*

*Proof before Answer* means the determination of facts before the issues of law are heard.

*Prorogation* is the Arbiter's power to extend the duration of the submission.

*Recovery* is the Scottish term for discovery of documents.

*Registration for preservation and execution* means the registration of a judgment or Decree Arbitral in the Books of Council and Session for execution against the losing party. It is the first step in obtaining a diligence for that purpose.

*Specification, lack of,* means, in English terminology, that the particulars in the pleadings are insufficient.

*Specific implement* is equivalent to specific performance in England.

*Submission* means arbitration agreement: see also *ordinary submission* and *ancillary submission.*

*Warrant* means (in the context of Rule 31) the equivalent of a *subpoena ad testificandum.*

# Chapter 12

# COMMENTARY ON THE SCOTTISH RULES

## Introduction

While Scotland has its own law and procedures which in many ways differ considerably from those which obtain in the rest of the United Kingdom, the ICE Conditions of Contract are applied with equal ease, and without amendment, both sides of the Border. Moreover, the manner in which civil engineering projects are managed and claims negotiated is generally the same, regardless of where the Works are located. In drafting the ICE Arbitration Procedure for Scotland, therefore, it seemed to be reasonable to try to ensure that, as far as possible, disputes referred to arbitration in Scotland could be resolved using procedures familiar in other parts of the country. Indeed, it became clear before the Procedure for Scotland was published that this was what a number of Contractors and Employers with experience in Scotland wanted.

Accordingly, the Procedure for Scotland has been drafted largely on the basis of that for England and Wales, while making proper provision for the traditional customs and practices of commercial arbitration in Scotland. However, the result is much more than a mere "translation" of the English Procedure into Scottish terminology. For this reason, the following commentary on the Rules for Scotland is written with the Sassenach in mind in the hope that, given suitable guidance, the newcomer to Scottish arbitration will be able to play his part with confidence and dispatch.

Scottish legal terms are used throughout the Rules, and no comment on that account is needed. A short glossary will be found at the end of the preceding chapter covering those terms the meaning of which is not immediately apparent to an English eye. For the rest, an absence of comment means that that particular Rule is essentially the same as the corresponding English Rule, and the commentary on the latter in Chapters 7, 8, 9 and 10 will apply equally to the former.

Where the English and Scottish Rules differ the English version is set out as a footnote for ease of reference. Where the English commentary applies equally to the Scottish Rule, the page on which it may be found is given.

## APPOINTMENT AND POWERS[1]

### PART A: REFERENCE AND APPOINTMENT

#### Rule 1: Notice to Refer

1.1 A dispute or difference shall be deemed to arise when a claim or assertion

---

[1] See Chapter 7.

made by one party is rejected by the other party and that rejection is not accepted. Subject only to Clause 66(1) of the *ICE Conditions of Contract* (if applicable) either party may then invoke arbitration by serving a *Notice to Refer* on the other party.

1.2    The Notice to Refer shall list the matters which the issuing party wishes to be referred to arbitration. Where Clause 66 of the ICE Conditions of Contract applies the Notice to Refer shall also state the date when the matters listed therein were referred to the Engineer for his decision under Clause 66(1) and the date on which the Engineer gave his decision thereon or that he has failed to do so.

For commentary, see p. 51.

## Rule 2: Appointment of sole Arbiter by agreement

2.1    After serving the Notice to Refer either party may serve upon the other a *Notice to Concur* in the appointment of an Arbiter listing therein the names and addresses of any persons he proposes as Arbiter.

2.2    Within 28 days thereafter the other party shall
   (a)   agree in writing to the appointment of one of the persons listed in the Notice to Concur

or   (b)   send to the Applicant a list of alternative persons.

2.3    Once agreement has been reached the issuing party shall write to the person so selected inviting him to accept the appointment enclosing a copy of the Notice to Refer and documentary evidence of the other party's agreement.

2.4    If the person so selected accepts the appointment he shall notify the issuing party in writing and send a copy to the other party. The date of posting or service as the case may be of this notification shall be deemed to be the date on which the Arbiter's appointment is completed.

For commentary, see p. 53. Note that the time limit in Rule 2.2 for Scotland is longer than the 14 days allowed in England.

## Rule 3: Appointment of sole Arbiter by the President

3.1    If within six weeks from service of the Notice to Concur the parties fail to appoint an Arbiter in accordance with Rule 2 either party may then apply to the President to appoint an Arbiter. The parties may also agree to apply to the President without a Notice to Concur.

3.2    Such application shall be in writing and shall include copies of the Notice to Refer, the Notice to Concur (if any) and any other relevant documents. The application shall be accompanied by the appropriate fee.

3.3    The Institution will send a copy of the application to the other party stating that the President intends to make the appointment on a specified date. Having first contacted an appropriate person and obtained his agreement the President will make the appointment on the specified date or such later date as may be appropriate which shall then be deemed to be the date on which the Arbiter's appointment is completed. The Institution will notify both parties and the Arbiter in writing as soon as possible thereafter.

For commentary, see p. 54. Note that the time limit in Rule 3.1 for Scotland is longer than the one month allowed in England.

## Rule 4: Notice of further disputes or differences

4.1.    At any time before the Arbiter's appointment is completed either party may put forward further disputes or differences to be referred to him. This shall be done by serving upon the other party an additional Notice to Refer in accordance with Rule 1.

4.2   Once his appointment is completed the Arbiter shall have jurisdiction over any issue connected with and necessary to the determination of any dispute or difference already referred to him whether or not the connected issue has first been referred to the Engineer for his decision under Clause 66(1) of the ICE Conditions of Contract.

For commentary, see p. 55.

## PART B: POWERS OF THE ARBITER

### Rule 5: Power to control the proceedings

5.1   The Arbiter shall be empowered to appoint a Clerk and Legal Adviser, in which case all communications between the parties and the Arbiter shall be through the Clerk.

5.2   The Arbiter may exercise any or all of the powers set out or necessarily to be implied in this Procedure on such terms or conditions as he thinks fit. These terms or conditions may include orders as to payment of expenses, time for compliance and the consequences of non–compliance.

5.3   This Procedure shall apply in addition to any other powers which the Arbiter may have under the Law of Scotland. Provided always that if any provision of this Procedure should conflict with the general law applicable to arbitration procedure this Procedure shall take precedence unless and to the extent that the parties shall have expressly agreed to the contrary.

Scottish Rule 5.1 gives the Arbiter power to appoint a Clerk and Legal Adviser in accordance with the common law procedure in Scottish arbitrations. It has no English equivalent. English Rules 5.1 and 5.2 are accordingly renumbered 5.2 and 5.3 respectively for the Scottish Procedure.

Rule 5.3 has been expanded to give precedence to the Procedure for Scotland over the general law, should there be any conflict, unless the parties otherwise agree.[1]

### Rule 6: Power to order protective measures

6.1   The Arbiter shall have power
  (a)   to give directions for the detention storage sale or disposal of the whole or any part of the subject matter of the dispute at the expense of one or both of the parties
  (b)   to give directions for the preservation of any document or thing which is or may become evidence in the arbitration
  (c)   to order the deposit of money or other security to secure the whole or any part of the amount(s) in dispute
  (d)   to order the deposit of money or other security to secure the expenses of one or more of the parties
and (e)   to order the deposit of money or other security as security for the fees and outlays of himself and his Clerk.

---

[1]   Compare this provision with the stipulation in many sections of the English Arbitration Act 1950 that the statutory powers shall vest in the Arbitrator unless a contrary intention is expressed in the arbitration agreement.

6.2   Money ordered to be deposited under this Rule shall be paid without delay into a special deposit or joint deposit under the directions of the Arbiter.

The Scottish and English versions of this Rule both achieve the same result but the means to that end differ in some respects. Thus Scottish Rules 6.1(d) and 6.1(e) substitute the deposit of money for the English security for costs and, by Rule 6.2, such monies are to be paid into a deposit (account) and not to a stakeholder.

Rule 6.1(e) also makes provision for safeguarding the fees and outlays of the Arbiter's Clerk.[1]

## Rule 7: Power to order concurrent Hearings

7.1   Where disputes or differences have arisen under two or more contracts each concerned wholly or mainly with the same subject matter and the resulting arbitrations have been referred to the same Arbiter he may with the agreement of all the parties concerned or where this procedure is applicable to each of the arbitrations upon the application of one of the parties being a party to all the contracts involved order that the whole or any part of the matters at issue shall be heard together upon such terms and conditions as the Arbiter thinks fit.

7.2   Where an order for concurrent Hearings has been made under Rule 7.1 the Arbiter shall nevertheless make and publish separate Decrees Arbitral unless the parties otherwise agree but the Arbiter may if he thinks fit prepare one combined set of Reasons to cover all the Decrees Arbitral.

This Rule is the same as in the Procedure for England, save for the addition of one phrase which does not alter the sense of the text. For commentary, see p. 58.

## Rule 8: Powers at the Hearing

8.1   The Arbiter may hear the parties their representatives and/or witnesses at any time or place and may adjourn the arbitration for any period on the application of any party or as he thinks fit.

8.2   Any party may be represented by any person including in the case of a company or other legal entity a director officer employee or beneficiary of such company or entity. In particular, a person shall not be prevented from representing a party because he is or may be also a witness in the proceedings. Nothing shall prevent a party from being represented by different persons at different times.

8.3   Nothing in these Rules or in any other rule custom or practice shall prevent the Arbiter from starting to hear the arbitration once his appointment is completed or at any time thereafter.

8.4   Any meeting with or summons before the Arbiter at which both parties are represented shall if the Arbiter so directs be treated as part of the hearing of the arbitration.

8.5   The Arbiter may require witnesses to be examined on oath or affirmation and is empowered to administer oaths or to take affirmations.

8.6   Without prejudice to his general powers under the Law of Scotland the Arbiter shall have power to award damages and interest or, at his discretion, to order specific implement.

---

[1]   Provisions linking the Clerk's fees and outlays with those of the Arbiter also appear in Rules 17.2, 21.1, 23.1, 29.2 and 29.4.

Rules 8.1, 8.2, 8.3 and 8.4 are the same in both Procedures.

Rules 8.5 and 8.6 are necessary in the Procedure for Scotland to equip the Arbiter with powers which in England are vested in the Arbitrator unless a contrary intention is expressed in the arbitration agreement. Thus Rule 8.5 is the Scottish equivalent of s. 12(3) of the English Arbitration Act 1950 and, in Rule 8.6, the power to order specific implement is similarly equivalent to s. 15 of the 1950 Act covering the remedy of specific performance.

The power to award interest in Rule 8.6 is, it seems, rather wider than the analogous power of an Arbitrator in England.[1]

## Rule 9: Power to appoint Assessors

9.1   The Arbiter may appoint a legal technical or other Assessor to assist him in the conduct of the arbitration.

9.2   Further and/or alternatively the Arbiter may rely upon his own knowledge and expertise to such extent as he thinks fit.

Scottish Rules 9.1 and 9.2 are effectively the same as English Rules 9.1 and 9.3 respectively.

English Rule 9.2[2] is omitted from the Procedure for Scotland. Having themselves chosen or acquiesced in the appointment of the Arbiter, the parties are prepared to rely on his own knowledge and expertise. Should some aspect of the dispute prove to be outside the Arbiter's specialist experience, the correct procedure in Scottish eyes is to appoint an appropriate Assessor or to rely on the testimony of experts called by the parties; in either event, the provider of the outside expertise is himself involved in the reference even though, in the case of an Assessor, he cannot be questioned by the parties.

Curiously, although the Scots are averse to the Arbiter's seeking outside advice, he may seek that of his Clerk. Yet there is no similar prohibition on the Clerk's seeking outside advice and then passing it on to the Arbiter as his own.

## PROCEDURE[3]

### PART C: PROCEDURE BEFORE THE HEARING

## Rule 10: The Preliminary Meeting

10.1   As soon as possible after accepting the appointment the Arbiter may summon the parties to a Preliminary Meeting for the purpose of giving such directions about the procedure to be adopted in the arbitration as he considers necessary.

10.2   At the Preliminary Meeting the parties and the Arbiter may consider whether and to what extent

---

[1]   See Chapter 4.
[2]   The English Rule 9.2 is as follows:
   9.2   The Arbitrator may seek legal technical or other advice on any matter arising out of or in connection with the proceedings.
[3]   See Chapter 8.

(a) Part F (Short Procedure) or Part G (Special Procedure for Experts) of these Rules shall apply

(b) the arbitration may proceed on documents only

(c) progress may be facilitated and expense saved by determining some of the issues in advance of or after the main Hearing

(d) the parties may enter into an exclusion agreement (if they have not already done so) in accordance with Section 3 of the Administration of Justice (Scotland) Act 1972 so as to exclude the appeal rights given by that Section

and in general may consider such other steps as may in their view minimise delay and expedite the determination of the issues between the parties.

10.3    If the parties so wish they may themselves as an alternative to a preliminary meeting agree directions and, within such time as the Arbiter may direct, submit them to the Arbiter for his approval. In so doing the parties shall state whether or not they wish Part F or Part G of these Rules to apply. The Arbiter may then approve the directions as submitted or—having first consulted the parties —may vary them or substitute his own as he thinks fit except that the Arbiter (other than in an Interim Arbitration) shall have no power to direct the parties to proceed by way of Rule 10.2 (a), (b) or (d). In an Interim Arbitration the Arbiter shall have powers to order proceeding by way of Rule 10.2 (a) and (c) but not to order procedure under Rule 10.2 (b) or (d).

Preliminary Meetings under this Rule are essentially the same whether in England or in Scotland. But while in England the holding of such meetings is the rule rather than the exception, in general the reverse is true in Scotland. Thus the main difference between the two Procedures is that under the Procedure for England a Preliminary Meeting is mandatory,[1] while under the Procedure for Scotland it is optional.

The English Arbitration Act 1979 does not apply to Scotland, so the Scottish Rule 10.2(d) cites instead s. 3 of the Administration of Justice (Scotland) Act 1972. The rights of appeal under that section are by way of case stated and are ". . . subject to express provision to the contrary in an agreement to refer to arbitration . . .".[2]

Consistent with the Scottish preference for the parties themselves to agree the procedure if at all possible, the Scottish Rule 10.3 carries a qualification that the Arbiter cannot impose the provisions of Rule 10.2 beyond a decision for "split" Hearings.[3] In the case of an Interim Arbitration this qualification is somewhat different, and is discussed later.[4]

## Rule 11: Pleadings and production of documents

11.1    Unless otherwise agreed or ordered by the Arbiter the pleadings in the arbitration will consist of claims and answers, statements of facts and counter-claims and answers and Closed Records in the usual Scottish form. Pleadings shall be adjusted in the usual Scottish manner before the closing of the Record. After the closing of the Record the pleading may be amended at the discretion of the

---

[1]  Unless, of course, the Arbitrator agrees to waive it.

[2]  S. 3(1). See also p. 104, *ante*. Useful summaries of case-stated procedure may be found in Weir's *Arbitration in Scotland*, pp. 90–92 and (although written with English procedure in mind) in Mustill & Boyd's *Commercial Arbitration*, app. 3.

[3]  Rule 10.2(c).

[4]  See p. 125, *post*.

Arbiter by way of Minute of Amendment and Answers thereto. If agreed or ordered by the Arbiter an Open Record will be made up and utilised for the purposes of adjustment of the pleadings. The pleadings will include pleas–in–law in Scottish form including preliminary pleas where appropriate.

11.2   Where, after a hearing, the Arbiter holds that pleadings are irrelevant, incompetent or lacking in specification, he may at his discretion permit amendment if sought but, if not sought or sought but refused, may make a decision giving effect to preliminary pleas alleging irrelevance, incompetence or lack of specification with the effect of rejecting in whole or in part the case of a party or the answer by a party to the case of the other party. Such decisions on such preliminary pleas shall constitute Part Decrees Arbitral or Decrees Arbitral as the case may be.

11.3   The Arbiter may order any party at any stage in the arbitration whether before or after the closing of the Record to lodge any document in his possession, custody or power which relates either generally or specifically to matters raised in the pleadings.

Rule 11 of the Procedure for Scotland is based firmly on conventional Scottish procedures and, as such, bears little relationship with the English Rule other than the power to order recovery of documents in Scottish Rule 11.3, which is comparable with discovery under English Rule 11.2.

Scottish Rules 11.1 and 11.2 provide for the full range of pleadings, adjustments, Open and Closed Records familiar to Scottish litigants and which are discussed in Chapter 11. The provision at the end of Rule 11.1 for preliminary pleas gives scope for separate Hearings on matters of law which, if properly used, should result in significant savings of time and expense.[1]

Rule 11.2 empowers the Arbiter to entertain further amendment of pleadings after a Hearing and to deal with a defaulting party by making a Part Decree Arbitral or even a final Decree Arbitral striking out that party's claim or answer. While an English Arbitrator may similarly give leave to amend, it has recently been held that he cannot strike out a party's case for want of prosecution,[2] and his alternative sanction of proceedings *ex parte* to a further Hearing is quite different from the Scottish Arbiter's powers.[3]

## Rule 12: Procedural meetings

12.1   The Arbiter may at any time call such procedural meetings as he deems necessary to identify or clarify the issues to be decided and the procedures to be adopted. For this purpose the Arbiter may request particular persons to attend on behalf of the parties.

12.2   Any party may lodge an incidental Motion at any time on the subject of

---

[1]   In Scotland it is quite common to try matters of law separately from matters of fact. Indeed, the leading case of *Donoghue* v. *Stevenson*, despite its status as the source of the modern *English* law of negligence, was for Scotland merely a preliminary application to the Court of Session to determine whether fact or law should be tried first.

[2]   *Bremer Vulkan Schiffbau* v. *South India Shipping* [1981] A.C. 989; see also p. 75, *ante*. Powers to strike out can, however, be obtained in England under s. 5 of the Arbitration Act 1979; see p. 15, *ante*.

[3]   There is, it seems, nothing to prevent the parties to an English arbitration from adopting the Scottish procedure in this respect, but few parties in England seem to favour such a solution.

procedure in the arbitration. If the Motion be opposed or if the Arbiter be uncertain about its desirability he may fix a hearing on the Motion: alternatively he may deal with the Motion by correspondence or otherwise as he thinks fit.

12.3   Where there are no pleadings under Rule 11 the Arbiter may issue an order that either or both parties shall prepare in writing and shall serve upon the other party and the Arbiter any or all of the following

(*a*)   a summary of that party's case

(*b*)   a summary of that party's evidence

(*c*)   a statement or summary of the issues between the parties

(*d*)   a list and/or a summary of the documents relied upon

(*e*)   a statement or summary of any other matters likely to assist the resolution of the disputes or differences between the parties.

For commentary, see p. 67.

## Rule 13: Preparation for the Hearing

13.1   In addition to his powers under Rules 11 and 12 the Arbiter shall also have power

(*a*)   to order that the parties shall agree facts as facts and figures as figures where possible

(*b*)   to order the parties jointly to prepare a bundle of all documents relevant to the arbitration. The bundle shall thereby be deemed to have been entered in evidence without further proof and without having to be read out at the Hearing. Provided always that either party may at the Hearing challenge any document in the bundle

(*c*)   to order before the Hearing that any experts whose reports have been exchanged shall be examined by the Arbiter in the presence of the parties or their legal representatives and not by the parties or their legal representatives themselves. Where such procedure is followed after all experts have been examined by the Arbiter any party may seek permission from the Arbiter to put questions after having first given notice to the Arbiter of the questions. A decision whether or not to permit a party to ask particular questions will be at the sole discretion of the Arbiter.

13.2   Before the Hearing the Arbiter may and shall if so requested by the parties read the documents to be used at the Hearing. For this or any other purpose the Arbiter may require all such documents to be delivered to him at such time and place as he may specify.

The only material difference between the English and Scottish version of this Rule is that the Scottish Rule 13.1(c) requires the Arbiter to issue any order thereunder before the Hearing and provides that a party wishing to put questions to a witness under this procedure must first get leave to do so from the Arbiter. Otherwise, for commentary, see p. 68.

## Rule 14: Decree Arbitral *ad interim*

14.1   The Arbiter may at any time make a Decree Arbitral *ad interim* and for this purpose shall have power to award payment by one party to another of a sum representing a reasonable proportion of the final nett amount which in his opinion that party is likely to be ordered to pay after determination of all the issues in the arbitration and after taking into account any answer or counterclaims upon which the other party may be entitled to rely.

14.2   The Arbiter shall have powers to order the party against whom a Decree Arbitral *ad interim* is made to pay part or all of the sum awarded into a special deposit or joint deposit.

14.3   A Decree Arbitral *ad interim* shall be final and binding upon the parties unless and until it is varied by any subsequent Decree Arbitral made and published by the same Arbiter or by any other arbiter having jurisdiction over the matters in dispute. Any such subsequent Decree Arbitral may order repayment of monies paid in accordance with the Decree Arbitral *ad interim*.

The Scottish Rule 14 is essentially the same as the English Rule but, as a Decree Arbitral *ad interim* is a normal remedy available in Scottish arbitration, the text is somewhat simpler.

As with Rule 6,[1] payments under Rule 14.2 are to be made to a deposit account rather than to a stakeholder. The sanction in default, contained in the second sentence of the English version,[2] is not needed in Scotland, as the other party can simply enforce the Decree by summary diligence.[3]

The English Rule 14.3[2] is omitted from the Procedure for Scotland as expenses relating to a Decree Arbitral *ad interim* will be recoverable in the same manner as those relating to any other kind of Decree. In consequence the English Rule 14.4 becomes the Scottish Rule 14.3.


## PART D: PROCEDURE AT THE HEARING

### Rule 15: The Hearing

15.1   At or before the Hearing and after hearing representations on behalf of each party the Arbiter shall determine the order in which the parties shall present their cases and/or the order in which the issues shall be heard and determined.

15.2   The Arbiter may order any submission or speech by or on behalf of any party to be put into writing and delivered to him and to the other party. A party so ordered shall be entitled if he so wishes to enlarge upon or vary any such submission orally.

15.3   The Arbiter may on the application of either party or *ex proprio motu* hear and determine any issue or issues separately.

15.4   If a party fails to appear at the Hearing and provided that the absent party has had notice of the Hearing or the Arbiter is satisfied that all reasonable steps have been taken to notify him of the Hearing the Arbiter may issue notice intimating to the absent party that if he does not appear or is not represented at a Hearing fixed in the notice the Arbiter may dispose of the arbitration by default and may then so proceed.

---

[1]   See p. 115, *ante*.
[2]   The English Rules 14.2 and 14.3 are as follows:
      14.2   The Arbitrator shall have power to order the party against whom a Summary Award is made to pay part or all of the sum awarded to a stakeholder. In default of compliance with such an order the Arbitrator may order payment of the whole sum in the Summary Award to the other party.
      14.3   The Arbitrator shall have power to order payment of costs in relation to a Summary Award including power to order that such costs shall be paid forthwith.
[3]   The sanction is needed in England because, by its nature, it will be exercised *after* the Summary Award has been made and, if it were omitted, the default could lack a remedy unless and until some later Award is made. On the other hand, its inclusion for Scotland, as well as being unnecessary, might be regarded by the Scottish Courts as being penal and therefore unenforceable.

This Rule is in substance the same as in the Procedure for England, save that in Rule 15.4 the Arbiter is expressly required to adjourn a Hearing and to issue a preremptory notice to a party failing to appear before proceeding *ex parte*.[1] Otherwise, for commentary, see p. 73.

## Rule 16: Evidence

16.1 The Arbiter may order a party to submit in advance of the Hearing a list of the witnesses he intends to call. That party shall not thereby be bound to call any witness so listed and may add to the list so submitted at any time.

16.2 No expert evidence shall be admissible except by leave of the Arbiter. Leave may be given on such terms and conditions as the Arbiter sees fit. Unless the Arbiter otherwise orders such terms shall be deemed to include a requirement that a precognition from each expert containing the substance of the evidence to be given shall be served upon the other party within a reasonable time before the Hearing.

16.3 The Arbiter may order disclosure or exchange of precognitions relating to factual issues. The Arbiter may also order any party to prepare and disclose in advance a list of points or questions to be put in cross-examination of any witness.

16.4 Where a list of questions is disclosed whether pursuant to an order of the Arbiter or otherwise the party making disclosure shall not be bound to put any question therein to the witness unless the Arbiter so orders. Where the party making disclosure puts a question not so listed in cross-examination the Arbiter may disallow the expenses thereby occasioned.

16.5 The Arbiter may order that any precognition which has been disclosed shall stand as the evidence in chief of the witness provided that the other party has been or will be given an opportunity to cross-examine the witness thereon. The Arbiter may also at any time before such cross-examination order the witness or some other identified person to deliver written answers to questions arising out of the precognition.

16.6 The Arbiter may himself put questions to any witness and/or require the parties to conduct enquiries tests or investigations. Subject to his agreement the parties may ask the Arbiter to conduct or arrange for any enquiry test or investigation.

For commentary, see p. 75.


## PART E: AFTER THE HEARING

## Rule 17: The Decree Arbitral

17.1 Upon the closing of the Hearing (if any) and after having considered all the evidence and submissions the Arbiter will prepare and publish his Decree Arbitral, Part Decree Arbitral or Decree Arbitral *ad interim*.

17.2 When the Arbiter has made and published his Decree Arbitral or a Decree Arbitral *ad interim* under Rule 14 or a Part Decree Arbitral under Rule 15 he will inform the parties that he has done so and shall specify how and where it may be taken up and upon what conditions if any in regard to payment of the fees and outlays of himself and his Clerk.

For commentary, see p. 78.

---

[1] In England as well, the Arbitrator will normally adjourn and issue a preremptory notice, but Rule 15.4 does not compel him to do so.

## Rule 18: Reasons

18.1  Whether requested by any party to do so or not the Arbiter may at his discretion state his Reasons for all or any part of his Decrees Arbitral, Part Decrees Arbitral or Decrees Arbitral *ad interim*. Such Reasons may form part of the Decrees Arbitral, Part Decrees Arbitral or Decrees Arbitral *ad interim* or may be contained in a separate document.

18.2  Reasons prepared as a separate document may be delivered with the Decree Arbitral, Part Decree Arbitral or Decree Arbitral *ad interim*, or later as the Arbiter thinks fit.

The Scottish Rules 18.1 and 18.2 are equivalent to the English Rules 18.1 and 18.3 respectively. In Scotland (as in England before the Act of 1979) the giving of reasons is wholly within the Arbiter's discretion.

English Rules 18.2 and 18.4 are concerned with the provisions of s. 1 of the Arbitration Act 1979 and thus have no relevance in Scotland.

## Rule 19: Application to the Court

19.1  If any party applies to the Court of Session in any matter affecting the arbitration proceedings that party shall forthwith notify the Arbiter and the other parties.

As the English Arbitration Act 1979 does not apply to Scotland, the Scottish version of Rule 19.1 is simpler and the English Rule 19.2 is not needed. However, under the Scottish Rule the applicant party must inform the other parties as well as the Arbiter.

## SPECIAL PROCEDURES[1]

### *PART F: SHORT PROCEDURE*

## Rule 20: Short Procedure

20.1  Where the parties so agree (either of their own motion or at the invitation of the Arbiter) the arbitration shall be conducted in accordance with the following *Short Procedure*.

20.2  Each party shall set out his case in the form of a file containing

    (*a*)  a statement as to the orders or decrees he seeks

    (*b*)  a statement of his reasons for being entitled to such orders or decrees

and  (*c*)  copies of any documents on which he relies (including precognitions) identifying the origin and date of each document

and shall deliver copies of the said file to the other party and to the Arbiter in such manner and within such time as the Arbiter may direct.

20.3  After reading the parties' cases the Arbiter may require either or both parties to submit further documents or information in writing.

20.4  Within one calendar month of completing the foregoing steps the Arbiter shall fix a day when he shall meet the parties for the purpose of

    (*a*)  receiving any oral submissions which either party may wish to make

and/or  (*b*)  the Arbiter's putting questions to the parties their representatives or witnesses.

---

[1]  See Chapter 9.

For this purpose the Arbiter shall give notice of any particular person he wishes to question but no person shall be bound to appear before him unless separately cited by the Arbiter on an application to him.

20.5    Within one calendar month following the conclusion of the meeting under Rule 20.4 or such further period as the Arbiter may reasonably require the Arbiter shall make and publish his Decree Arbitral.

Save that in Scottish Rule 20.4 the Arbiter is given power to order that a named witness shall appear before him, the two versions of this Rule are identical. For commentary, see p. 84.

## Rule 21: Other matters relating to the Short Procedure

21.1    Unless the parties otherwise agree the Arbiter shall have no power to award expenses to either party and the Arbiter's own fees and charges and those of his Clerk shall be paid in equal shares by the parties. Where one party has agreed in advance to such fees and charges the other party by agreeing to this Short Procedure shall be deemed to have agreed likewise.

21.2    Either party may at any time before the Arbiter has made and published his Decree Arbitral under this Short Procedure require by written notice served on the Arbiter and the other party that the arbitration shall cease to be conducted in accordance with this Short Procedure. Save only for Rule 21.3 the Short Procedure shall thereupon no longer apply or bind the parties but any evidence already laid before the Arbiter shall be admissible in further proceedings as if it had been submitted as part of those proceedings and without further proof.

21.3    The party giving written notice under Rule 21.2 shall thereupon in any event become liable to pay

   (a) the whole of the Arbiter's fees and charges and those of his Clerk incurred up to the date of such notice

and   (b) a sum to be assessed by the Arbiter as reasonable compensation for the expenses (including any legal expense) incurred by the other party up to the date of such notice.

Payment in full of such charges shall be a condition precedent to that party's proceeding further in the arbitration unless the Arbiter otherwise directs. Provided that non-payment of the said charges shall not prevent the other party from proceeding in the arbitration.

For commentary, see p. 86.

## PART G: SPECIAL PROCEDURE FOR EXPERTS

## Rule 22: Special Procedure for Experts

22.1    Where the parties so agree (either of their own motion or at the invitation of the Arbiter) the hearing and determination of any issues of fact which depend upon the evidence of experts shall be conducted in accordance with the following *Special Procedure*.

22.2    Each party shall set out his case on such issues in the form of a file containing

   (a) a statement of the factual findings he seeks

   (b) a report or precognition from and signed by each expert upon whom that party relies

and   (c) copies of any other documents referred to in each expert's report or precognition or on which the party relies identifying the origin and date of each document and shall deliver copies of the said file to the other party and to the Arbiter in such manner and within such time as the Arbiter may direct.

22.3 After reading the parties' cases the Arbiter may view the site or the Works and may require either or both parties to submit further documents or information in writing.

22.4 Thereafter the Arbiter shall fix a day when he shall meet the experts whose reports or precognitions have been submitted. At the meeting each expert may address the Arbiter and put questions to any other expert representing the other party. The Arbiter shall so direct the meeting as to ensure that each expert has an adequate opportunity to explain his opinion and to comment upon any opposing opinion. No other person shall be entitled to address the Arbiter or question any expert unless the parties and the Arbiter so agree.

22.5 Thereafter the Arbiter may make and publish a Decree Arbitral or Part Decree Arbitral setting out with such details or particulars as may be necessary his decision upon the issues dealt with.

For commentary, see p. 88.

## Rule 23: Expenses under Special Procedure for Experts

23.1 The Arbiter may in his Decree Arbitral or Part Decree Arbitral make orders as to the payment of any expenses relating to the foregoing matters including his own fees and charges in connection therewith and those of his Clerk.

23.2 Unless the parties otherwise agree and so notify the Arbiter neither party shall be entitled to any expense in respect of legal representation assistance or other legal work relating to the disposal of issues under this Special Procedure.

For commentary, see p. 90.

# INTERIM ARBITRATION AND OTHER MATTERS[1]

## PART H: INTERIM ARBITRATION

## Rule 24: Interim Arbitration

24.1 Where the Arbiter is appointed and the arbitration is to proceed before completion or alleged completion of the Works then save in the case of a dispute arising under Clause 63 of the ICE Conditions of Contract the following provisions shall apply in addition to the foregoing Rules and the arbitration shall be called an *Interim Arbitration*.

24.2 In conducting an Interim Arbitration in terms of Clause 66(2) of the ICE Conditions of Contract the following conditions shall apply. The Arbiter shall apply the powers at his disposal with a view to concluding the Interim Arbitration as quickly as possible and thereby allowing or facilitating the timely completion of the Works.

24.3 Should an Interim Arbitration not be completed before receipt by the Arbiter of a copy of a certificate of completion by the Engineer issued under Clause 48 of the ICE Conditions of Contract the Arbiter shall within 28 days of the date of such certificate make and publish his Decree Arbitral, Part Decree

---

[1] See Chapter 10. Where the new (1985) Clause 66 applies, Rule 24 procedure may be used for any arbitration starting before substantial completion of the whole of the Works.

Arbitral or Decree Arbitral *ad interim* findings of fact or Interim Decision pursuant to Rule 24.4 hereunder on the basis of evidence given and submissions made up to that date together with such further evidence and submissions as he may in his discretion agree to receive during the said 28 days. Provided that before the expiry of the said 28 days the parties may otherwise agree and so notify the Arbiter.

24.4   In an Interim Arbitration the Arbiter may make and publish any or all of the following

> (*a*) a Decree Arbitral or a part Decree Arbitral on the matters at issue therein
>
> (*b*) findings of fact
>
> (*c*) a Decree Arbitral *ad interim* in accordance with Rule 14
>
> (*d*) an Interim Decision as defined in Rule 24.5.

A Decree under (*a*) above or a finding under (*b*) above shall be final and binding upon the parties in any subsequent proceedings. Provided that anything not expressly identified as falling under any of headings (*a*), (*b*) or (*c*) above shall be deemed to be an Interim Decision under heading (*d*). Provided also that the Arbiter shall not make an Interim Decision without first notifying the parties that he intends to do so.

24.5   An Interim Decision shall be final and binding upon the parties and upon the Engineer (if any) unless superseded by a Decree Arbitral, Part Decree Arbitral or Decree Arbitral *ad interim*.

24.6   The Arbiter in an Interim Arbitration shall have power to direct that Part F (Short Procedure) and/or Part G (Special Procedure for Experts) shall apply to the Interim Arbitration.

Interim Arbitration in Scotland generally follows English procedure save for the following.

(*a*) Rule 24.4 of the Procedure for England[1] is omitted. In consequence, the Arbiter has to rely on a Completion Certificate from the Engineer under Clause 48 of the ICE Conditions of Contract, and cannot decide it himself.[2] Rules 24.5, 24.6 and 24.7 are accordingly renumbered for the Scottish Procedure.

(*b*) Similarly, additional words have been inserted in Rule 24.3 which link completion specifically to the Engineer's Certificate. Once completion has been so certified, however, the Arbiter has 28 days in which to make his Decree instead of the 14 days allowed under the English Rule.

(*c*) Scottish Rule 24.4 is ostensibly the same as English Rule 24.5. But, in the last sentence, the words "Provided also that . . ." have replaced the English "Save as aforesaid . . .". At first sight, this appears to create an anomaly in that, as the Arbiter *must* give the parties notice before making an Interim Decision, it is difficult to see how anything not "expressly identified" can be deemed to be an Interim Decision where, having failed to give notice of such an intention, the Arbiter could otherwise be assumed to have intended to make some other decree or finding. However, the "deeming" provision is intended

---

[1]   The English Rule 24.4 is as follows.

> 24.4   For the purpose only of Rule 24.3 the Arbitrator shall decide finally whether and if so when the Works or the relevant parts thereof are complete.

[2]   Unless, of course, the fact of completion is the very matter which has been referred to arbitration. But in that event the reference is arguably not an Interim Arbitration at all.

only to save what would otherwise be an ambiguous result by adopting the mildest of the available alternatives—one, moreover, which is easily corrected by the Arbiter himself in a subsequent Decree—and in practice little difficulty is likely to arise.

(*d*) Scottish Rule 24.5 makes an Interim Decision final and binding unless and until superseded by a Decree Arbitral, Part Decree Arbitral or Decree Arbitral *ad interim*. The finality does not cease upon completion of the Works as the English Rule 24.6[1] provides. However, the difference is unlikely to lead to any difficulty in practice.

## *PART J: MISCELLANEOUS*

## Rule 25: Definitions

25.1 In these Rules the following definitions shall apply.

(*a*) 'Arbiter' includes a tribunal of two or more Arbiters with or without an Oversman.

(*b*) 'Institution' means the Institution of Civil Engineers.

(*c*) 'ICE Conditions of Contract' means The Conditions of Contract for use in connection with Works of Civil Engineering Construction published jointly by the Institution, the Association of Consulting Engineers and the Federation of Civil Engineering Contractors applicable to the contract between the parties.

(*d*) 'Other party' includes the plural unless the context otherwise requires.

(*e*) 'President' means the President for the time being of the Institution or any Vice-President acting on his behalf.

(*f*) 'Procedure' means the ICE Arbitration Procedure (Scotland) (1983) unless the context otherwise requires.

(*g*) 'Interim Arbitration' means an arbitration in accordance with Part H of these Rules. 'Interim Decision' means a decision as defined in Rule 24.5 hereof.

(*h*) Where the word 'he/him' appears it shall be deemed to read 'she/her' when appropriate.

Both versions of this Rule cover the same ground, save that the English Rule 25.1(g) (Award, Final Award and Interim Award) is not needed in Scotland and Scottish Rule 25.1(h) is covered in England by statute. English Rule 25.1(h) (Interim Arbitration) accordingly becomes Scottish Rule 25.1(g).

## Rule 26: Application of the ICE Procedure

26.1 This Procedure shall apply to arbitrations under the Law of Scotland.

---

[1] The English Rule 24.6 is as follows.

24.6 An *Interim Decision* shall be final and binding upon the parties and upon the Engineer (if any) until such time as the Works have been completed or any Award or decision under Rule 24.3 has been given. Thereafter the Interim Decision may be reopened by another Arbitrator appointed under these Rules and where such other Arbitrator was also the Arbitrator appointed to conduct the Interim Arbitration he shall not be bound by his earlier Interim Decision.

26.2  This Procedure shall not apply to arbitrations under the law of England and Wales for which a separate *ICE Arbitration Procedure* is available.

26.3  Where an arbitration is governed by the law of a country other than Scotland this Procedure may be applied to the extent that the applicable law permits.

Under the Procedure for Scotland the provisions of the English Rule 26.1[1] are omitted; Scottish Rule 26.1 merely echoes Clause 67 of the ICE Conditions of Contract. However, the substance of the English Rules 26.1(a) and 26.1(b) will apply by virtue of the provisions of Clause 66 of the ICE Conditions. The omission of English Rule 26.1(c) and the proviso thereto is of no great moment as the parties can agree to terminate the Arbiter's appointment at any time; all that is lost is the English requirement that they do so within 14 days of the Presidential appointment.

## Rule 27: Duration of Submission[2]

27.1  It is agreed that notwithstanding the lapse of a year and a day from the appointment of the Arbiter the submission shall endure until all matters referred are finally determined and that without the necessity of prorogation.

This Rule needs no comment; the Arbiter's jurisdiction is extended automatically. There is no equivalent Rule under the Procedure for England.

## Rule 28: Registration

28.1  The parties agree to the registration hereof and of any decrees to follow hereon for preservation and execution.

There is no equivalent Rule under the Procedure for England.

It is usual in Scotland to register an award in the Books of Council and Session. This will usually be done by one of the parties, but may also be done by the Arbiter. A valid award which is not so registered will afford a plea of *res judicata* as a defence to an action in the Courts on the same subject matter,[3] but positive enforcement of the award is best achieved by summary diligence after registration. Alternatively, an unregistered but valid award may be enforced by "decree conform".[4]

## Rule 29: Expenses

29.1  Save as elsewhere provided herein the Arbiter shall have power to order

---

[1]  The English version of Rule 26.1 is as follows.

26.1  This Procedure shall apply to the conduct of the arbitration if
   (a)  the parties at any time so agree
   (b)  the President when making an appointment so directs
   or  (c)  the Arbitrator so stipulates at the time of his appointment
   Provided that where this Procedure applies by virtue of the Arbitrator's stipulation under (c) above the parties may within 14 days of that appointment agree otherwise in which event the Arbitrator's appointment shall terminate and the parties shall pay his reasonable charges in equal shares.

[2]  See M. E. L. Weir's *Arbitration in Scotland*, p. 33.

[3]  *Ibid.*, p. 81.

[4]  See *Bell on Arbitration* (2nd edn), p. 357, para. 742.

any party or parties to the arbitration to meet wholly or partly the expenses of another party or other parties where such are craved and shall so far as legal expense is concerned intimate the scale upon which legal fees are to be taxed.

29.2   The Arbiter shall have power to order the parties to the arbitration or any one or more of them to meet his fees and outlays and the fees and outlays of his Clerk in such proportions as he may think fit. If his Clerk is legally qualified any such order shall include the scale upon which the Clerk's fees are to be taxed.

29.3   The fees of the Arbiter shall be as agreed or, failing agreement, such as are fair and reasonable in the circumstances and may include fees and outlays in respect of cancelled hearings.

29.4   Notwithstanding the provisions set out in this paragraph the parties shall be liable jointly and severally to the Arbiter for the fees and outlays of the Arbiter and his Clerk without prejudice to the rights of parties thereafter to seek relief from the other party or other parties in respect of any sums expended by them in excess of the sums they were ordered to pay.

There is no equivalent Rule under the Procedure for England.

This Rule is needed to give the Arbiter powers which an English Arbitrator is given by statute.[1] Rule 29.3 includes express power to charge for cancelled Hearings, a matter on which there is as yet no authority in England.

## Rule 30: Exclusion of liability

30.1   Neither the Institution nor its servants or agents nor the President shall be liable to any party for any act omission or misconduct in connection with any appointment made or any arbitration conducted under this Procedure.

Save for the numbering, Scottish Rule 30.1 is identical with English Rule 27.1.

## Rule 31: Assistance of the Court

31.1   The Arbiter may authorise any party to petition the Court for
   (*a*) a Warrant to compel the attendance of witnesses
   (*b*) the grant to a qualified person of a Commission to take evidence
   (*c*) a Commission to recover documents and material evidence.

There is no equivalent Rule under the Procedure for England.

This Rule covers in general terms the provisions of s. 12 of the English Arbitration Act 1950.[2] The Arbiter's authorisation will normally be required for any such application to the Court, unlike in England where a party may approach the Court without the Arbitrator's leave.

There is no equivalent in Scotland to the procedure under s. 5 of the English Act of 1979 whereby the Arbitrator may be granted the powers of a High Court Judge.

---

[1]   Arbitration Act 1950, s. 18.
[2]   Specifically, ss. 12(4), 12(5) and 12(6).

# OTHER APPLICATIONS

*Chapter 13*

# APPLICATION TO NORTHERN IRELAND AND THE REPUBLIC OF IRELAND

## Introduction

Although the ICE Arbitration Procedure (1983) was designed to fit in with current legislation applicable to England and Wales, namely the Arbitration Acts of 1950 and 1979, it is possible to use the Procedure, suitably modified, for arbitrations in both parts of Ireland.

It is useful to trace the history of the various Arbitration Acts. The Northern Ireland Arbitration Act dates from 1937 and a comparison between that Act, the 1954 Arbitration Act of the Republic of Ireland and the English Act of 1950 will demonstrate that the Northern Ireland Act sets the pattern for the other two. Indeed, in many sections the same wording is used in all three statutes. However, there are some real differences between them, not only in the numbering of sections but also in the scope of the statutes themselves.

The full text of each Act is set out in the appendices.[1] To facilitate comparison, the sections of each Act are listed in Table 1 together with the equivalent sections of the other two statutes.

## Appeals

The English Arbitration Act of 1979 has no Irish equivalent, and appeals procedures in either part of Ireland are still broadly the same as those which existed in England before 1979. Thus the "special case" procedure still applies in Northern Ireland and the Republic, either in the form of the consultative case during the course of a reference or as an Award in the form of a special case following the Hearing. Parties in Ireland may therefore still exercise the option of having matters of law decided by the Courts. Curiously, this could result in appeals originating in Northern Ireland reaching the House of Lords in England, despite the repeal of the special case procedure so far as England and Wales is concerned.

The absence of any Irish equivalent to the English 1979 Act affects a number of the rules of the ICE Arbitration Procedure, as noted below.

## Stay of proceedings

The English Arbitration Act of 1975 applies equally to Northern Ireland but not, of course, to the Republic. Thus in Northern Ireland, as in England and Wales, the Court continues to have a discretion[2] whether or not to grant a stay of proceedings in domestic litigation where there is also an

---

[1]   The English 1950 and 1979 Acts in Appendix I, the Irish Acts in Appendix II.
[2]   S. 4 in the 1950 and 1937 Acts; s. 1 in the 1975 Act.

**Table 1. Table of comparison**

| | Sections of the following Acts | | |
|---|---|---|---|
| | England and Wales 1950 Act | Northern Ireland 1937 Act | Republic of Ireland 1954 Act |
| Additional powers of Court re second schedule | 5 | 21 | — |
| Application of Part II to Scotland | 41 | — | — |
| Application of Part II to Northern Ireland | 42 | See 1937 Act generally | — |
| Application of section 3 of Legal Practitioners (Ireland) Act 1876, to Solicitors' costs in arbitrations | — | 23(4) | 32 |
| Application to statutory arbitrations | 31 | 28 | 48 |
| Arbitration agreements | 1 | 1 | 9 |
| Awards to which Part II applies | 35 | — | 54 |
| Bankruptcy | 3 | 3 | 11 |
| Conditions for enforcement of foreign Awards | 37 | — | 56 |
| Conduct of Proceedings | 12 | 13, 14, 24 | 19, 20, 21, 22 |
| Correction of slips | 17 | 13 | 28 |
| Costs, fees and interest | 18, 19A | 23 | 29,[1] 30, 31 |
| Court jurisdiction | 25 | — | 51, 53 |
| Court's power to remit Award | 22 | 15 | 36[1] |
| Court's power where Arbitrator not impartial | 24 | 10 | 39 |
| Court's power where Arbitrator removed or authority revoked | 25 | 8, 11 | 40 |
| Court Rules under Order of Court | — | 20 | — |
| Crown to be bound | 30 | — | 4 |
| Death of party | 2 | 2 | 10 |
| Effect of foreign Awards | 36 | — | 55 |
| Enforcement of Award | 26 | 16 | 41[1] |
| Evidence in foreign Awards | 38 | — | 57 |
| Exclusion of certain arbitrations | — | — | 5 |
| Extension of time for commencement | 27 | 19(5) | 42,[2] 43,[2] 44,[2] 45 |
| Finality of Awards | 16 | — | 27 |
| | | | *(continued)* |

[1] These sections may be restricted in certain cases by s. 17(5) of the Landlord and Tenant (Ground Rents) Act 1967.

[2] Now amended by ss. 9 and 11 of the Limitation Act 1957 and, in some cases, by ss. 11(1)(d) and 11(5)(b) of the Landlord and Tenant (Ground Rents) Act 1967.

**Table 1** (*continued*)

| | Sections of the following Acts | | |
|---|---|---|---|
| | England and Wales 1950 Act | Northern Ireland 1937 Act | Republic of Ireland 1954 Act |
| Interest on Awards | 20 | 17 | 34 |
| Interim Awards | 14 | 22(2) | 25 |
| Interpleader to arbitration | 5 | 21(2) | 13 |
| Meaning of arbitration agreement | 32 | 30 | 2 |
| Meaning of Final Award | 39 | — | 58 |
| Merchant Shipping Act | 29 | — | 46 |
| Modifications to Part 1 to apply to Scotland and Northern Ireland | 34 | — | — |
| Official Referee | 11 | — | — |
| Operation of Part I | 33 | 27 | — |
| Perjury | 26 | — | 7 |
| Power of Arbitrator to award interest | 19A[1] | — | — |
| Power of Court to appoint | 10[2] | 5 | 18 |
| Power of Court and Circuit Court to refer in certain cases | — | — | 49 |
| Power to stay proceedings | 4 | 4 | 5 (1980 Act)[3] |
| Power to supply vacancy | 7 | 6 | 15 |
| Removal of Arbitrator and setting aside | 23 | 7 | 37,[4] 38 |
| Saving for other rights etc. | 40 | — | 59 |
| Saving for pending proceedings | 43 | 27 | — |
| Short title, commencement and repeal | 44 | 31, 29 | 1, 6, 8 |
| Single Arbitrator | 6 | 5(a), 11 | 14 |
| Specific performance | 15 | — | 26 |
| Statement of case pending arbitration | — | — | 52 |
| Statement of special case | 21[5] | 22 | 35[6] |
| Taxation of Arbitrator's fees | 19 | 18 | 33 |
| Terms as to costs | 28 | 23 | 47 |
| Three Arbitrators | 9[7] | 12(1) | 17 |
| Time for making Award | 13 | 9 | 23, 24 |
| Umpires | 8[7] | 12(1) | 16 |

[1] Inserted by s. 15(6) of the Administration of Justice Act 1982.
[2] Amended by s. 6 of the 1979 Act.
[3] Formerly s. 12 of the 1954 Act, repealed by s. 4 of the 1980 Act.
[4] This section may be restricted in certain cases by s. 17(5) of the Landlord and Tenant (Ground Rents) Act 1967.
[5] Repealed by 1979 Act, s. 1(1).
[6] This section may be restricted by s. 45(4) of the Patents Act 1964.
[7] Amended by 1979 Act, s. 6.

arbitration agreement between the parties covering the same issues. But in non-domestic cases there is now no such discretion and the Court must grant a stay.

In the Republic under the 1954 Act the Court had a discretion to stay proceedings[1] whether the case was domestic or not. However, s. 4 of the Arbitration Act 1980[2] repealed s. 12 of the 1954 Act and provided that the Court must now make an order staying proceedings in virtually all cases, whether domestic or non-domestic.[3]

### Interest[4]

In England and Wales an Arbitrator is empowered to award interest, impliedly under s. 3 of the Law Reform (Miscellaneous Provisions) Act 1934 and (since the Administration of Justice Act 1982) expressly under s. 19A of the Arbitration Act 1950.[5] Neither of these measures applies to Northern Ireland[6] but s. 17 of the Law Reform (Miscellaneous Provisions) Act (Northern Ireland) 1937 is identical with s. 3 of the English 1934 Act and, although the provision has been construed slightly differently in the two countries, it seems that the power to award interest in Northern Ireland does extend to Arbitrators also.

In the Republic the Courts Act 1981 introduced a power to award interest in words virtually identical with those used in the English Act of 1934. In England this power was held to extend by implication to Arbitrators, but in the Republic it has been construed as applying only to "courts established by law",[7] thus excluding Arbitrators. However, there are, apparently, plans to correct this situation.[8]

In all three countries, an Award once made and published carries interest at the rate appropriate to a judgment debt.[9]

## Application of the ICE Procedure to Northern Ireland

*Rule 10 (The Preliminary Meeting)*

As exclusion agreements apply only to arbitrations under the English 1979 Act, Rule 10.2(d) should be deleted.

*Rule 15 (The Hearing)*

An extra Rule should be added to cover the consultative special case still available under s. 22 of the Northern Ireland Arbitration Act 1937. The following form is suggested.

---

[1] S. 12.

[2] See Appendix II.

[3] S. 5.

[4] See also Chapter 4.

[5] Inserted by s. 15(6) and Part IV of Schedule 1 to the 1972 Act.

[6] Although ss. 69 and 70 of the Administration of Justice Act 1982 extend powers to the Northern Irish Courts analogous to those given to the English Courts, Parliament seems to have forgotten to make similar provision for Arbitrators in the Province.

[7] i.e. those referred to in the Constitution: see *Mellowhide Products Ltd.* v. *Barry Agencies Ltd.* 1 (1983) I.L.T. 14.

[8] See article under "Ireland" by M. W. Abrahamson in *International Handbook on Commercial Arbitration*, Suppl. 2, ICCA, Aug., 1984.

[9] S. 20 in the 1950 Act; s. 17 in the 1937 Act; s. 34 in the 1954 Act.

"15.5 On the application of either party, or of his own motion, the Arbitrator may state a point of law for decision by the High Court in accordance with s. 22 of the Arbitration Act 1937. To this end the Arbitrator shall first inform the parties of the point(s) of law which he intends to put to the Court together with the facts he intends to find for that purpose. He shall then give each party a reasonable opportunity to comment thereon, to suggest further points of law, and to request the Arbitrator to make further findings of fact. The Arbitrator shall then ask one of the parties to make application under s. 22 of the Act on his behalf or shall himself make application to the Court. Thereafter the Arbitrator may adjourn the reference pending receipt of the judgment of the Court, or proceed with other matters at issue as he sees fit."

### Rule 17 (The Award)

As in Rule 15, an extra Rule should be added to cover the making of an Award in the form of a special case under s. 22 of the 1937 Act. The following form is suggested.

"17.3 Where an issue in the arbitration turns upon a point of law the Arbitrator may, on the application of either party or of his own motion, make an Award in the form of a special case in accordance with s. 22 of the Arbitration Act 1937. For this purpose he shall proceed in accordance with Rule 15.5."

### Rule 18 (Reasons)

Rules 18.2 and 18.4 should be deleted, as there is no power in the High Court of Northern Ireland to order the giving of reasons.[1]

### Rule 19 (Appeals)

Rule 19(1) should be modified to dispense with the reference to the question of leave to appeal and to substitute a reference to the special case procedures. The following revised form is suggested.

"19.1 If any party applies to the High Court for the decision of that Court on any matter of law under s. 22 of the Arbitration Act 1937 or for an order staying the arbitration proceedings or for any other purpose that party shall forthwith notify the Arbitrator of the application."

Similarly, in Rule 19(2) the words ". . . other than in compliance with an order of the High Court under s. 1(5) of the Arbitration Act 1979" should be deleted.

### Rule 24 (Interim Arbitration)

Although it is probably implicit, it would be wise to add a further Sub-Rule stipulating that a Final Award or an Interim Award may be made in the form of a special case. The following form is suggested.

"24.5(e) an Award under (a) above, but in the form of a special case for the decision of the High Court in accordance with s. 22 of the Arbitration Act 1937."

### Rule 25 (Definitions)

The reference in Rule 25.1(g) to the Arbitration Acts 1950–1979 should be

---

[1] But see Chapter 4 (at p. 31) for the giving of reasons other than as part of the Award.

deleted and replaced by one to the Arbitration Act 1937.

### Rule 26 (Application)

In the unlikely event of an arbitration under Northern Irish law's being held in Scotland, it might be necessary to delete Rule 26. However, even if not deleted, the parties are free at any time to agree that a procedure other than that of Scotland shall apply.

## Application of the ICE Procedure to the Republic of Ireland

### Rule 3 (Appointment by the President)

This Rule may be used (with any necessary amendment) where the appointing authority is not the President of the ICE. It could therefore apply even to Statutory Arbitrations.

### Rule 10 (The Preliminary Meeting)

As exclusion agreements apply only to arbitrations under the English 1979 Act, Rule 10.2(d) should be deleted.

### Rule 15 (The Hearing)

An extra Rule should be added to cover the consultative special case still available under s. 35[1] of the Arbitration Act 1954. The following form is suggested.

> "15.5 On the application of either party, or of his own motion, the Arbitrator may state a point of law for decision by the High Court in accordance with s. 35 of the Arbitration Act 1954. To this end the Arbitrator shall first inform the parties of the point(s) of law which he intends to put to the Court together with the facts he intends to find for that purpose. He shall then give each party a reasonable opportunity to comment thereon, to suggest further points of law, and to request the Arbitrator to make further findings of fact. The Arbitrator shall then ask one of the parties to make application under s. 35 of the Act on his behalf or shall himself make application to the Court. Thereafter the Arbitrator may adjourn the reference pending receipt of the judgment of the Court, or proceed with other matters at issue as he sees fit."

### Rule 17 (The Award)

As in Rule 15, an extra Rule should be added to cover the making of an Award in the form of a special case under s. 35[2] of the 1954 Act. The following form is suggested.

> "17.3 Where an issue in the arbitration turns upon a point of law the Arbitrator may, on the application of either party or of his own motion, make an Award in the form of a special case in accordance with s. 35 of the Arbitration Act 1954. For this purpose he shall proceed in accordance with Rule 15.5."

### Rule 18 (Reasons)

Rules 18.2 and 18.4 should be deleted, as there is no power in the High Court of the Republic to order the giving of reasons.

---

[1]  But see Chapter 4 (at p. 31) for the giving of reasons other than as part of the Award.

[2]  S. 35 may be restricted in certain cases by s. 45(4) of the Patents Act 1964.

*Rule 19 (Appeals)*[1]

Rule 19(1) should be modified to dispense with the reference to the question of leave to appeal and to substitute a reference to the special case procedures.[2] The following revised form is suggested.

> "19.1 If any party applies to the High Court for the decision of that Court on any matter of law under s. 35 of the Arbitration Act 1954 or for an order staying the arbitration proceedings or for any other purpose that party shall forthwith notify the Arbitrator of the application."

Similarly, in Rule 19(2) the words ". . . other than in compliance with an order of the High Court under s. 1(5) of the Arbitration Act 1979" should be deleted.

*Rule 24 (Interim Arbitration)*

Although it is probably implicit, it would be wise to add a further Sub-Rule stipulating that a Final Award or an Interim Award may be made in the form of a special case. The following form is suggested.,

> "24.5(e) An Award under (a) above, but in the form of a special case for the decision of the High Court in accordance with s. 35[2] of the Arbitration Act 1954."

*Rule 25 (Definitions)*

The reference in Rule 25.1(g) to the Arbitration Acts 1950–1979 should be deleted and replaced by one to the Arbitration Act 1954.

*Rule 26 (Application)*

In the unlikely event of an arbitration under Irish law's being held in Scotland, it might be necessary to delete Rule 26. However, even if not deleted, the parties are free at any time to agree that a procedure other than that of Scotland shall apply.

*Costs*

In considering the question of costs under Rules 14.3, 16.4, 21.1, 23.1 or 23.2 it should be borne in mind that the discretion given to an Arbitrator or Umpire in respect of the costs of the Reference and the Award by s. 29 of the 1954 Act may be restricted by s. 17(5) of the Landlord and Tenant (Ground Rents) Act 1967, where the dispute affects ground rents.

*Periods of limitation*

Periods of limitation are covered in ss. 42, 43 and 44 of the 1954 Act, as amended by ss. 9 and 11 of the Limitation Act 1957. Ss. 11(1)(d) and 11(5)(b) of the Landlord and Tenant (Ground Rents) Act 1967 will also apply where the dispute affects ground rents.

---

[1] The Court's power to remit an Award (s. 36), to remove an Arbitrator or Umpire (s. 37) or to enforce an Award (s. 41) may be restricted in certain cases by s. 17(5) of the Landlord and Tenant (Ground Rents) Act 1967.

[2] S. 35 may be restricted in certain cases by s. 45(4) of the Patents Act 1964.

**Effects of other statutory provisions**

The provisions of the Arbitration Act 1954 have been modified in some respects by subsequent legislation. The relevant parts of these statutes will be found in Appendix II but may be summarised as follows.

*Limitation Act 1957.* Ss. 9 and 11 amend ss. 42, 43 and 44 of the Act of 1954 (application, accrual and powers to extend periods of limitation).

*Patents Act 1964.* S. 45(4) may restrict the provisions of s. 35 of the Act of 1954 (Statement of Case).

*Landlord and Tenant (Ground Rents) Act 1967.* Ss. 11(1)(d) and 11(5)(b) may modify periods of limitation (ss. 42, 43 and 44 of the Act of 1954). S. 17(5) may restrict the Arbitrator's or Umpire's discretion with respect to costs under s. 29 of the Act of 1954. It may also restrict the Court's power to remit an Award (s. 36), to remove an Arbitrator or Umpire (s. 37) or to enforce an Award (s. 41).

*Chapter 14*

# APPLICATION OF THE ICE PROCEDURE UNDER OTHER FORMS OF CONTRACT

The use of the ICE Arbitration Procedure is by no means limited to disputes arising under contracts based on the ICE Conditions of Contract. With a few modifications, the Procedure may be used under most commonly encountered forms of construction contract, and individual parts or Rules may be adopted in any form of dispute resolution, including litigation.[1]

In the following notes the means of applying the Procedure under several of the more usual forms of contract are set out. The relevant arbitration clauses will be found in Appendix III.

### The ICE Overseas Conditions[2]

When the ICE Conditions of Contract were first introduced, a complementary form of contract known as the "Overseas (Civil) Conditions" was produced for Works situated abroad. This has now largely been displaced by the FIDIC Conditions (see below), but is still in use to some extent for work in the Middle East.

The arbitration clause[3] is essentially the same as Clause 66 of the main ICE Conditions, so the ICE Arbitration Procedure may be applied as it stands.

### The FIDIC Conditions[4]

This form of contract has many similarities with the ICE Conditions, including the requirement that disputes shall first be referred to the Engineer.[5] Many Third-World or developing countries are also adopting their own forms of contract, which follow the FIDIC pattern more or less closely.[6]

A dispute in respect of which a decision of the Engineer has not become final[7] is required to be settled "... under the Rules of Conciliation and

---

[1]  The Official Referees now use a range of special orders to speed up business, many of which are similar to parts of the ICE Procedure.
[2]  Prepared by the Association of Consulting Engineers jointly with the Export Group for the Construction Industries and approved by the ICE.
[3]  Virtually identical with the version used in the fourth edition of the ICE Conditions of Contract.
[4]  The *Conditions of Contract (International) for Works of Civil Engineering Construction*, third edition (March, 1977), issued jointly by the Fédération Internationale des Ingénieurs-Conseils (FIDIC) and the Fédération Internationale Européene de la Construction (FIEC).
[5]  Clause 67.
[6]  The most usual amendment to Clause 67 is to substitute local procedural law for the ICC Rules and to provide for three arbitrators.
[7]  i.e. where the three months' period for referring the dispute to arbitration has yet to expire.

Arbitration of the International Chamber of Commerce by one or more arbitrators appointed under such Rules ...".[1] Under the ICC Rules, the procedural law to be applied in the arbitration comprises those Rules and, where the Rules are silent, any rules which the parties or, failing them, the arbitrator may settle.[2] Accordingly, there is no objection in principle to the importation of other procedural rules and, in particular, the ICE Arbitration Procedure.

However, the possibility of conflict between the parties' wishes on the procedure to be adopted and the views of the arbitrator(s) cannot be ruled out, nor can the attitude of the ICC (as the appointing authority) to the importation of other procedural rules be anticipated. The parties should therefore make known their views on procedure as early as possible to ensure, so far as is possible, that the arbitrator(s) will agree and that the ICC will raise no objection.

Consideration at this stage should also be given to the possible effect on procedure of the proper law of the Contract.[3]

In using the ICE Procedure under a FIDIC form of contract the following specific points should be noted.

*Rule 3 (Appointment by President).* Rule 3 is inapplicable and should be deleted (but see below, p. 141).

*Rule 11.2 (Discovery).* If a right to discovery of documents is not available under the procedural law applicable to the arbitration, this Rule may be ineffective.

*Rules 18.2, 18.4 and 19 (Reasons and Appeals).* Rules 18.2, 18.4 and 19 are specific to the arbitration law of England and Wales and will only apply if that is the procedural law applicable to the arbitration.

*Rule 24 (Interim Arbitration).* Under Clause 67 of the FIDIC Conditions an arbitration may proceed at any time, and "Interim Arbitration" does not exist thereunder as a separate procedure.

If Rule 24 is left as printed it will apply to any arbitration which "... is to proceed before completion or alleged completion of the Works ...".[4] In this event there will be conflict with Clause 67 which provides that the obligations of the Employer, Engineer and Contractor are not to be altered by the arbitration's being conducted during the progress of the Works. The parties (and the Engineer) should therefore specifically agree what the effect is to be of a decision under Clause 67 which is given before completion, and either amend Clause 67 or delete Rule 24.

*Rule 26.1 (Application of Procedure).* Rule 26.1 will be inappropriate, but in any event it cannot apply unless the parties have agreed to use the Procedure.

---

[1] Clause 67.
[2] ICC Art. 11.
[3] Specified in Clause 5(1)(b) and Part II of the FIDIC Conditions.
[4] Rule 24.1.

## Choice of arbitrator under the FIDIC Conditions

It is not always realised (and Clause 67 does not make it clear) that the parties are free to choose their own arbitrator by agreement and that, once so chosen, that arbitrator will be appointed by the ICC Art. 2(3) of the ICC Rules provides that

> "Where the parties have agreed that the disputes shall be settled by a sole arbitrator they may by agreement nominate him for confirmation by the Court [i.e. the ICC's Court of Arbitration]. If the parties fail so to nominate a sole arbitrator within 30 days from the date when the Claimant's Request for Arbitration has been communicated to the other party, the sole arbitrator shall be appointed by the Court."

The snag with leaving the appointment to the ICC is that the resulting arbitrator will usually be a lawyer of a nationality other than that of either of the parties. The FIDIC Conditions are wholly English in concept and English construction law is a highly specialised field. Moreover, Clause 67 expressly empowers the arbitrator

> ". . . to open up, revise and review any decision, opinion, direction, certificate or valuation of the Engineer . . ."

Exercise of this power may well necessitate the application of purely engineering knowledge and skills. It is therefore desirable that the arbitrator shall be a qualified Engineer or, if the issues are predominantly of a legal nature, at least a lawyer familiar with English construction law. It is therefore in the parties' own interest to try to agree on their own arbitrator rather than leaving it all to the ICC.

## The JCT Forms of Contract[1]

The JCT Forms of Contract, also known as the Standard Forms of Building Contract, exist in several versions, either with or without bills of quantity, for use by private individuals or local authorities. The latest edition was issued in 1980 but the previous edition of 1963 continues in use. There is also an "intermediate" form issued in 1984 which has many similarities to the 1980 edition. All the various forms provide for mandatory arbitration of disputes,[2] but, surprisingly, neither the JCT nor the RIBA (which administers arbitrations) has ever made use of a specific arbitration procedure.

Fortunately, all versions of the JCT Forms contain common provisions for reference to arbitration. These allow appointment of arbitrators by the President of the RIBA and restrict the categories of dispute which may proceed to a Hearing before practical completion of the Works. Unlike the ICE Conditions, there is no requirement that disputes should be referred to the Architect as a condition precedent to arbitration.

In using the ICE Procedure under a JCT Form of Contract the following specific points should be noted.

---

[1] Issued by the Joint Contracts Tribunal (JCT)—see Keating's *Building Contracts* (4th edn), p. 281 for the JCT constituent bodies.

[2] Clause 35 (1963 edition); Art. 5 (JCT 80 and IFC 84).

*Rule 3 (Appointment by President).* Rule 3 is inapplicable and should be deleted.

*Rule 24 (Interim Arbitration).* Rule 24 may be applied as it stands save that, in any particular dispute, the parties should consider whether it is appropriate to have an Interim Decision under Rule 24.6.[1]

*Rule 26 (Application of Procedure).* Rule 26 will be inappropriate, but in any event it cannot apply unless the parties have agreed to use the Procedure.

### The FCEC Form of Sub-Contract (March 1973 version)[2]

The familiar "Blue Form", although not issued or sanctioned by the ICE,[3] is in widespread use for all types of civil engineering sub-contracting, both where the Main Contractor chooses his own Sub-Contractor and where the Sub-Contractor is nominated by the Engineer or Employer.

The arbitration clause[4] makes provision for three different situations. The first is where the dispute concerns only the parties to the Sub-Contract. Here the matter is to be referred to an arbitrator agreed between the parties in the usual way or, in default of agreement, appointed by the President of the ICE.[5] The second is where the dispute touches or concerns both Main and Sub-Contract. Provided that an arbitrator has not already been agreed or appointed pursuant to Clause 18(1), the Main Contractor may require the dispute to be referred to an arbitrator appointed under the Main Contract, if such arbitrator is willing so to act.[6] The third is where a dispute which touches or concerns both Main and Sub-Contract is made the subject of proceedings in any Court in connection with the Main Contract. The Main Contractor may then abrogate Clause 18(1) unless an arbitrator has already been agreed or appointed thereunder, and the Sub-Contractor may then be joined as a third party to the Court proceedings.[7]

The ICE Procedure is not referred to in the "Blue Form", so its use thereunder requires the parties' specific agreement. In a purely Sub-Contract dispute, use of the Procedure is desirable to secure the advantages it offers in speed and economy. Its application is essential where both Sub-Contract and Main Contract disputes are to be heard by the same arbitrator and the latter proceedings are subject to the ICE Procedure; indeed, should the parties fail to agree on this, the joint arbitrator might well make it a

---

[1] The JCT Forms do not allow Interim Arbitration on a dispute following termination of the Contract—cf. Clause 63 of the ICE Conditions.

[2] Issued by the Federation of Civil Engineering Contractors (FCEC) and designed for use in conjunction with the ICE Conditions. A new Form was issued in September, 1984, and is discussed below.

[3] Strictly speaking, the ICE Conditions are the responsibility of the Standing Joint Committee (CCSJC) of the ICE, the FCEC and the Association of Consulting Engineers.

[4] Clause 18.

[5] Clause 18(1).

[6] Clause 18(2).

[7] Clause 18(3).

condition of his accepting the dual appointment that the Procedure should be adopted in both references.

Where a Sub-Contract arbitrator is appointed before the Main Contract dispute arises (so that a joint appointment is not permitted), it is still open to the Employer and the Main Contractor to agree to appoint the same person as arbitrator under the Main Contract. Where they do so agree and the Sub-Contract arbitration is already subject to the ICE Procedure, the arbitrator will then have power under Rule 7.1 to order a concurrent Hearing of the disputes. Indeed, in the case of Presidential appointments, the President may well have regard to this useful power when considering whom to appoint in connection with existing related disputes.

In using the ICE Procedure under the FCEC Form of Sub-Contract the following specific points should be noted.

*Rule 3 (Appointment by President).* Rule 3 will apply, as the President of the ICE is the appointing authority specified in both FCEC Clause 18 and ICE Clause 66. The applicant party should notify the Institution of any other related disputes for which concurrent Hearings may be sought (for example, under other Sub-Contracts) so that consideration can be given to the appointment of the same person as arbitrator in each case.

*Rule 24 (Interim Arbitration).* Under the FCEC Form there is no stipulation as to the time when arbitral proceedings may commence. Where a dispute arises solely under the Sub-Contract, neither the Employer nor the Engineer will be party to or bound by the proceedings, so there is little need to achieve an award before completion of the relevant part of the Works.

In concurrent proceedings, however, it is essential that the same procedure shall apply to both disputes. Problems will therefore arise whenever an Interim Arbitration under the Main Contract is to run concurrently with a Sub-Contract reference as, if the Sub-Contract Works have been completed, Rule 24 will not apply to that reference.

One solution could be to amend Rule 24.1 to read

> "24.1 Where the Arbitrator is appointed and *a Sub-Contract* arbitration is to proceed before completion or alleged completion of the *relevant part of the Main Contract* Works then ... the following provisions shall apply *to the Sub-Contract arbitration* in addition to ... "

It is suggested that each Sub-Contract dispute should be assessed on its merits on whether the parties will benefit from the application of Rule 24.

## The FCEC Form of Sub-Contract (September 1984 version)

The changes wrought by the September 1984 revision of Clause 18 are discussed in Chapter 6, the main ones being the introduction of a direct reference to the ICE Arbitration Procedure in Clause 18(1) and the provision that Clause 66 of the Main Contract Conditions is to apply to the Sub-Contract Arbitration.[1]

It follows that, in applying the ICE Procedure to a reference under the

---

[1]  Clauses 18(2) and 18(4).

revised "Blue Form", it will not be necessary to amend Rule 24.1 as suggested above for the earlier version. Otherwise, the matters discussed in Chapters 7–10 will still apply, bearing in mind that the references to ICE Clause 66 in Clause 18 can refer either to the old or to the new versions of that Clause. Thus, where the old form of Clause 66 applies, the Sub-Contract arbitration may be constrained by the former distinction between references under Clause 66(2) and other arbitrations, the latter not being permitted to proceed before substantial completion of the whole of the Main Contract Works. Where the Sub-Contract Works are completed well before the Main Contract Works, this may well be a serious disadvantage to the Sub-Contractor unless he can persuade the Main Contractor to agree to proceed earlier. Where the new form of Clause 66 applies, this problem does not arise, as arbitrations thereunder may proceed at any time.

*Chapter 15*

# ARBITRATIONS WITH A FOREIGN ELEMENT

Arbitrations involving a foreign element give rise to a number of questions about the law and procedure to be applied. Where the arbitration is conducted in England and Wales, either because the contract so provides or because the parties so agree, the way in which these questions are answered can be stated, since they depend on English law. Where the arbitration is conducted abroad, however, the answers depend upon the domestic law of that particular country. This branch of law, in which the law applicable to international disputes is determined, is called "conflict of laws".

### The proper law of the contract

Under English rules of conflict of laws,[1] most matters concerning disputes in contract are determined in accordance with the "proper law" of the contract. This can be chosen by the parties, either expressly or by implication. Where there is no such choice, the law to be applied is that of the country having the closest connection with the contract, and will be determined having regard, *inter alia*, to matters such as the country in which the contract was made, the country in which it was to be performed, the place and currency of payment and the nationality of the parties. In practice, most contracts of any substance contain an express choice of the governing or proper law; for example, the FIDIC Conditions of Contract contain an express clause requiring the parties to choose the law which is to govern the contract.[2]

In an arbitration conducted in England and arising out of a contract which is subject to foreign law, the arbitrator must construe and apply the contract in accordance with that law. If the requirements of the relevant foreign law are unclear, they may be proved by adducing evidence from an appropriately qualified expert witness.[3] But where the proper law is that of a member country of the British Commonwealth, the law will often be substantially the same as English law, save for the effect of any local statutes. Or in the Middle East, and in other countries having a less developed legal system, it may be found that there are no principles of law which are particularly applicable. In all such cases the arbitrator should assume (as will the English Courts) that the relevant law is the same as English law unless the contrary is proved.[4]

---

[1] For a wider discussion of the subject, see *Halsbury's Laws* (4th edn), vol. 8.
[2] Clause 5(1) and Part II.
[3] Such a witness need not be formally qualified in the appropriate foreign law, provided that his knowledge has been acquired by experience or a course of study; see, for example, Phipson's *Manual of the Law of Evidence* (11th edn), p. 23.
[4] *Halsbury's Laws* (4th edn), vol. 8, para. 794.

## Procedural law

The procedure to be followed in any arbitration may be controlled to a greater or lesser extent by the procedural law of the country in which the proceedings are conducted. Thus, for example, in some countries it is unlawful for the arbitrator to take evidence on oath, and in others the proceedings will be invalid unless a formal minute or *procés verbal* is executed. It has been held that, under English law, the procedural law applicable is prima facie that of the country in which the proceedings are conducted,[1] but that the parties may themselves agree that some other procedural law shall apply.[2]

## Enforcement of awards

A further problem involving conflict of laws is the enforcement of English awards abroad and of foreign awards in England. In general, these matters are governed by international conventions which have the effect of limiting the grounds on which an award may be challenged. But this depends on whether a particular country has ratified the convention on which it is sought to rely.

There are a number of relevant conventions, of which only two are of any practical importance. The first is the Geneva Convention of 1927, ratified in the United Kingdom by the Arbitration Act 1950. It provides for the enforcement of awards in Convention countries provided that both parties are the subjects of, and the award is made in, Convention countries. However, these countries do not include much of the Middle East and Africa, so the use of this Convention is rather restricted.

The second is the New York Convention of 1958, drawn up under the auspices of the United Nations. It was ratified in the United Kingdom by the Arbitration Act 1975 and provides for reciprocal enforcement where an award is obtained in a Convention country. While enforcement is possible only in a Convention country, the nationality of the parties is immaterial. This convention can therefore be used to enforce an award against a non-Convention national who has assets in a Convention country. The list of States who have acceded to the New York Convention is more extensive than that applicable to the Geneva Convention and includes some Middle Eastern[3] and African States.

Where an award has to be enforced without benefit of either Convention, the means to be employed will depend entirely upon the internal law of the country in which enforcement is sought. Relevant considerations may be the form of the award, whether or not the dispute is one which is actionable under the law of the country of enforcement, the nationalities of the parties, and many others.[4] Many countries will not enforce an award which does

---

[1] *James Miller* v. *Whitworth Street Estates* [1970] A.C. 583.

[2] For a fuller discussion of the many problems which can arise, see Mustill & Boyd's *Commercial Arbitration*, ch. 4.

[3] Ratification may have retrospective effect; see *Minister of Public Works, Kuwait* v. *Snow* [1984] A.C. 426; 2 W.L.R. 340 (H.L.).

[4] For example, awards in favour of Israeli parties are not enforceable in many Arab countries, while some other countries will not enforce contracts involving work carried out in South Africa.

not include reasons and this will clearly be a factor which the arbitrator must consider when drafting his award. Indeed, the question of enforcement may well have a decisive influence on where the arbitration is to be conducted.

## Application of the Conventions to Scotland and Ireland

By Part II of the English Arbitration Act 1950 the Geneva Convention of 1927 applies to Scotland[1] and to Northern Ireland.[2] By Part V of the Arbitration Act 1954 of Eire, the Convention also applies to that country.

Section 3(b) of the English Arbitration Act 1975 applies the New York Convention of 1958 to Scotland, and s. 3(c) applies it to Northern Ireland. In Eire, Part III of the Arbitration Act 1980 applies the Convention to that country.

Part IV of the Eire Act of 1980 also applies the Washington Convention of 1965 to that country. So far, this Convention does not apply to any part of the United Kingdom.

## International arbitrations heard in England

Where an arbitration with a foreign element is to be heard in England or Wales the parties may avail themselves of the provisions of the Arbitration Act 1979 to exclude the Court's jurisdiction. This is achieved by entering into an exclusion agreement under s. 3 of the Act.[3] But, while in the case of a "domestic" arbitration this can be done only after a dispute has arisen, the parties to a "non-domestic" arbitration may (with certain exceptions) incorporate an exclusion agreement into their contract at any time.[4]

## The UNCITRAL "model law"

A "model law" for international arbitration is currently being considered by the Commission on International Trade and Law of the United Nations Organisation and seems likely to be finalised during the Summer of 1985.[5] As it is not an international convention, formal ratification by Member States will not be required, but the intention is that in due course most States, and in particular Third-World and developing countries, shall incorporate its provisions into their domestic law.

Where it is so promulgated, the "model law" may well have some effect on the conduct of international construction arbitrations. However, the incorporation of such provisions into the law of the United Kingdom is likely to remain a topic of debate for some time.

---

[1] S. 41.

[2] S. 42.

[3] See p. 42, *ante*; see also Appendix VII.

[4] For further discussion see Gibson-Jarvie & Hawker's *Guide to Commercial Arbitration under the 1979 Act* (CIArb, 1980), ch. 4.

[5] The final text of the "model law" was agreed at a meeting of the Commission in Vienna on 21st June, 1985. The General Assembly was expected formally to note its existence and to commend its adoption by Member States at its December, 1985 meeting.

# APPENDICES

# STATUTE LAW APPLICABLE TO ENGLAND AND WALES

**Arbitration Act 1950** (14 Geo. 6 Ch. 27)

An Act to consolidate the Arbitration Acts 1889 to 1934

Part I

GENERAL PROVISIONS AS TO ARBITRATION

*Effect of arbitration agreements, &c.*

**1. Authority of arbitrators and umpires to be irrevocable.**—The authority of an arbitrator or umpire appointed by or by virtue of an arbitration agreement shall, unless a contrary intention is expressed in the agreement, be irrevocable except by leave of the High Court or a judge thereof.

**2. Death of party.**—(1) An arbitration agreement shall not be discharged by the death of any party thereto, either as respects the deceased or any other party, but shall in such an event be enforceable by or against the personal representative of the deceased.

(2) The authority of an arbitrator shall not be revoked by the death of any party by whom he was appointed.

(3) Nothing in this section shall be taken to affect the operation of any enactment or rule of law by virtue of which any right of action is extinguished by the death of a person.

**3. Bankruptcy.**—(1) Where it is provided by a term in a contract to which a bankrupt is a party that any differences arising thereout or in connection therewith shall be referred to arbitration, the said term shall, if the trustee in bankruptcy adopts the contract, be enforceable by or against him so far as relates to any such differences.

(2) Where a person who has been adjudged bankrupt had, before the commencement of the bankruptcy, become a party to an arbitration agreement, and any matter to which the agreement applies requires to be determined in connection with or for the purposes of the bankruptcy proceedings, then, if the case is one to which subsection (1) of this section does not apply, any other party to the agreement or, with the consent of the committee of inspection, the trustee in bankruptcy, may apply to the court having jurisdiction in the bankruptcy proceedings for an order directing that the matter in question shall be referred to arbitration in accordance with the agreement, and that court may, if it is of opinion that, having regard to all the circumstances of the case, the matter ought to be determined by arbitration, make an order accordingly.

**4. Staying court proceedings where there is submission to arbitration.**—(1) If any party to an arbitration agreement, or any person claiming through or under him, commences any legal proceedings in any court against any other party to the agreement, or any person claiming through or under him, in respect of any matter agreed to be referred, any party to those legal proceedings may at any time after appearance, and before delivering any pleadings or taking any other steps in the proceedings, apply to that court to stay the proceedings, and that court or a judge thereof, if satisfied that there is no sufficient reason why the matter should not be referred in accordance with the agreement, and that the applicant was, at the time when the proceedings were commenced, and still remains, ready and willing to do all things necessary to the proper conduct of the arbitration, may make an order staying the proceedings.

(2) [Repealed].[1]

**5. Reference of interpleader issues to arbitration.**—Where relief by way of interpleader is granted and it appears to the High Court that the claims in question are matters to which an arbitration agreement, to which the claimants are parties, applies, the High Court may direct the issue between the claimants to be determined in accordance with the agreement.

*Arbitrators and umpires*

**6. When reference is to a single arbitrator.**—Unless a contrary intention is expressed therein, every arbitration agreement shall, if no other mode of reference is provided, be deemed to include a provision that the reference shall be to a single arbitrator.

**7. Power of parties in certain cases to supply vacancy.**—Where an arbitration agreement provides that the reference shall be to two arbitrators, one to be appointed by each party then, unless a contrary intention is expressed therein —

(a) if either of the appointed arbitrators refuses to act, or is incapable of acting, or dies, the party who appointed him may appoint a new arbitrator in his place;

(b) if, on such a reference, one party fails to appoint an arbitrator, either originally, or by way of substitution as aforesaid, for seven clear days after the other party having appointed his arbitrator, has served the party making default with notice to make the appointment, the party who has appointed an arbitrator may appoint that arbitrator to act as sole arbitrator in the reference and his award shall be binding on both parties as if he had been appointed by consent:

Provided that the High Court or a judge thereof may set aside any appointment made in pursuance of this section.

**8. Umpires.**—(1) Unless a contrary intention is expressed therein, every arbitration agreement shall, where the reference is to two arbitrators, be deemed to include a provision that the two arbitrators may appoint an umpire at any time after they are themselves appointed, and shall do so forthwith if they cannot agree.[2]

(2) Unless a contrary intention is expressed therein, every arbitration agreement shall, where such a provision is applicable to the reference, be deemed to include a provision that if the arbitrators have delivered to any party to the arbitration agreement, or to the umpire, a notice in writing stating that they cannot agree, the umpire may forthwith enter on the reference in lieu of the arbitrators.

(3) At any time after the appointment of an umpire, however appointed, the High Court may, on the application of any party to the reference and notwithstanding anything to the contrary in the arbitration agreement, order that the umpire shall

---

[1]  Repealed by s. 8(2)(a) of the Arbitration Act 1975.
[2]  As amended by s. 6(1) of the Arbitration Act 1979.

enter upon the reference in lieu of the arbitrators and as if he were a sole arbitrator.

**9. Majority award of three arbitrators.**—Unless the contrary intention is expressed in the arbitration agreement, in any case where there is a reference to three arbitrators, the award of any two of the arbitrators shall be binding.[1]

**10. Power of court in certain cases to appoint an arbitrator or umpire.**—
(1) In any of the following cases—
  (*a*) where an arbitration agreement provides that the reference shall be to a single arbitrator, and all the parties do not, after differences have arisen, concur in the appointment of an arbitrator;
  (*b*) if an appointed arbitrator refuses to act, or is incapable of acting, or dies, and the arbitration agreement does not show that it was intended that the vacancy should not be supplied and the parties do not supply the vacancy;
  (*c*) where the parties or two arbitrators are required or are at liberty to appoint an umpire or third arbitrator and do not appoint him;[2]
  (*d*) where an appointed umpire or third arbitrator refuses to act, or is incapable of acting, or dies, and the arbitration agreement does not show that it was intended that the vacancy should not be supplied, and the parties or arbitrators do not supply the vacancy;
any party may serve the other parties or the arbitrators, as the case may be, with a written notice to appoint or, as the case may be, concur in appointing, an arbitrator, umpire or third arbitrator, and if the appointment is not made within seven clear days after the service of the notice, the High Court or a judge thereof may, on application by the party who gave the notice, appoint an arbitrator, umpire or third arbitrator who shall have the like powers to act in the reference and make an award as if he had been appointed by consent of all parties.
(2) In any case where —
  (*a*) an arbitration agreement provides for the appointment of an arbitrator or umpire by a person who is neither one of the parties nor an existing arbitrator (whether the provision applies directly or in default of agreement by the parties or otherwise), and
  (*b*) that person refuses to make the appointment or does not make it within the time specified in the agreement or, if no time is so specified, within a reasonable time
any party to the agreement may serve the person in question with a written notice to appoint an arbitrator or umpire and, if the appointment is not made within seven clear days after the service of the notice, the High Court or a judge thereof may, on the application of the party who gave the notice, appoint an arbitrator or umpire who shall have the like powers to act in the reference and make an award as if he had been appointed in accordance with the terms of the agreement.[3]

**11. Reference to official referee.**—Where an arbitration agreement provides that the reference shall be to an official referee, any official referee to whom application is made shall, subject to any order of the High Court or a judge thereof as to transfer or otherwise, hear and determine the matters agreed to be referred.

*Conduct of proceedings, witnesses, &c.*

**12. Conduct of proceedings, witnesses, &c.**—(1) Unless a contrary intention is expressed therein, every arbitration agreement shall, where such a provision is

---

[1]  As amended by s. 6(2) of the Arbitration Act 1979.
[2]  As amended by s. 6(3) of the Arbitration Act 1979.
[3]  As amended by s. 6(4) of the Arbitration Act 1979.

applicable to the reference, be deemed to contain a provision that the parties to the reference, and all persons claiming through them respectively, shall, subject to any legal objection, submit to be examined by the arbitrator or umpire, on oath or affirmation, in relation to the matters in dispute, and shall, subject as aforesaid, produce before the arbitrator or umpire all documents within their possession or power respectively which may be required or called for, and do all other things which during the proceedings on the reference the arbitrator or umpire may require.

(2) Unless a contrary intention is expressed therein, every arbitration agreement shall, where such a provision is applicable to the reference, be deemed to contain a provision that the witnesses on the reference shall, if the arbitrator or umpire thinks fit, be examined on oath or affirmation.

(3) An arbitrator or umpire shall, unless a contrary intention is expressed in the arbitration agreement, have power to administer oaths to, or take the affirmations of, the parties to and witnesses on a reference under the agreement.

(4) Any party to a reference under an arbitration agreement may sue out a writ of subpoena ad testificandum or a writ of subpoena duces tecum, but no person shall be compelled under any such writ to produce any document which he could not be compelled to produce on the trial of an action, and the High Court or a judge thereof may order that a writ of subpoena ad testificandum or of subpoena duces tecum shall issue to compel the attendance before an arbitrator or umpire of a witness wherever he may be within the United Kingdom.

(5) The High Court or a judge thereof may also order that a writ of habeas corpus ad testificandum shall issue to bring up a prisoner for examination before an arbitrator or umpire.

(6) The High Court shall have, for the purpose of and in relation to a reference, the same power of making orders in respect of—

(a)  security for costs;

(b)  discovery of documents and interrogatories;

(c)  the giving of evidence by affidavit;

(d)  examination on oath of any witness before an officer of the High Court or any other person, and the issue of a commission or request for the examination of a witness out of the jurisdiction;

(e)  the preservation, interim custody or sale of any goods which are the subject matter of the reference;

(f)  securing the amount in dispute in the reference;

(g)  the detention, preservation or inspection of any property or thing which is the subject of the reference or as to which any question may arise therein, and authorising for any of the purposes aforesaid any persons to enter upon or into any land or building in the possession of any party to the reference, or authorising any samples to be taken or any observation to be made or experiment to be tried which may be necessary or expedient for the purpose of obtaining full information or evidence; and

(h)  interim injunctions or the appointment of a receiver;

as it has for the purpose of and in relation to an action or matter in the High Court:

Provided that nothing in this subsection shall be taken to prejudice any power which may be vested in an arbitrator or umpire of making orders with respect to any of the matters aforesaid.

*Provisions as to awards*

**13. Time for making award.**—(1) Subject to the provisions of subsection (2) of section twenty-two of this Act, and anything to the contrary in the arbitration agreement, an arbitrator or umpire shall have power to make an award at any time.

(2) The time, if any, limited for making an award, whether under this Act or

otherwise, may from time to time be enlarged by order of the High Court or a judge thereof, whether that time has expired or not.

(3) The High Court may, on the application of any party to a reference, remove an arbitrator or umpire who fails to use all reasonable dispatch in entering on and proceeding with the reference and making an award, and an arbitrator or umpire who is removed by the High Court under this subsection shall not be entitled to receive any remuneration in respect of his services.

For the purposes of this subsection, the expression 'proceeding with a reference' includes, in a case where two arbitrators are unable to agree, giving notice of that fact to the parties and to the umpire.

**14. Interim awards.**—Unless a contrary intention is expressed therein, every arbitration agreement shall, where such a provision is applicable to the reference, be deemed to contain a provision that the arbitrator or umpire may, if he thinks fit, make an interim award, and any reference in this Part of this Act to an award includes a reference to an interim award.

**15. Specific performance.**—Unless a contrary intention is expressed therein, every arbitration agreement shall, where such a provision is applicable to the reference, be deemed to contain a provision that the arbitrator or umpire shall have the same power as the High Court to order specific performance of any contract other than a contract relating to land or any interest in land.

**16. Awards to be final.**—Unless a contrary intention is expressed therein, every arbitration agreement shall, where such a provision is applicable to the reference, be deemed to contain a provision that the award to be made by the arbitrator or umpire shall be final and binding on the parties and the persons claiming under them respectively.

**17. Power to correct slips.**—Unless a contrary intention is expressed in the arbitration agreement, the arbitrator or umpire shall have power to correct in an award any clerical mistake or error arising from any accidental slip or omission.

*Costs, fees and interest*

**18. Costs.**—(1) Unless a contrary intention is expressed therein, every arbitration agreement shall be deemed to include a provision that the costs of the reference and award shall be in the discretion of the arbitrator or umpire, who may direct to and by whom and in what manner those costs or any part thereof shall be paid, and may tax or settle the amount of costs to be so paid or any part thereof, and may award costs to be paid as between solicitor and client.

(2) Any costs directed by an award to be paid shall, unless the award otherwise directs, be taxable in the High Court.

(3) Any provision in an arbitration agreement to the effect that the parties or any party thereto shall in any event pay their or his own costs of the reference or award or any part thereof shall be void, and this Part of this Act shall, in the case of an arbitration agreement containing any such provision, have effect as if that provision were not contained therein:

Provided that nothing in this subsection shall invalidate such a provision when it is a part of an agreement to submit to arbitration a dispute which has arisen before the making of that agreement.

(4) If no provision is made by an award with respect to the costs of the reference, any party to the reference may, within fourteen days of the publication of the award or such further time as the High Court or a judge thereof may direct, apply to the arbitrator for an order directing by and to whom those costs shall be paid, and

thereupon the arbitrator shall, after hearing any party who may desire to be heard, amend his award by adding thereto such directions as he may think proper with respect to the payment of the costs of the reference.

(5) Section sixty-nine of the Solicitors Act 1932 (which empowers a court before which any proceeding is being heard or is pending to charge property recovered or preserved in the proceeding with the payment of solicitors' costs) shall apply as if an arbitration were a proceeding in the High Court, and the High Court may make declarations and orders accordingly.

**19. Taxation of arbitrator's or umpire's fees.**—(1) If in any case an arbitrator or umpire refuses to deliver his award except on payment of the fees demanded by him, the High Court may, on an application for the purpose, order that the arbitrator or umpire shall deliver the award to the applicant on payment into court by the applicant of the fees demanded, and further that the fees demanded shall be taxed by the taxing officer and that out of the money paid into court there shall be paid out to the arbitrator or umpire by way of fees such sum as may be found reasonable on taxation and that the balance of the money, if any, shall be paid out to the applicant.

(2) An application for the purposes of this section may be made by any party to the reference unless the fees demanded have been fixed by a written agreement between him and the arbitrator or umpire.

(3) A taxation of fees under this section may be reviewed in the same manner as a taxation of costs.

(4) The arbitrator or umpire shall be entitled to appear and be heard on any taxation or review of taxation under this section.

**19A. Power of arbitrator to award interest.**—(1) Unless a contrary intention is expressed therein, every arbitration agreement shall, where such a provision is applicable to the reference, be deemed to contain a provision that the arbitrator or umpire may, if he thinks fit, award simple interest at such rate as he thinks fit —
  (a)  on any sum which is the subject of the reference but which is paid before the award, for such period ending not later than the date of the payment as he thinks fit; and
  (b)  on any sum which he awards, for such period ending not later than the date of the award as he thinks fit.

(2) The power to award interest conferred on an arbitrator or umpire by subsection (1) above is without prejudice to any other power of an arbitrator or umpire to award interest.[1]

**20. Interest on awards.**—A sum directed to be paid by an award shall, unless the award otherwise directs, carry interest as from the date of the award and at the same rate as a judgment debt.

*Special cases, remission and setting aside of awards, &c.*

**21. Statement of case.**—[Repealed][2]

**22. Power to remit award.**—(1) In all cases of reference to arbitration the High Court or a judge thereof may from time to time remit the matters referred, or any of them, to the reconsideration of the arbitrator or umpire.

(2) Where an award is remitted, the arbitrator or umpire shall, unless the order otherwise directs, make his award within three months after the date of the order.

---

[1]  S. 19A was added by s. 15(6) and Sched. 2, Part IV, of the Administration of Justice Act 1982.
[2]  Repealed by s. 8(3)(b) of the Arbitration Act 1979.

**23. Removal of arbitrator and setting aside of award.**—(1) Where an arbitrator or umpire has misconducted himself or the proceedings, the High Court may remove him.

(2) Where an arbitrator or umpire has misconducted himself or the proceedings, or an arbitration or award has been improperly procured, the High Court may set the award aside.

(3) Where an application is made to set aside an award, the High Court may order that any money made payable by the award shall be brought into court or otherwise secured pending the determination of the application.

**24. Power of court to give relief where arbitrator is not impartial or the dispute involves question of fraud.**—(1) Where an agreement between any parties provides that disputes which may arise in the future between them shall be referred to an arbitrator named or designated in the agreement, and after a dispute has arisen any party applies, on the ground that the arbitrator so named or designated is not or may not be impartial, for leave to revoke the authority of the arbitrator or for an injunction to restrain any other party or the arbitrator from proceeding with the arbitration, it shall not be a ground for refusing the application that the said party at the time when he made the agreement knew, or ought to have known, that the arbitrator, by reason of his relation towards any other party to the agreement or of his connection with the subject referred, might not be capable of impartiality.

(2) Where an agreement between any parties provides that disputes which may arise in the future between them shall be referred to arbitration, and a dispute which so arises involves the question whether any such party has been guilty of fraud, the High Court shall, so far as may be necessary to enable that question to be determined by the High Court, have power to order that the agreement shall cease to have effect and power to give leave to revoke the authority of any arbitrator or umpire appointed by or by virtue of the agreement.[1]

(3) In any case where by virtue of this section the High Court has power to order that an arbitration agreement shall cease to have effect or to give leave to revoke the authority of an arbitrator or umpire, the High Court may refuse to stay any action brought in breach of the agreement.

**25. Power of court where arbitrator is removed or authority of arbitrator is revoked.**—(1) Where an arbitrator (not being a sole arbitrator), or two or more arbitrators (not being all the arbitrators) or an umpire who has not entered on the reference is or are removed by the High Court or the Court of Appeal, the High Court may, on the application of any party to the arbitration agreement, appoint a person or persons to act as arbitrator or arbitrators or umpire in place of the person or persons so removed.

(2) Where the authority of an arbitrator or arbitrators or umpire is revoked by leave of the High Court or the Court of Appeal, or a sole arbitrator or all the arbitrators or an umpire who has entered on the reference is or are removed by the High Court or the Court of Appeal, the High Court may, on the application of any party to the arbitration agreement, either—

   (*a*)  appoint a person to act as sole arbitrator in place of the person or persons removed; or

   (*b*)  order that the arbitration agreement shall cease to have effect with respect to the dispute referred.

(3) A person appointed under this section by the High Court or the Court of Appeal, as an arbitrator or umpire shall have the like power to act in the reference

---

[1]   But see s. 3(3) of the Arbitration Act 1979.

and to make an award as if he had been appointed in accordance with the terms of the arbitration agreement.

(4) Where it is provided (whether by means of a provision in the arbitration agreement or otherwise) that an award under an arbitration agreement shall be a condition precedent to the bringing of an action with respect to any matter to which the agreement applies, the High Court or the Court of Appeal, if it orders (whether under this section or under any other enactment) that the agreement shall cease to have effect as regards any particular dispute, may further order that the provision making an award a condition precedent to the bringing of an action shall also cease to have effect as regards that dispute.[1]

### *Enforcement of award*

**26. Enforcement of award.**—(1) An award on an arbitration agreement may, by leave of the High Court or a judge thereof, be enforced in the same manner as a judgment or order to the same effect, and where leave is so given, judgment may be entered in terms of the award.

(2) If—

(a) the amount sought to be recovered does not exceed the current limit on jurisdiction in s. 40 of the County Courts Act 1959, and

(b) a county court so orders,

it shall be recoverable (by execution issued from the county court or otherwise) as if payable under an order of that court and shall not be enforceable under subsection (1) above.

(3) An application to the High Court under this section shall preclude an application to a county court, and an application to a county court under this section shall preclude an application to the High Court.[2]

### *Miscellaneous*

**27. Power of court to extend time for commencing arbitration proceedings.**—Where the terms of an agreement to refer future disputes to arbitration provide that any claims to which the agreement applies shall be barred unless notice to appoint an arbitrator is given or an arbitrator is appointed or some other step to commence arbitration proceedings is taken within a time fixed by the agreement, and a dispute arises to which the agreement applies, the High Court, if it is of opinion that in the circumstances of the case undue hardship would otherwise be caused, and notwithstanding that the time so fixed has expired, may, on such terms, if any, as the justice of the case may require, but without prejudice to the provisions of any enactment limiting the time for the commencement of arbitration proceedings, extend the time for such period as it thinks proper.

**28. Terms as to costs, &c.**—Any order made under this Part of this Act may be made on such terms as to costs or otherwise as the authority making the order thinks just.[3]

**29. Extension of s. 496 of the Merchant Shipping Act 1894.**—(1) In subsection (3) of section four hundred and ninety-six of the Merchant Shipping Act 1894 (which requires a sum deposited with a wharfinger by an owner of goods to be repaid unless legal proceedings are instituted by the shipowner), the expression 'legal proceedings' shall be deemed to include arbitration.

---

[1] References to the Court of Appeal added by para. 11 of Sched. 3 to the Administration of Justice Act 1970.

[2] Ss. 26(2) and 26(3) were added by s. 18(2) of the Administration of Justice Act 1977.

[3] Proviso repealed by s. 8(2)(b) of the Arbitration Act 1975.

(2) For the purposes of the said section four hundred and ninety-six, as amended by this section, an arbitration shall be deemed to be commenced when one party to the arbitration agreement serves on the other party or parties a notice requiring him or them to appoint or concur in appointing an arbitrator, or, where the arbitration agreement provides that the reference shall be to a person named or designated in the agreement, requiring him or them to submit the dispute to the person so named or designated.

(3) Any such notice as is mentioned in subsection (2) of this section may be served either —

(*a*) by delivering it to the person on whom it is to be served; or

(*b*) by leaving it at the usual or last known place of abode in England of that person; or

(*c*) by sending it by post in a registered letter addressed to that person at his usual or last known place of abode in England;

as well as in any other manner provided in the arbitration agreement; and where a notice is sent by post in manner prescribed by paragraph (c) of this subsection, service thereof shall, unless the contrary is proved, be deemed to have been effected at the time at which the letter would have been delivered in the ordinary course of post.

**30. Crown to be bound.**—This Part of this Act shall apply to any arbitration to which His Majesty, either in right of the Crown or of the Duchy of Lancaster or otherwise, or the Duke of Cornwall, is a party.[1]

**31. Application of Part I to statutory arbitrations.**—(1) Subject to the provisions of section thirty-three of this Act, this Part of this Act, except the provisions thereof specified in subsection (2) of this section, shall apply to every arbitration under any other Act (whether passed before or after the commencement of this Act) as if the arbitration were pursuant to an arbitration agreement and as if that other Act were an arbitration agreement, except in so far as this Act is inconsistent with that other Act or with any rules or procedure authorised or recognised thereby.

(2) The provisions referred to in subsection (1) of this section are subsection (1) of section two, section three, [subsection (2) of section four,] section five, subsection (3) of section eighteen and sections twenty-four, twenty-five, twenty-seven and twenty-nine.[2]

**32. Meaning of 'arbitration agreement'.**—In this Part of this Act, unless the context otherwise requires, the expression 'arbitration agreement' means a written agreement to submit present or future differences to arbitration, whether an arbitrator is named therein or not.

**33. Operation of Part I.**—This Part of this Act shall not affect any arbitration commenced (within the meaning of subsection (2) of section twenty-nine of this Act) before the commencement of this Act, but shall apply to an arbitration so commenced after the commencement of this Act under an agreement made before the commencement of this Act.

**34. Extent of Part I.**—Save as aforesaid, none of the provisions of this Part of this Act shall extend to Scotland or Northern Ireland.[3]

---

[1] As amended by s. 8(2)(c) of the Arbitration Act 1975.
[2] As amended by s. 8(2)(d) of the Arbitration Act 1975.
[3] As amended by s. 8(2)(e) of the Arbitration Act 1975.

Part II

## ENFORCEMENT OF CERTAIN FOREIGN AWARDS

**35. Awards to which Part II applies.**—(1) This Part of this Act applies to any award made after the twenty-eighth day of July, nineteen hundred and twenty-four —

(a) in pursuance of an agreement for arbitration to which the protocol set out in the First Schedule to this Act applies; and

(b) between persons of whom one is subject to the jurisdiction of some one of such Powers as His Majesty, being satsified that reciprocal provisions have been made, may by Order in Council declare to be parties to the convention set out in the Second Schedule to this Act, and of whom the other is subject to the jurisdiction of some other of the Powers aforesaid; and

(c) in one of such territories as His Majesty, being satisfied that reciprocal provisions have been made, may by Order in Council declare to be territories to which the the said convention applies;

and an award to which this Part of this Act applies is in this Part of this Act referred to as 'a foreign award'.

(2) His Majesty may by a subsequent Order in Council vary or revoke any Order previously made under this section.

(3) Any Order in Council under section one of the Arbitration (Foreign Awards) Act 1930, which is in force at the commencement of this Act shall have effect as if it had been made under this section.[1]

**36. Effect of foreign awards.**—(1) A foreign award shall, subject to the provisions of this Part of this Act, be enforceable in England either by action or in the same manner as the award of an arbitrator is enforceable by virtue of section twenty-six of this Act.

(2) Any foreign award which would be enforceable under this Part of this Act shall be treated as binding for all purposes on the persons as between whom it was made, and may accordingly be relied on by any of those persons by way of defence, set off or otherwise in any legal proceedings in England, and any references in this Part of this Act to enforcing a foreign award shall be construed as including references to relying on an award.

**37. Conditions for enforcement of foreign awards.**—(1) In order that a foreign award may be enforceable under this Part of this Act it must have —

(a) been made in pursuance of an agreement for arbitration which was valid under the law by which it was governed;

(b) been made by the tribunal provided for in the agreement or constituted in manner agreed upon by the parties;

(c) been made in conformity with the law governing the arbitration procedure;

(d) become final in the country in which it was made;

(e) been in respect of a matter which may lawfully be referred to arbitration under the law of England;

and the enforcement thereof must not be contrary to the public policy or the law of England.

(2) Subject to the provisions of this subsection, a foreign award shall not be enforceable under this Part of this Act if the court dealing with the case is satisfied that —

---

[1] The Contracting States for the purposes of the protocol in the First Schedule are listed in Mustill & Boyd's *Commercial Arbitration*, pp. 638–640.

(a)   the award has been annulled in the country in which it was made; or

(b)   the party against whom it is sought to enforce the award was not given notice of the arbitration proceedings in sufficient time to enable him to present his case, or was under some legal incapacity and was not properly represented; or

(c)   the award does not deal with all the questions referred or contains decisions on matters beyond the scope of the agreement for arbitration.

Provided that, if the award does not deal with all the questions referred, the court may, if it thinks fit, either postpone the enforcement of the award or order its enforcement subject to the giving of such security by the person seeking to enforce it as the court may think fit.

(3) If a party seeking to resist the enforcement of a foreign award proves that there is any ground other than the non-existence of the conditions specified in paragraphs (a), (b) and (c) of subsection (1) of this section, or the existence of the conditions specified in paragraphs (b) and (c) of subsection (2) of this section, entitling him to contest the validity of the award, the court may, if it thinks fit, either refuse to enforce the award or adjourn the hearing until after the expiration of such period as appears to the court to be reasonably sufficient to enable that party to take the necessary steps to have the award annulled by the competent tribunal.

**38. Evidence.**—(1) The party seeking to enforce a foreign award must produce—

(a)   the original award or a copy thereof duly authenticated in manner required by the law of the country in which it was made; and

(b)   evidence proving that the award has become final; and

(c)   such evidence as may be necessary to prove that the award is a foreign award and that the conditions mentioned in paragraphs (a), (b) and (c) of subsection (1) of the last foregoing section are satisfied.

(2) In any case where any document required to be produced under subsection (1) of this section is in a foreign language, it shall be the duty of the party seeking to enforce the award to produce a translation certified as correct by a diplomatic or consular agent of the country to which that party belongs, or certified as correct in such other manner as may be sufficient according to the law of England.

(3) Subject to the provisions of this section, rules of court may be made under section [84 of the Supreme Court Act 1981], with respect to the evidence which must be furnished by a party seeking to enforce an award under this Part of this Act.[1]

**39. Meaning of 'final award'.**—For the purpose of this Part of this Act, an award shall not be deemed final if any proceedings for the purpose of contesting the validity of the award are pending in the country in which it was made.

**40. Saving for other rights, &c.**—Nothing in this Part of this Act shall—

(a)   prejudice any rights which any person would have had of enforcing in England any award or of availing himself in England of any award if neither this Part of this Act nor Part I of the Arbitration (Foreign Awards) Act 1930, had been enacted; or

(b)   apply to any award made on an arbitration agreement governed by the law of England.

**41. Application of Part II to Scotland.**—(1) The following provisions of this section shall have effect for the purpose of the application of this Part of this Act to Scotland.

(2) For the references to England there shall be substituted references to Scotland.

---

[1]   Amended by Sched. 5 of the Supreme Court Act 1981.

(3) For subsection (1) of section thirty-six there shall be substituted the following subsection: —

'(1) A foreign award shall, subject to the provisions of this Part of this Act, be enforceable by action, or, if the agreement for arbitration contains consent to the registration of the award in the Books of Council and Session for execution and the award is so registered, it shall, subject as aforesaid, be enforceable by summary diligence'.

(4) For subsection (3) of section thirty-eight there shall be substituted the following subsection: —

'(3) The Court of Session shall, subject to the provision of this section, have power, exercisable by statutory instrument, to make provision by Act of Sederunt with respect to the evidence which must be furnished by a party seeking to enforce in Scotland an award under this Part of this Act'.[1]

**42. Application of Part II to Northern Ireland.**—(1) The following provisions of this section shall have effect for the purpose of the application of this Part of this Act to Northern Ireland.

(2) For the references to England there shall be substituted references to Northern Ireland.

(3) For subsection (1) of section thirty-six there shall be substituted the following subsection: —

'(1) A foreign award shall, subject to the provisions of this Part of this Act, be enforceable either by action or in the same manner as the award of an arbitrator under the provisions of the Common Law Procedure Amendment Act (Ireland) 1856 was enforceable at the date of the passing of the Arbitration (Foreign Awards) Act 1930'.

(4) [Repealed][2]

**43. Saving for pending proceedings.**—[Repealed][3]


Part III

GENERAL

**44. Short title, commencement and repeal.**—(1) This Act may be cited as the Arbitration Act 1950.

(2) This Act shall come into operation on the first day of September, nineteen hundred and fifty.

(3) The Arbitration Act 1889, the Arbitration Clauses (Protocol) Act 1924, and the Arbitration Act 1934 are hereby repealed except in relation to arbitrations commenced (within the meaning of subsection (2) of section twenty-nine of this Act) before the commencement of this Act, and the Arbitration (Foreign Awards) Act 1930 is hereby repealed; and any reference in any Act or other document to any enactment hereby repealed shall be construed as including a reference to the corresponding provision of this Act.

---

[1] As amended by the Statutory Instruments Act 1946 and the Law Reform (Miscellaneous Provisions) (Scotland) Act 1966.
[2] S. 42(4) was repealed by s. 122(2) and Sched. 7 of the Judicature (Northern Ireland) Act 1978.
[3] Repealed by the Statute Law (Revision) Act 1978.

FIRST SCHEDULE[1]

The First Schedule sets out the terms of the protocol signed on behalf of His Majesty at a meeting of the assembly of the League of Nations held on 24th September, 1923.

SECOND SCHEDULE[2]

The Second Schedule sets out the Convention on the Execution of Foreign Arbitral Awards (the Geneva Convention) of 1927.

---

[1]   See Mustill & Boyd's *Commercial Arbitration*, pp. 643–644.
[2]   *Ibid.*, pp. 644–647.

# Arbitration Act 1975 (1975 c. 3)

An Act to give effect to the New York Convention on the Recognition and Enforcement of Foreign Arbitral Awards.

*Effect of arbitration agreement on court proceedings*

**1. Staying court proceedings where party proves arbitration agreement.—** (1) If any party to an arbitration agreement to which this section applies, or any person claiming through or under him, commences any legal proceedings in any court against any other party to the agreement, or any person claiming through or under him, in respect of any matter agreed to be referred, any party to the proceedings may at any time after appearance, and before delivering any pleadings or taking any other steps in the proceedings, apply to the court to stay the proceedings; and the court, unless satisfied that the arbitration agreement is null and void, inoperative or incapable of being performed or that there is not in fact any dispute between the parties with regard to the matter agreed to be referred, shall make an order staying the proceedings.

(2) This section applies to any arbitration agreement which is not a domestic arbitration agreement; and neither section 4(1) of the Arbitration Act 1950 nor section 4 of the Arbitration Act (Northern Ireland) 1937 shall apply to an arbitration agreement to which this section applies.

(3) In the application of this section to Scotland, for the references to staying proceedings there shall be substituted references to sisting proceedings.

(4) In this section 'domestic arbitration agreement' means an arbitration agreement which does not provide, expressly or by implication, for arbitration in a State other than the United Kingdom and to which neither —

- (a) an individual who is a national of, or habitually resident in, any State other than the United Kingdom; nor
- (b) a body corporate which is incorporated in, or whose central management and control is exercised in, any State other than the United Kingdom;

is a party at the time the proceedings are commenced.

*Enforcement of Convention awards*

**2. Replacement of former provisions.—**Sections 3 to 6 of this Act shall have effect with respect to the enforcement of Convention awards; and where a Convention award would, but for this section, be also a foreign award within the meaning of Part II of the Arbitration Act 1950, that Part shall not apply to it.

**3. Effect of Convention awards.—**(1) A Convention award shall, subject to the following provisions of this Act, be enforceable —

- (a) in England and Wales, either by action or in the same manner as the award of an arbitrator is enforceable by virtue of section 26 of the Arbitration Act 1950;
- (b) in Scotland, either by action or, in a case where the arbitration agreement contains consent to the registration of the award in the Books of Council and Session for execution and the award is so registered, by summary diligence;
- (c) in Northern Ireland, either by action or in the same manner as the award of an arbitrator is enforceable by virtue of section 16 of the Arbitration Act (Northern Ireland) 1937.

(2) Any Convention award which would be enforceable under this Act shall be treated as binding for all purposes on the persons as between whom it was made, and may accordingly be relied on by any of those persons by way of defence, set off or otherwise in any legal proceedings in the United Kingdom; and any reference in

this Act to enforcing a Convention award shall be construed as including references to relying on such an award.

**4. Evidence.**—The party seeking to enforce a Convention award must produce —

(a) the duly authenticated original award or a duly certified copy of it; and

(b) the original arbitration agreement or a duly certified copy of it; and

(c) where the award or agreement is in a foreign language, a translation of it certified by an official or sworn translator or by a diplomatic or consular agent.

**5. Refusal of enforcement.**—(1) Enforcement of a Convention award shall not be refused except in the cases mentioned in this section.

(2) Enforcement of a Convention award may be refused if the person against whom it is invoked proves —

(a) that a party to the arbitration agreement was (under the law applicable to him) under some incapacity; or

(b) that the arbitration agreement was not valid under the law to which the parties subjected it or, failing any indication thereon, under the law of the country where the award was made; or

(c) that he was not given proper notice of the appointment of the arbitrator or of the arbitration proceedings or was otherwise unable to present his case; or

(d) (subject to subsection (4) of this section) that the award deals with a difference not contemplated by or not falling within the terms of the submission to arbitration or contains decisions on matters beyond the scope of the submission to arbitration; or

(e) that the composition of the arbitral authority or the arbitral procedure was not in accordance with the agreement of the parties or, failing such agreement, with the law of the country where the arbitration took place; or

(f) that the award has not yet become binding on the parties, or has been set aside or suspended by a competent authority of the country in which, or under the law of which, it was made.

(3) Enforcement of a Convention award may also be refused if the award is in respect of a matter which is not capable of settlement by arbitration, or if it would be contrary to public policy to enforce the award.

(4) A Convention award which contains decisions on matters not submitted to arbitration may be enforced to the extent that it contains decisions on matters submitted to arbitration which can be separated from those on matters not so submitted.

(5) Where an application for the setting aside or suspension of a Convention award has been made to such a competent authority as is mentioned in subsection (2)(f) of this section, the court before which enforcement of the award is sought may, if it thinks fit, adjourn the proceedings and may, on the application of the party seeking to enforce the award, order the other party to give security.

**6. Saving.**—Nothing in this Act shall prejudice any right to enforce or rely on an award otherwise than under this Act or Part II of the Arbitration Act 1950.

*General*

**7. Interpretation.**—(1) In this Act —

'arbitration agreement' means an agreement in writing (including an agreement contained in an exchange of letters or telegrams) to submit to arbitration present or future differences capable of settlement by arbitration;

'Convention award' means an award made in pursuance of an arbitration agreement in the territory of a State, other than the United Kingdom, which is a party to the New York Convention; and

'the New York Convention' means the Convention on the Recognition and Enforcement of Foreign Arbitral Awards adopted by the United Nations Conference on International Commercial Arbitration on 10th June 1958.

(2) If Her Majesty by Order in Council declares that any State specified in the Order is a party to the New York Convention the Order shall, while in force, be conclusive evidence that that State is a party to that Convention.[1]

(3) An Order in Council under this section may be varied or revoked by a subsequent Order in Council.

**8. Short title, repeals, commencement and extent.**—(1) This Act may be cited as the Arbitration Act 1975.

(2) The following provisions of the Arbitration Act 1950 are hereby repealed, that is to say —

(*a*) section 4(2);

(*b*) in section 28 the proviso;

(*c*) in section 30 the words '(except the provisions of subsection (2) of section 4 thereof)';

(*d*) in section 31(2) the words 'subsection (2) of section 4'; and

(*e*) in section 34 the words from the beginning to 'save as aforesaid'.

(3) This Act shall come into operation on such date as the Secretary of State may by order made by statutory instrument appoint.

(4) This Act extends to Northern Ireland.

---

[1]   The States which are parties to the New York Convention are listed in Mustill & Boyd's *Commercial Arbitration*, p. 653.

## Arbitration Act 1979 (1979 c. 42)

An Act to amend the law relating to arbitrations and for purposes connected therewith.

**1. Judicial review of arbitration awards.**—(1) In the Arbitration Act 1950 (in this Act referred to as 'the principal Act') section 21 (statement of case for a decision of the High Court) shall cease to have effect and, without prejudice to the right of appeal conferred by subsection (2) below, the High Court shall not have jurisdiction to set aside or remit an award on an arbitration agreement on the ground of errors of fact or law on the face of the award.

(2) Subject to subsection (3) below, an appeal shall lie to the High Court on any question of law arising out of an award made on an arbitration agreement; and on the determination of such an appeal the High Court may by order —

    (*a*)   confirm, vary or set aside the award; or

    (*b*)   remit the award to the reconsideration of the arbitrator or umpire together with the court's opinion on the question of law which was the subject of the appeal;

and where the award is remitted under paragraph (b) above the arbitrator or umpire shall, unless the order otherwise directs, make his award within three months after the date of the order.

(3) An appeal under this section may be brought by any of the parties to the reference —

    (*a*)   with the consent of all the other parties to the reference; or

    (*b*)   subject to section 3 below, with the leave of the court.

(4) The High Court shall not grant leave under subsection (3)(b) above unless it considers that, having regard to all the circumstances, the determination of the question of law concerned could substantially affect the rights of one or more of the parties to the arbitration agreement; and the court may make any leave which it gives conditional upon the applicant complying with such conditions as it considers appropriate.

(5) Subject to subsection (6) below, if an award is made and, on an application made by any of the parties to the reference —

    (*a*)   with the consent of all the other parties to the reference, or

    (*b*)   subject to section 3 below, with the leave of the court,

it appears to the High Court that the award does not or does not sufficiently set out the reasons for the award, the court may order the arbitrator or umpire concerned to state the reasons for his award in sufficient detail to enable the court, should an appeal be brought under this section, to consider any question of law arising out of the award.

(6) In any case where an award is made without any reason being given, the High Court shall not make an order under subsection (5) above unless it is satisfied —

    (*a*)   that before the award was made one of the parties to the reference gave notice to the arbitrator or umpire concerned that a reasoned award would be required; or

    (*b*)   that there is some special reason why such a notice was not given.

(6A) Unless the High Court gives leave, no appeal shall lie to the Court of Appeal from a decision of the High Court —

    (*a*)   to grant or refuse leave under subsection 3(b) or 5(b) above; or

    (*b*)   to make or not to make an order under subsection (5) above.[1]

(7) No appeal shall lie to the Court of Appeal from a decision of the High Court on an appeal under this section unless —

    (*a*)   the High Court or the Court of Appeal gives leave; and

    (*b*)   it is certified by the High Court that the question of law to which its decision

---

[1]   S. 1(6A) was added by s. 148(2) of the Supreme Court Act 1981.

relates either is one of general public importance or is one which for some other special reason should be considered by the Court of Appeal.

(8) Where the award of an arbitrator or umpire is varied on appeal, the award as varied shall have effect (except for the purposes of this section) as if it were the award of the arbitrator or umpire.

**2. Determination of preliminary point of law by court.**—(1) Subject to subsection (2) and section 3 below, on an application to the High Court made by any of the parties to a reference —

(*a*)   with the consent of an arbitrator who has entered on the reference or, if an umpire has entered on the reference, with his consent, or

(*b*)   with the consent of all the other parties,

the High Court shall have jurisdiction to determine any question of law arising in the course of the reference.

(2) The High Court shall not entertain an application under subsection (1)(a) above with respect to any question of law unless it is satisfied that —

(*a*)   the determination of the application might produce substantial savings in costs to the parties; and

(*b*)   the question of law is one in respect of which leave to appeal would be likely to be given under section 1(3)(b) above.

(2A)  Unless the High Court gives leave, no appeal shall lie to the Court of Appeal from a decision of the High Court to entertain or not to entertain an application under subsection 1(a) above. [1]

(3) A decision of the High Court under [subsection (1) above][2] shall be deemed to be a judgment of the court within the meaning of section [16 of the Supreme Court Act 1981][2] (appeals to the Court of Appeal), but no appeal shall lie from such a decision unless —

(*a*)   the High Court or the Court of Appeal gives leave; and

(*b*)   it is certified by the High Court that the question of law to which its decision relates either is one of general public importance or is one which for some other special reason should be considered by the Court of Appeal.

**3. Exclusion agreements affecting rights under sections 1 and 2.**—(1) Subject to the following provisions of this section and section 4 below —

(*a*)   the High Court shall not, under section 1(3)(b) above, grant leave to appeal with respect to a question of law arising out of an award, and

(*b*)   the High Court shall not, under section 1(5)(b) above, grant leave to make an application with respect to an award, and

(*c*)   no application may be made under section 2(1)(a) above with respect to a question of law,

if the parties to the reference in question have entered into an agreement in writing (in this section referred to as an 'exclusion agreement') which excludes the right of appeal under section 1 above in relation to that award or, in a case falling within paragraph (c) above, in relation to an award to which the determination of the question of law is material.

(2) An exclusion agreement may be expressed so as to relate to a particular award, to awards under a particular reference or to any other description of awards, whether arising out of the same reference or not; and an agreement may be an exclusion agreement for the purposes of this section whether it is entered into before or after the passing of this Act and whether or not it forms part of an arbitration agreement.

(3) In any case where —

---

[1]  Added by s. 148 of the Supreme Court Act 1981.
[2]  Amended by s. 148(3) of the Supreme Court Act 1981.

(a) an arbitration agreement, other than a domestic arbitration agreement, provides for disputes between the parties to be referred to arbitration, and

(b) a dispute to which the agreement relates involves the question whether a party has been guilty of fraud, and

(c) the parties have entered into an exclusion agreement which is applicable to any award made on the reference of that dispute,

then, except in so far as the exclusion agreement otherwise provides, the High Court shall not exercise its powers under section 24(2) of the principal Act (to take steps necessary to enable the question to be determined by the High Court) in relation to that dispute.

(4) Except as provided by subsection (1) above, sections 1 and 2 above shall have effect notwithstanding anything in any agreement purporting —

(a) to prohibit or restrict access to the High Court; or

(b) to restrict the jurisdiction of that court; or

(c) to prohibit or restrict the making of a reasoned award.

(5) An exclusion agreement shall be of no effect in relation to an award made on, or a question of law arising in the course of a reference under, a statutory arbitration, that is to say, such an arbitration as is referred to in subsection (1) of section 31 of the principal Act.

(6) An exclusion agreement shall be of no effect in relation to an award made on, or a question of law arising in the course of a reference under, an arbitration agreement which is a domestic arbitration agreement unless the exclusion agreement is entered into after the commencement of the arbitration in which the award is made or, as the case may be, in which the question of law arises.

(7) In this section 'domestic arbitration agreement' means an arbitration agreement which does not provide, expressly or by implication, for arbitration in a State other than the United Kingdom and to which neither —

(a) an individual who is a national of, or habitually resident in, any State other than the United Kingdom, nor

(b) a body corporate which is incorporated in, or whose central management and control is exercised in, any State other than the United Kingdom,

is a party at the time the arbitration agreement is entered into.

**4. Exclusion agreements not to apply in certain cases.**–(1) Subject to subsection (3) below, if an arbitration award or a question of law arising in the course of a reference relates, in whole or in part, to —

(a) a question or claim falling within the Admiralty jurisdiction of the High Court, or

(b) a dispute arising out of a contract of insurance, or

(c) a dispute arising out of a commodity contract,

an exclusion agreement shall have no effect in relation to the award or question unless either —

(i) the exclusion agreement is entered into after the commencement of the arbitration in which the award is made or, as the case may be, in which the question of law arises, or

(ii) the award or question relates to a contract which is expressed to be governed by a law other than the law of England and Wales.

(2) In subsection (1)(c) above 'commodity contract' means a contract —

(a) for the sale of goods regularly dealt with on a commodity market or exchange in England or Wales which is specified for the purposes of this section by an order made by the Secretary of State; and

(b) of a description so specified.

(3) The Secretary of State may by order provide that subsection (1) above —

(a) shall cease to have effect; or

(b) subject to such conditions as may be specified in the order, shall not apply to any exclusion agreement made in relation to an arbitration award of a description so specified;

and an order under this subsection may contain such supplementary, incidental and transitional provisions as appear to the Secretary of State to be necessary or expedient.

(4) The power to make an order under subsection (2) or subsection (3) above shall be exercisable by statutory instrument which shall be subject to annulment in pursuance of a resolution of either House of Parliament.

(5) In this section 'exclusion agreement' has the same meaning as in section 3 above.

**5. Interlocutory orders.**—(1) If any party to a reference under an arbitration agreement fails within the time specified in the order or, if no time is so specified, within a reasonable time to comply with an order made by the arbitrator or umpire in the course of the reference, then, on the application of the arbitrator or umpire or of any party to the reference, the High Court may make an order extending the powers of the arbitrator or umpire as mentioned in subsection (2) below.

(2) If an order is made by the High Court under this section, the arbitrator or umpire shall have power, to the extent and subject to any conditions specified in that order, to continue with the reference in default of appearance or of any other act by one of the parties in like manner as a judge of the High Court might continue with proceedings in that court where a party fails to comply with an order of that court or a requirement of rules of court.

(3) Section 4(5) of the Administration of Justice Act 1970 (jurisdiction of the High Court to be exercisable by the Court of Appeal in relation to judge-arbitrators and judge-umpires) shall not apply in relation to the power of the High Court to make an order under this section, but in the case of a reference to a judge-arbitrator or judge-umpire that power shall be exercisable as in the case of any other reference to arbitration and also by the judge-arbitrator or judge-umpire himself.

(4) Anything done by a judge-arbitrator or judge-umpire in the exercise of the power conferred by subsection (3) above shall be done by him in his capacity as judge of the High Court and have effect as if done by that court.

(5) The preceding provisions of this section have effect notwithstanding anything in any agreement but do not derogate from any powers conferred on an arbitrator or umpire, whether by an arbitration agreement or otherwise.

(6) In this section 'judge-arbitrator' and 'judge-umpire' have the same meaning as in Schedule 3 to the Administration of Justice Act 1970.

**6. Minor amendments relating to awards and appointment of arbitrators and umpires.**—(1) In subsection (1) of section 8 of the principal Act (agreements where reference is to two arbitrators deemed to include provision that the arbitrators shall appoint an umpire immediately after their own appointment) —

(a) for the words 'shall appoint an umpire immediately' there shall be substituted the words 'may appoint an umpire at any time'; and

(b) at the end there shall be added the words 'and shall do so forthwith if they cannot agree'.

(2) For section 9 of the principal Act (agreements for reference to three arbitrators) there shall be substituted the following section: —

**9. 'Majority award of three arbitrators.**—Unless the contrary intention is expressed in the arbitration agreement, in any case where there is a reference to three arbitrators, the award of any two of the arbitrators shall be binding'.

(3) In section 10 of the principal Act (power of court in certain cases to appoint an arbitrator or umpire) in paragraph (c) after the word 'are', in the first place where it

occurs, there shall be inserted the words 'required or are' and the words from 'or where' to the end of the paragraph shall be omitted.

(4) At the end of section 10 of the principal Act there shall be added the following subsection: —

'(2) In any case where —

(a) an arbitration agreement provides for the appointment of an arbitrator or umpire by a person who is neither one of the parties nor an existing arbitrator (whether the provision applies directly or in default of agreement by the parties or otherwise), and

(b) that person refuses to make the appointment or does not make it within the time specified in the agreement or, if no time is so specified, within a reasonable time,

any party to the agreement may serve the person in question with a written notice to appoint an arbitrator or umpire and, if the appointment is not made within seven clear days after the service of the notice, the High Court or a judge thereof may, on the application of the party who gave the notice, appoint an arbitrator or umpire who shall have the like powers to act in the reference and make an award as if he had been appointed in accordance with the terms of the agreement'.

**7. Application and interpretation of certain provisions of Part I of principal Act.**—(1) References in the following provisions of Part I of the principal Act to that Part of that Act shall have effect as if the preceding provisions of this Act were included in that Part, namely, —

(a)  section 14 (interim awards);

(b)  section 28 (terms as to costs of orders);

(c)  section 30 (Crown to be bound);

(d)  section 31 (application to statutory arbitrations); and

(e)  section 32 (meaning of 'arbitration agreement').

(2) Subsections (2) and (3) of section 29 of the principal Act shall apply to determine when an arbitration is deemed to be commenced for the purposes of this Act.

(3) For the avoidance of doubt, it is hereby declared that the reference in subsection (1) of section 31 of the principal Act (statutory arbitrations) to arbitration under any other Act does not extend to arbitration under section 92 of the County Courts Act 1959 (cases in which proceedings are to be or may be referred to arbitration) and accordingly nothing in this Act or in Part I of the principal Act applies to arbitration under the said section 92.

**8. Short title, commencement, repeals and extent.**—(1) This Act may be cited as the Arbitration Act 1979.

(2) This Act shall come into operation on such day as the Secretary of State may appoint by order made by statutory instrument; and such an order —

(a)  may appoint different days for different provisions of this Act and for the purposes of the operation of the same provision in relation to different descriptions of arbitration agreement; and

(b)  may contain such supplementary, incidental and transitional provisions as appear to the Secretary of State to be necessary or expedient.

(3) In consequence of the preceding provisions of this Act, the following provisions are hereby repealed, namely —

(a)  in paragraph (c) of section 10 of the principal Act the words from 'or where' to the end of the paragraph;

(b)  section 21 of the principal Act;

(c)  in paragraph 9 of Schedule 3 to the Administration of Justice Act 1970, in sub-paragraph (1) the words '21(1) and (2)' and sub-paragraph (2).

(4) This Act forms part of the law of England and Wales only.

## Rules of the Supreme Court

ORDER 73

*Arbitration proceedings*

**1. Arbitration proceedings not to be assigned to Chancery Division (O. 73, r. 1).**—[Revoked]

**2. Matters for a judge in court (O. 73, r. 2).**–(1) Every application to the Court—

(*a*)  to remit an award under section 22 of the Arbitration Act 1950, or

(*b*)  to remove an arbitrator or umpire under section 23(1) of that Act, or

(*c*)  to set aside an award under section 23(2) thereof, or

(*d*)  [Revoked]

(*e*)  to determine, under section 2(1) of that Act, any question of law arising in the course of a reference,

must be made by originating motion to a single judge in court.

(2)  Any appeal to the High Court under section 1(2) of the Arbitration Act 1979 shall be made by originating motion to a single judge in court and notice thereof may be included in the notice of application for leave to appeal, where leave is required.

(3)  An application for a declaration that an award made by an arbitrator or umpire is not binding on a party to the award on the ground that it was made without jurisdiction may be made by originating motion to a single judge in court, but the foregoing provision shall not be taken as affecting the judge's power to refuse to make such a declaration in proceedings begun by motion.

**3. Matters for judge in chambers or master (O. 73, r. 3).**—(1) Subject to the foregoing provisions of this Order and the provisions of this rule, the jurisdiction of the High Court or a judge thereof under the Arbitration Act 1950 and the jurisdiction of the High Court under the Arbitration Act 1975 and the Arbitration Act 1979 may be exercised by a judge in chambers, a master or the Admiralty Registrar.

(2)  Any application

(*a*)  for leave to appeal under s. 1(2) of the Arbitration Act 1979, or

(*b*)  under s. 1(5) of that Act (including any application for leave), or

(*c*)  under s. 5 of that Act,

shall be made to a judge in chambers.

(3)  Any application to which this rule applies shall, where an action is pending, be made by summons in the action, and in any other case by an originating summons which shall be in Form No. 10 in Appendix A.

(4)  Where an application is made under section 1(5) of the Arbitration Act 1979 (including any application for leave) the summons must be served on the arbitrator or umpire and on any other party to the reference.

**4. Applications in district registries (O. 73, r. 4).**—An application under section 12(4) of the Arbitration Act 1950 for an order that a writ of subpoena ad testificandum or of subpoena duces tecum shall issue to compel the attendance before an arbitrator or umpire of a witness may, if the attendance of the witness is required within the district of any district registry, be made at that registry, instead of at the Central Office, at the option of the applicant.

**5. Time-limits and other special provisions as to appeals and applications under the Arbitration Acts (O. 73, r. 5).**—(1) An application to the Court —

(*a*)  to remit an award under section 22 of the Arbitration Act 1950, or

(*b*)  to set aside an award under section 23(2) of that Act or otherwise, or

(*c*)  to direct an arbitrator or umpire to state the reasons for an award under section 1(5) of the Arbitration Act 1979,

must be made, and the summons or notice must be served, within 21 days after the award has been made and published to the parties.

(2)  In the case of an appeal to the Court under section 1(2) of the Arbitration Act 1979, the notice must be served, and the appeal entered, within 21 days after the award has been made and published to the parties:

Provided that, where reasons material to the appeal are given on a date subsequent to the publication of the award, the period of 21 days shall run from the date on which the reasons are given.

(3)  An application, under section 2(1) of the Arbitration Act 1979, to determine any question of law arising in the course of a reference, must be made, and notice thereof served, within 14 days after the arbitrator or umpire has consented to the application being made, or the other parties have so consented.

(4)  For the purpose of paragraph (2) the consent must be given in writing.

(5)  In the case of every appeal or application to which this rule applies, the notice of originating motion or, as the case may be, the originating summons, must state the grounds of the appeal or application and, where the appeal or application is founded on evidence by affidavit, or is made with the consent of the arbitrator or umpire or of the other parties, a copy of every affidavit intended to be used, or, as the case may be, of every consent given in writing, must be served with that notice.

**6. Applications and appeals to be heard by Commercial Judges.**—(1) Any matter which is required, by rule 2 or 3, to be heard by a judge, shall be heard by a Commercial Judge, unless any such judge otherwise directs.

(2)  Nothing in the foregoing paragraph shall be construed as preventing the powers of a Commercial Judge from being exercised by any judge of the High Court.

**7. Service out of the jurisdiction of summons, notice, etc. (O. 73, r. 7).**—(1)  Service out of the jurisdiction —

(*a*)  of an originating summons for the appointment of an arbitrator or umpire, or

(*b*)  of notice of an originating motion to remove an arbitrator or umpire or to remit or set aside an award, or

(*c*)  of an originating summons or notice of an originating motion under the Arbitration Act 1979, or

(*d*)  of any order made on such a summons or motion as aforesaid,

is permissible with the leave of the Court provided that the arbitration to which the summons, motion or order relates is governed by English law or has been, is being, or is to be held, within the jurisdiction.

(1A)  Service out of the jurisdiction of an originating summons for leave to enforce an award is permissible with the leave of the Court whether or not the arbitration is governed by English law.

(2)  An application for the grant of leave under this rule must be supported by an affidavit stating the grounds on which the application is made and showing in what place or country the person to be served is, or probably may be found; and so such leave shall be granted unless it shall be made sufficiently to appear to the Court that the case is a proper one for service out of the jurisdiction under this rule.

(3)  Order 11, rules 5, 6 and 8, shall apply in relation to any such summons, notice or order as is referred to in paragraph (1) as they apply in relation to a writ.

**8. Registration in High Court of foreign awards (O. 73, r. 8).**—Where an award is made in proceedings on an arbitration in any part of Her Majesty's dominions or other territory to which Part I of the Foreign Judgments (Reciprocal Enforcement) Act 1933 extends, being a part to which Part II of the Administration of Justice Act 1920 extended immediately before the said Part I was extended thereto, then, if the award has, in pursuance of the law in force in the place where it was made, become enforceable in the same manner as a judgment given by a court in that place, Order 71 shall apply in relation to the award as it applies in relation to a judgment given by that court, subject, however, to the following modifications: —

(a) for references to the country of the original court there shall be substituted references to the place where the award was made; and

(b) the affidavit required by rule 3 of the said Order must state (in addition to the other matters required by that rule) that to the best of the information or belief of the deponent the award has, in pursuance of the law in force in the place where it was made, become enforceable in the same manner as a judgment given by a court in that place.

**9. Registration of awards under Arbitration (International Investment Disputes) Act 1966 (O. 73, r. 9).**—(1) In this rule and in any provision of these rules as applied by this rule —

"the Act of 1966" means the Arbitration (International Investment Disputes) Act 1966;

"award" means an award rendered pursuant to the Convention;

"the Convention" means the Convention referred to in section 1(1) of the Act of 1966;

"judgment creditor" and "judgment debtor" means respectively the person seeking recognition or enforcement of an award and the other party to the award.

(2) Subject to the provisions of this rule, the following provisions of Order 71, namely, rules 1, 3(1) (except sub-paragraphs (c)(iv) and (d) thereof) 7 (except paragraph (3)(c) and (d) thereof), and 10(3) shall apply with the necessary modifications in relation to an award as they apply in relation to a judgment to which Part II of the Foreign Judgments (Reciprocal Enforcement) Act 1933 applies.

(3) An application to have an award registered in the High Court under section 1 of the Act of 1966 shall be made by originating summons which shall be in Form No. 10 in Appendix A.

(4) The affidavit required by Order 71, rule 3, in support of an application for registration shall—

(a) in lieu of exhibiting the judgment or a copy thereof, exhibit a copy of the award certified pursuant to the Convention, and

(b) in addition to stating the matters mentioned in paragraph 3(1)(c)(i) and (ii) of the said rule 3, state whether at the date of the application the enforcement of the award has been stayed (provisionally or otherwise) pursuant to the Convention and whether any, and if so what, application has been made pursuant to the Convention which, if granted, might result in a stay of the enforcement of the award.

(5) There shall be kept in the Central Office under the direction of the senior master a register of the awards ordered to be registered under the Act of 1966 and particulars shall be entered in the register of any execution issued on such an award.

(6) Where it appears to the court on granting leave to register an award or on an application made by the judgment debtor after an award has been registered —

(a) that the enforcement of the award has been stayed (whether provisionally or otherwise) pursuant to the Convention, or

(b) that an application has been made pursuant to the Convention which, if granted, might result in a stay of the enforcement of the award, the court shall, or, in the case referred to in sub-paragraph (b) may, stay execution of the award for such time as it considers appropriate in the circumstances.

(7) An application by the judgment debtor under paragraph (6) shall be made by summons and supported by affidavit.

**10. Enforcement of arbitration awards (O. 73, r. 10).**—(1) An application for leave under section 26 of the Arbitration Act 1950 or under section 3(1)(a) of the Arbitration Act 1975 to enforce an award on an arbitration agreement in the same manner as a judgment or order may be made ex parte but the Court hearing the application may direct a summons to be issued.

(2) If the Court directs a summons to be issued, the summons shall be an originating summons which shall be in Form No. 10 in Appendix A.

(3) An application for leave must be supported by affidavit —

(a) exhibiting
   (i)  where the application is under section 26 of the Arbitration Act 1950, the arbitration agreement and the original award or, in either case, a copy thereof;
   (ii) where the application is under section 3(1)(a) of the Arbitration Act 1975, the documents required to be produced by section 4 of that Act,

(b) stating the name and the usual or last known place of abode or business of the applicant (hereinafter referred to as "the creditor") and the person against whom it is sought to enforce the award (hereinafter referred to as "the debtor") respectively,

(c) as the case may require, either that the award has not been complied with or the extent to which it has not been complied with at the date of the application.

(4) An order giving leave must be drawn up by or on behalf of the creditor and must be served on the debtor by delivering a copy to him personally or by sending a copy to him at his usual or last known place of abode or business or in such other manner as the Court may direct.

(5) Service of the order out of the jurisdiction is permissible without leave, and Order 11, rules 5, 6 and 8, shall apply in relation to such an order as they apply in relation to a writ.

(6) Within 14 days after service of the order or, if the order is to be served out of the jurisdiction, within such other period as the Court may fix, the debtor may apply to set aside the order and the award shall not be enforced until after the expiration of that period or, if the debtor applies within that period to set aside the order, until after the application is finally disposed of.

(7) The copy of that order served on the debtor shall state the effect of paragraph (6).

(8) In relation to a body corporate this rule shall have effect as if for any reference to the place of abode or business of the creditor or the debtor there were substituted a reference to the registered or principal address of the body corporate; so, however, that nothing in this rule shall affect any enactment which provides for the manner in which a document may be served on a body corporate.

# STATUTE LAW APPLICABLE TO SCOTLAND, NORTHERN IRELAND AND THE REPUBLIC OF IRELAND

## *STATUTE LAW APPLICABLE TO SCOTLAND*

*Note* The Arbitration Act 1975 and Part II of the Arbitration Act 1950 also apply to Scotland: see Appendix I.

### The 25th Act of the Articles of Regulation 1695

"That, for the cutting off of groundless and expensive pleas and processes in time coming, the Lords of Session sustain no reduction of any decreet-arbitral that shall be pronounced hereafter upon a Subscribed Submission, at the instance of either of the parties-submitters, upon any cause or reason whatsoever, unless that of corruption, bribery, or falsehood, to be alleged against the judges-arbitrators who pronounced the same."

---

### Arbitration (Scotland) Act, 1894 (1894 c. 13)

I. *Reference to Arbiter not named, etc., not to be invalid.*—From and after the passing of this Act an agreement to refer to arbitration shall not be invalid or ineffectual by reason of the reference being to a person not named, or to a person to be named by another person, or to a person merely described as the holder for the time being of any office or appointment.

II. *On Failure to concur in Nomination of Single Arbiter, Court may appoint.*—Should one of the parties to an agreement to refer to a single arbiter refuse to concur in the nomination of such arbiter, and should no provision have been made for carrying out the reference in that event, or should such provision have failed, an arbiter may be appointed by the Court, on the application of any party to the agreement, and the arbiter so appointed shall have the same powers as if he had been duly nominated by all the parties.

III. *On Failure of one Party to nominate Arbiter, Court may appoint.*—Should one of the parties to an agreement to refer to two arbiters refuse to name an arbiter, in terms of the agreement, and should no provision have been made for carrying out the reference in that event, or should such provision have failed, an arbiter may be appointed by the Court, on the application of the other party, and the arbiter so appointed shall have the same powers as if he had been duly nominated by the party so refusing.

IV. *Arbiters may devolve on Oversman unless otherwise agreed.*—Unless the agree-

175

ment to refer shall otherwise provide, arbiters shall have power to name an oversman on whom the reference shall be devolved in the event of their differing in opinion. Should the arbiters fail to agree in the nomination of an oversman, the Court may, on the application of any party to the agreement, appoint an oversman. The decision of such oversman, whether he has been named by the arbiters or appointed by the Court, shall be final.

V. *Act not to apply to Certain Agreements.*—This Act shall not apply to any agreement, made before its passing, to refer to an arbiter not named or to be named by another person, or merely described as the holder for the time being of an office or appointment, if any party to such agreement shall, before the passing of this Act, or within six months thereafter, have intimated to the other party by writing that he declines to be bound by such agreement.

VI. *Interpretation.*—For the purposes of this Act the expression 'the Court' shall mean any Sheriff having jurisdiction, or any Lord Ordinary of the Court of Session; except that where —

(a)   any arbiter appointed is; or

(b)   in terms of the agreement to refer to arbitration an arbiter or oversman to be appointed must be,

a Senator of the College of Justice, 'the Court' shall mean the Inner House of the Court of Session.[1]

VII. *Extent of Act and Short Title.*—This Act shall apply to Scotland only, and may be cited as the Arbitration (Scotland) Act, 1894.

---

## Administration of Justice (Scotland) Act, 1972, s. 3

3.—(1) Subject to express provision to the contrary in an agreement to refer to arbitration, the arbiter or oversman may, on the application of a party to the arbitration, and shall, if the Court of Session on such an application so directs, at any stage in the arbitration state a case for the opinion of that Court on any question of law arising in the arbitration.

(2) This section shall not apply to an arbitration under any enactment which confers a power to appeal to or state a case for the opinion of a court or tribunal in relation to that arbitration.

(3) This section shall not apply to any form of arbitration relating to a trade dispute within the meaning of the Industrial Courts Act 1919 or relating to an industrial dispute within the meaning of the Industrial Relations Act 1971; to any other arbitration arising from a collective agreement within the meaning of the said Act of 1971; or to proceedings before the Industrial Arbitration Board described in section 124 of that Act.

(4) This section shall not apply in relation to an agreement to refer to arbitration made before the commencement of this Act.

---

[1]   As amended by s. 17(4) of the Law Reform (Miscellaneous Provisions) (Scotland) Act 1980.

*STATUTE LAW APPLICABLE TO NORTHERN IRELAND*[1]

*Note* The Arbitration Act 1975 and Part II of the Arbitration Act 1950 also apply to Northern Ireland: see Appendix I.

## Arbitration Act (Northern Ireland) 1937 (1 Edw. 8 & 1 Geo. 6, Ch. 8.)

An Act to amend the law relating to arbitrations, and to make provision for other matters connected therewith. [7th July, 1937.]

*References under arbitration agreements.*

**1. Provisions as to arbitration agreements and references thereunder.—** (1) A reference under an arbitration agreement shall, unless a contrary intention is expressed therein, be irrevocable, except by leave of the court, and shall have the same effect in all respects as if it had been made an order of court.

(2) An arbitration agreement shall, unless a contrary intention is expressed therein, be deemed to include the provisions set forth in the First Schedule to this Act, so far as they are applicable to the reference under the agreement.

**2. Arbitration agreement not to be discharged by death of party thereto.—**(1) An arbitration agreement shall not be discharged by the death of any party thereto, either as respects the deceased or any other party, but shall in such an event be enforceable by or against the personal representative of the deceased.

(2) The authority of an arbitrator shall not be revoked by the death of any party by whom he was appointed.

**3. Provisions in case of bankruptcy.—**(1) Where an arbitration agreement forms part of a contract to which a bankrupt is a party, the said agreement shall, if the assignee or the trustee in bankruptcy does not disclaim the contract, be enforceable by or against him so far as it relates to any difference arising out of, or in connection with, such contract.

(2) Where a person who has been adjudged bankrupt had before the commencement of the bankruptcy become a party to an arbitration agreement and any matter to which the agreement applies requires to be determined in connection with or for the purposes of the bankruptcy proceedings, then, if the case is one to which subsection (1) of this section does not apply, any other party to the agreement or the assignee, or, with the consent of the committee of inspection, the trustee in bankruptcy, may apply to the court having jurisdiction in the bankruptcy proceedings for an order directing that the matter in question shall be referred to arbitration in accordance with the agreement, and that court may, if it is of opinion that, having regard to all the circumstances of the case, the matter ought to be determined by arbitration, make an order accordingly.

**4. Power to stay proceedings.—**If any party to an arbitration agreement, or any person claiming through or under him, commences any proceedings in any court against any other party to the agreement, or any person claiming through or under him, in respect of any matter agreed to be referred, any party to such proceedings may at any time after appearance, and before delivering any pleadings or taking any other steps in the proceedings, apply to that court to stay the proceedings, and that court, if satisfied that there is no sufficient reason why the matter should not be referred in accordance with the agreement, and that the applicant was, at the time when the proceedings were commenced, and still remains,

---

[1] See p. 132 for a table comparing the Irish statutes with those for England and Wales.

ready and willing to do all things necessary to the proper conduct of the arbitration, may make an order staying the proceedings.

*Provisions as to arbitrators and umpires under arbitration agreements.*

**5. Power for the court in certain cases to appoint an arbitrator, umpire or third arbitrator**—In any of the following cases, namely: —

(a) where an arbitration agreement provides that the reference shall be to a single arbitrator, and all the parties do not after differences have arisen concur in the appointment of an arbitrator;

(b) if an appointed arbitrator refuses to act, or is incapable of acting, or dies, and the arbitration agreement or the reference under the agreement does not show that it was intended that the vacancy should not be supplied, and the parties do not supply the vacancy;

(c) where the parties or two arbitrators are at liberty to appoint an umpire or third arbitrator, or where two arbitrators are required to appoint an umpire, and do not appoint him;

(d) where an appointed umpire or third arbitrator refuses to act, or is incapable of acting, or dies, and the arbitration agreement or the reference under the agreement does not show that it was intended that the vacancy should not be supplied, and the parties or arbitrators do not supply the vacancy;

any party may serve the other parties or the arbitrators, as the case may be, with a written notice that in default of concurrence in appointing an arbitrator, umpire or third arbitrator, as the case may be, an application will be made to the court under this section.

If the appointment is not made within seven days after the day of service of the notice, the court may, on application by the party who gave the notice, appoint an arbitrator, umpire, or third arbitrator, who shall have the like powers to act in the reference and make an award as if he had been appointed by consent of all parties.

**6. Power of parties in certain cases to supply vacancy.**—Where an arbitration agreement provides that the reference shall be to two arbitrators, one to be appointed by each party, then, unless the agreement expresses a contrary intention —

(a) if either of the appointed arbitrators refuses to act, or is incapable of acting, or dies, the party who appointed him may appoint a new arbitrator in his place;

(b) if, on such a reference, one party fails to appoint an arbitrator, either originally or by way of substitution as aforesaid, for seven clear days after the other party, having appointed his arbitrator, has served the party making default with notice to make the appointment, the party who has appointed an arbitrator may appoint that arbitrator to act as sole arbitrator in the reference, and his award shall be binding on both parties as if he had been appointed by consent:

Provided that the court may set aside any appointment made in pursuance of paragraph (b) of this section.

**7. Power of court to remove arbitrator or umpire and to set aside award.**—
(1) Where an arbitrator or umpire has misconducted himself or the proceedings, the court may remove him.

(2) Where an arbitrator or umpire has misconducted himself or the proceedings, or an arbitration or award has been improperly procured, the court may set aside the award.

**8. Removal of arbitrator or umpire on failure to use due dispatch.**—(1) The court may, on the application of any party to a reference under an arbitration agreement, remove an arbitrator or umpire who fails to use all reasonable dispatch in entering on and proceeding with the reference and making an award.

(2) An arbitrator or umpire who is removed by the court under this section shall not be entitled to receive any remuneration in respect of his services.

(3) For the purposes of this section the expression "proceeding with a reference" includes, in a case where two arbitrators are unable to agree, giving notice of that fact to the parties and to the umpire.

**9. Provisions as to time for making an award.**—(1) Subject to the provisions of section fifteen of this Act and anything to the contrary in the arbitration agreement, an arbitrator or umpire shall have power to make an award at any time.

(2) Where an arbitration agreement provides that the award shall be delivered within a certain time, or where an award has been remitted under the provisions of section fifteen of this Act, the time for making the award may from time to time be enlarged by order of the court whether the time for making the award has expired or not.

**10. Power of court to give relief where arbitrator is not impartial or dispute referred involves question of fraud.**—(1) Where an agreement between any parties provides that disputes which may arise in the future between them shall be referred to an arbitrator named or designated in the agreement, and after a dispute has arisen any party applies, on the ground that the arbitrator so named or designated is not or may not be impartial, for leave to revoke the reference under the agreement or for an injunction to restrain any other party or the arbitrator from proceeding with the arbitration, it shall not be a ground for refusing the application that the said party at the time when he made the agreement knew, or ought to have known, that the arbitrator by reason of his relation towards any other party to the agreement or of his connection with the subject referred might not be capable of impartiality.

(2) Where an agreement between any parties provides that disputes which may arise in the future between them shall be referred, and a dispute which so arises involves the question whether any party has been guilty of fraud, the court shall, so far as may be necessary to enable that question to be determined by the court, have power to order that the agreement shall cease to have effect and power to give leave to revoke any reference made thereunder.

(3) In any case where by virtue of this section the court has power to order that an arbitration agreement shall cease to have effect or to give leave to revoke a reference under an arbitration agreement, the court may refuse to stay any action brought in breach of the agreement.

**11. Power of court where arbitrator is removed or appointment of arbitrator is revoked.**—(1) Where an arbitrator (not being a sole arbitrator), or two or more arbitrators (not being all the arbitrators), or an umpire who has not entered on the reference, is or are removed by the court, the court may, on the application of any party to the arbitration agreement, appoint a person or persons to act as arbitrator or arbitrators or umpire in place of the person or persons so removed.

(2) Where the appointment of an arbitrator or arbitrators or umpire is revoked by leave of the court, or a sole arbitrator or all the arbitrators or an umpire who has entered on the reference is or are removed by the court, the court may, on the application of any party to the arbitration agreement, either —

(a) appoint a person to act as sole arbitrator in place of the person or persons removed; or

(b) order that the arbitration agreement shall cease to have effect with respect to the dispute referred.

(3) A person appointed under this section by the court as an arbitrator or umpire shall have the like power to act in the reference and to make an award as if he had been appointed in accordance with the terms of the arbitration agreement.

(4) Where it is provided (whether by means of a provision in the arbitration agreement or otherwise) that an award under an arbitration agreement shall be a condition precedent to the bringing of an action with respect to any matter to which the agreement applies, the court, if it orders (whether under this section or any other enactment) that the agreement shall cease to have effect as regards any particular dispute, may further order that the provision making an award a condition precedent to the bringing of an action shall also cease to have effect as regards that dispute.

**12. Provisions applicable where three arbitrators appointed and as to umpires.**—(1) Where an arbitration agreement provides that the reference shall be to three arbitrators, one to be appointed by each party and the third to be appointed by the two appointed by the parties, the agreement shall have effect as if it provided for the appointment of an umpire, and not for the appointment of a third arbitrator by the two arbitrators appointed by the parties.

(2) Where an arbitration agreement provides that the reference shall be to three arbitrators to be appointed otherwise than as mentioned in the foregoing subsection, the award of any two of the arbitrators shall be binding.

(3) At any time after the appointment of an umpire, however appointed, the court may, on the application of any party to the reference, and notwithstanding anything to the contrary in the arbitration agreement, order that the umpire shall enter on the reference in lieu of the arbitrators and as if he were a sole arbitrator.

**13. Power of arbitrators.**—The arbitrators or umpire acting under a reference in an arbitration agreement shall, unless the arbitration agreement or the reference thereunder expresses a contrary intention, have power to administer oaths to or take the affirmations of the parties and witnesses appearing, and to correct in an award any clerical mistake or error arising from any accidental slip or omission.

**14. Attendance of witnesses.**—Any party to a reference under an arbitration agreement may sue out a writ of subpoena ad testificandum, or a writ of subpoena duces tecum, but no person shall be compelled under any such writ to produce any document which he could not be compelled to produce on the trial of an action:

Provided that no writ shall issue under this section unless the arbitrator has entered on the reference or has been called on to act by notice in writing from a party to the reference and has agreed to do so.

*Provisions as to awards under arbitration agreements.*

**15. Power to remit award.**—(1) In all cases of reference to arbitration the court may from time to time remit the matters referred, or any of them, to the reconsideration of the arbitrators or umpire.

(2) Subject to the provisions of section nine of this Act, where an award is remitted the arbitrators or umpire shall, unless the order otherwise directs, make their award within three months after the date of the order.

**16. Entry of judgment in terms of award.**—An award on a reference under an arbitration agreement may, by leave of the court, be entered as a judgment in terms of the award, and shall thereupon have the same force and effect as a judgment or order of the court.

**17. Interest on awards.**—A sum directed to be paid by an award shall, unless the award otherwise directs, carry interest as from the date of the award and at the same rate as a judgment debt.

**18. Taxation of arbitrator's or umpire's fees.**—(1) If in any case an arbitrator or umpire refuses to deliver his award except on payment of the fees demanded by him, the court may, on an application for the purpose, order that the arbitrator or umpire shall deliver the award to the applicant on payment into court by the applicant of the fees demanded, and further that the fees demanded shall be taxed by the taxing master, and that out of the money paid into court there shall be paid out to the arbitrator or umpire by way of fees such sum as may be found reasonable on taxation, and that the balance of the money, if any, shall be paid out to the applicant.

(2) An application for the purposes of this section may be made by any party to the reference unless the fees demanded have been fixed by a written agreement between him and the arbitrator or umpire.

(3) A taxation of fees under this section may be reviewed in the same manner as a taxation of costs.

(4) The arbitrator or umpire shall be entitled to appear and be heard on any taxation or review of taxation under this section.

*Limitation of time for proceedings under arbitration agreements.*

**19. Limitation of time for commencing arbitration proceedings.**—(1) The statutes of limitation shall apply to an arbitration under an arbitration agreement as they apply to proceedings in the court.

(2) Notwithstanding any term in an arbitration agreement to the effect that no cause of action shall accrue in respect of any matter required by the agreement to be referred until an award is made under the agreement, a cause of action shall, for the purpose of the statutes of limitation both as originally enacted and as applying to arbitrations, be deemed to have accrued in respect of any such matter at the time when it would have accrued but for that term in the agreement.

(3) For the purpose of this section and for the purpose of the statutes of limitation as applying to arbitrations, an arbitration shall be deemed to be commenced when one party to the arbitration agreement serves on the other party or parties a notice requiring him or them to appoint an arbitrator, or, where the arbitration agreement provides that the reference shall be to a person named or designated in the agreement, serves on the other party or parties a notice requiring him or them to submit the dispute to the person so named or designated.

(4) Any such notice as is mentioned in the preceding sub-section may be served —

(*a*)   by delivering it to the person on whom it is to be served; or

(*b*)   by leaving it at the usual or last known place of abode in Northern Ireland of that person; or

(*c*)   by sending it by post in a registered letter addressed to that person at his usual or last known place of abode in Northern Ireland;

as well as in any other manner provided in the arbitration agreement; and where a notice is sent by post in manner prescribed by paragraph (c) of this sub-section, service thereof shall, unless the contrary is proved, be deemed to have been effected at the time at which the letter would have been delivered in the ordinary course of post.

(5) Where the terms of an agreement to refer future disputes to arbitration provide that any claims to which the agreement applies shall be barred unless notice to appoint an arbitrator is given, or an arbitrator is appointed, or some other step to commence arbitration proceedings is taken within a time fixed by the agreement, and a dispute arises to which the agreement applies, the court, if it is of opinion that

in the circumstances of the case undue hardship would otherwise be caused, and notwithstanding that the time so fixed has expired, may, on such terms, if any, as the justice of the case may require, but without prejudice to the foregoing provisions of this section, extend the time for such period as it thinks proper.

(6) Where the court orders that an award be set aside or orders, after the commencement of an arbitration, that the arbitration agreement shall cease to have effect with respect to the dispute referred, the court may further order that the period between the commencement of the arbitration and the date of the order of the court shall be excluded in computing the time prescribed by the statutes of limitation for the commencement of proceedings (including arbitration) with respect to the dispute referred.

(7) For the purposes of this section the expression "the statutes of limitation" includes any enactment limiting the time within which any particular proceeding may be commenced.

*References under order of court.*

**20. Power to make rules as to references under order of court.**—(1) Rules of court may be made providing that—

    (*a*)   in any cause or matter (other than a criminal proceeding by the Crown) if the question in dispute consists wholly or in part of matters of account, the court may at any time order the whole cause or matter, or any question or issue of fact arising therein to be tried before a referee or arbitrator respectively agreed on by the parties, or before an officer of the court;

    (*b*)   in all cases of reference to a referee or arbitrator under an order of the court in any cause or matter, the referee or arbitrator shall be deemed to be an officer of the court and shall have such authority, and shall conduct the reference in such manner, as may be prescribed by the said rules, and, subject thereto, as the court may direct;

    (*c*)   the report or award of any referee or arbitrator on any such reference shall, unless set aside by the court, be equivalent to the verdict of a jury;

    (*d*)   the remuneration to be paid to any referee or arbitrator to whom any matter is referred under order of the court shall be determined by the court.

Upon the making of such rules of court the following provisions of this section shall come into operation, and the rules may provide for any matters for which provision may be necessary in order to give full effect to this section, and may prescribe anything which is to be prescribed thereunder.

(2) The court shall, as to references under an order of a court, have all the powers which are by this Act conferred on the court as to references under arbitration agreements.

(3) The provisions of sections six to twenty of the Common Law Procedure Amendment Act (Ireland), 1856, relating to the reference of matters of account under order of court to an arbitrator, master of the court, or assistant barrister, and sections sixty-three and sixty-four of the Debtors (Ireland) Act, 1840, so far as they relate to references by order of court, shall cease to have effect.

*General.*

**21. Additional powers of court.**—(1) The court shall have, for the purpose of and in relation to a reference, the same power of making orders in respect of any of the matters set out in the Second Schedule to this Act as it has for the purpose of and in relation to an action or matter in the court:

Provided that nothing in the foregoing provision shall be taken to prejudice any power which may be vested in an arbitrator or umpire of making orders with respect to any of the matters aforesaid.

(2) Where relief by way of interpleader is granted and it appears to the court that the claims in question are matters to which an arbitration agreement, to which the claimants are parties, applies, the court may direct the issue between the claimants to be determined in accordance with the agreement.

(3) Where an application is made to set aside an award the court may order that any money made payable by the award shall be brought into court or otherwise secured pending the determination of the application.

**22. Statement of case by arbitrator or umpire.**—(1) An arbitrator or umpire may, and shall if so ordered by the court, state —

(*a*)  any question of law arising in the course of the reference; or

(*b*)  an award or any part of an award;

in the form of a special case for the determination of the court.

(2) A special case with respect to an interim award or with respect to a question of law arising in the course of a reference may be stated, or may be ordered by the court to be stated, notwithstanding that proceedings under the reference are still pending.

**23. Provisions as to costs.**—(1) Any order made under this Act by the court may be made on such terms as to costs or otherwise as the court thinks just.

(2) Any provision in an arbitration agreement to the effect that the parties or any party thereto shall in any event pay their or his own costs of the reference or award or any part thereof shall be void:

Provided that nothing herein shall invalidate such a provision when it is part of an agreement to submit to arbitration a dispute which has arisen before the making of such agreement.

(3) If no provision is made by an award with respect to the costs of the reference, any party to the reference may, within fourteen days of the publication of the award or such further time as a court may direct, apply to the arbitrator for an order directing by and to whom such costs shall be paid, and thereupon the arbitrator shall, after hearing any party who may desire to be heard, amend his award by adding thereto such directions as he may think proper with respect to the payment of the costs of the reference.

(4) Section three of the Legal Practitioners (Ireland) Act, 1876, which empowers a court before which any proceeding has been heard or is depending to charge property recovered or preserved in the proceeding with the payment of solicitors' costs, shall apply as if an arbitration were a proceeding in the court, and the court may make declarations and orders accordingly.

**24. Additional powers to compel attendance of witnesses.**—(1) The court may order that a writ of subpoena ad testificandum or of subpoena duces tecum shall issue to compel the attendance of a witness before any referee, arbitrator or umpire.

(2) The court may also order that a writ of habeas corpus ad testificandum shall issue to bring up a prisoner for examination before any referee, arbitrator or umpire.

**25. Exercise of jurisdiction conferred on the court.**—The jurisdiction conferred on the court by this Act shall be exercisable in such manner as may be provided by rules of court, and such rules may, in particular, confer all or any of the said jurisdiction upon a judge sitting in court or, if so provided, upon a judge in chambers.

**26. Penalty for perjury.**—Any person who wilfully and corruptly gives false evidence before any referee, arbitrator or umpire shall be liable to the penalties for wilful and corrupt perjury.

**27. Saving for pending arbitrations.**—Subject as hereinafter provided, the provisions of this Act shall not affect any arbitration which has been commenced within the meaning of section nineteen of this Act before the date on which this Act comes into operation, but shall apply to any arbitration so commenced after the said date under an arbitration agreement made before the said date.

**28. Application of Act to statutory arbitrations.**—This Act, except the provisions thereof set out in the Third Schedule to this Act, shall apply in relation to every arbitration under any other Act passed before or after the commencement of this Act, as if the arbitration were pursuant to an arbitration agreement and as if that other Act were an arbitration agreement, except in so far as this Act is inconsistent with that other Act or with any rules or procedure authorised or recognised thereby.

*Supplemental.*

**29. Repeals.**—(1) The enactments set out in the Fourth Schedule to this Act are hereby repealed to the extent specified in the third column of that Schedule.

(2) Any enactment or instrument referring to any enactment repealed by this Act shall be construed as referring to this Act.

**30. Interpretation.**—(1) In this Act, unless the context otherwise requires, the following expressions have the meanings hereby assigned to them, that is to say: —

"Act" and "enactment" include an Act or enactment passed by the Parliament of the United Kingdom in so far as it relates to a matter in respect of which the Parliament of Northern Ireland has power to make laws:

"Arbitration agreement" means a written agreement to refer present or future differences to arbitration, whether an arbitrator is named therein or not:

"Assignee" means the official assignee appointed in Northern Ireland under section fifty-nine of the Irish Bankrupt and Insolvent Act, 1857, as amended by section four of the Supreme Court of Judicature (Ireland) (No. 2) Act, 1897, and includes the assignee (if any) chosen by the creditors to act with the official assignee:

"Court" means the High Court:

"Judge" means a judge of the High Court:

"Rules of court" means rules of the Supreme Court made under section sixty-one of the Supreme Court of Judicature Act (Ireland), 1877, as amended by the Supreme Court of Judicature (Ireland) (No. 2) Act, 1897.

(2) References in this Act to an award include references to an interim award.

(3) References in this Act to enactments of the Parliament of the United Kingdom shall be construed as references to those enactments as they apply in Northern Ireland.

**31. Short title and commencement.**—(1) This Act may be cited as the Arbitration Act (Northern Ireland), 1937.

(2) This Act shall come into operation on the first day of January, nineteen hundred and thirty-eight.

FIRST SCHEDULE.

*Provisions to be implied in arbitration agreements.*

1. If no other mode of reference is provided the reference shall be to a single arbitrator.

2. If the reference is to two arbitrators the two arbitrators shall appoint an umpire immediately after they are themselves appointed.

3. If the arbitrators have delivered to any party to the arbitration agreement, or to

the umpire, a notice in writing stating that they cannot agree, the umpire may forthwith enter on the reference in lieu of the arbitrators.

4. The parties to the reference and all persons claiming through them respectively shall, subject to any legal objection, submit to be examined by the arbitrators or umpire on oath or affirmation in relation to the matters in dispute and shall, subject as aforesaid, produce before the arbitrators or umpire all books, deeds, papers, accounts, writings and documents within their possession or power respectively which may be required or called for, and do all other things which during the proceedings on the reference the arbitrators or umpire may require.

5. The witnesses on the reference shall, if the arbitrators or umpire think fit, be examined on oath or affirmation.

6. The arbitrators or umpire shall have the same power as the Court to order specific performance of any contract, other than a contract relating to land or any interest in land.

7. The award to be made by the arbitrators or umpire shall be final and binding on the parties and the persons claiming under them respectively.

8. The arbitrators or umpire may, if they think fit, make an interim award.

9. The costs of the reference and award shall be in the discretion of the arbitrators or umpire who may direct to, and by whom, and in what manner, those costs, or any part thereof, shall be paid and may tax or settle the amount of costs to be so paid, or any part thereof, and may award costs to be paid as between solicitor and client.

SECOND SCHEDULE.

*Matters in respect of which the Court may make Orders.*

1. Security for costs.
2. Discovery of documents and interrogatories.
3. The giving of evidence by affidavit.
4. Examination on oath of any witness before an officer of the court or any other person, and the issue of a commission or request for the examination of a witness out of the jurisdiction.
5. The preservation, interim custody, or sale, of any goods which are the subject matter of the reference.
6. Securing the amount in dispute in the reference.
7. The detention, preservation or inspection of any property or thing which is the subject of the reference or as to which any question may arise therein, and authorising for any of the purposes aforesaid any persons to enter upon or into any land or building in the possession of any party to the reference, or authorising any samples to be taken or any observation to be made or experiment to be tried which may be necessary or expedient for the purpose of obtaining full information or evidence.
8. Interim injunctions or the appointment of a receiver.

THIRD SCHEDULE.

*Provisions of Act which do not apply to statutory arbitrations.*

Sub-section (1) of section two.
Section three.
Section ten.
Section eleven.
Section nineteen.
Sub-section (2) of section twenty-one.
Sub-section (2) of section twenty-three.

FOURTH SCHEDULE.

*Enactments repealed.*

*STATUTE LAW APPLICABLE TO THE REPUBLIC OF IRELAND*[1]

## Arbitration Act 1954 (No. 26 of 1954)

An Act to make further and better provision in respect of arbitrations.

Part I.

PRELIMINARY AND GENERAL.

**1. Short title and commencement.**—(1) This Act may be cited as the Arbitration Act, 1954.

(2) This Act (except subsection (2) of section 12 and Part V) shall come into operation on the 1st day of January, 1955.

(3) Subsection (2) of section 12 and Part V of this Act shall come into operation on such day as may be fixed for that purpose by order of the Government.

**2. Interpretation generally.**—(1) In this Act —

"arbitration agreement" means a written agreement to refer present or future differences to arbitration, whether an arbitrator is named therein or not;

"the Convention of 1927" means the Convention on the Execution of Foreign Arbitral Awards done at Geneva on the 26th day of September, 1927, set out in the Second Schedule to this Act;

"the Court" means the High Court;

"the operative date" means the 1st day of January, 1955;

"the Protocol of 1923" means the Protocol on Arbitration Clauses opened at Geneva on the 24th day of September, 1923, set out in the First Schedule to this Act;

"State authority" means any authority being —

    (*a*)   a Minister of State,

    (*b*)   the Commissioners of Public Works in Ireland,

    (*c*)   the Irish Land Commission, or

    (*d*)   the Revenue Commissioners;

"the statutes of limitation" includes any enactment limiting the time within which any particular proceedings may be commenced.

(2) References in this Act to an award include references to an interim award.

**3. Commencement of arbitration.**—(1) For the purposes of this Act and for the purpose of the statutes of limitation as applying to arbitrations and of section 496 of the Merchant Shipping Act, 1894, as amended by section 46 of this Act, an arbitration shall be deemed to be commenced when one party to the arbitration agreement serves on the other party or parties a written notice requiring him or them to appoint or concur in appointing an arbitrator or, where the arbitration agreement provides that the reference shall be to a person named or designated in the agreement, requiring him or them to submit the dispute to the person so named or designated.

(2)(*a*) A notice under subsection (1) of this section may be served—

    (i)   by delivering it to the person to whom it is to be served,

    (ii)  by leaving it at the place in the State at which that person ordinarily resides or carries on business,

    (iii) by sending it by registered post in an envelope addressed to that person at the place in the State at which he ordinarily resides or carries on business,

---

[1]   See p. 132 for a table comparing the Irish statutes with those for England and Wales.

(iv)    in any other manner provided in the arbitration agreement.

(b) For the purposes of this subsection, a company registered under the Companies Acts, 1908 to 1924, shall be deemed to carry on business at its registered office in the State and every other body corporate and every unincorporated body shall be deemed to carry on business at its principal office or place of business in the State.

**4. State authorities to be bound.**—This Part, Part II (except subsection (2) of section 12) and Part III of this Act shall apply to an arbitration under an arbitration agreement to which a State authority is a party.

**5. Exclusion of certain arbitrations.**—Notwithstanding anything contained in this Act, this Act does not apply to —

(a) an arbitration under an agreement providing for the reference to, or the settlement by, arbitration of any question relating to the terms or conditions of employment or the remuneration of any employees, including persons employed by or under the State or local authorities, or

(b) an arbitration under section 70 of the Industrial Relations Act, 1946 (No. 26 of 1946).

**6. Operation of Parts II and III.**—(1) Part II of this Act shall not affect any arbitration under an arbitration agreement which has commenced before the operative date, but shall apply to any arbitration commenced on or after the operative date under an arbitration agreement made before the operative date.

(2) Part III of this Act shall not affect any arbitration under any other Act which has commenced before the operative date, but shall apply to any arbitration commenced on or after the operative date under any other Act passed before, on, or after the operative date.

**7. Penalty for giving false evidence.**—Any person who, upon any examination upon oath or affirmation before an arbitrator or umpire or in any affidavit in proceedings before an arbitrator or umpire, wilfully and corruptly gives false evidence or wilfully and corruptly swears or affirms anything which is false, being convicted thereof, shall be liable to the penalties for wilful and corrupt perjury.

**8. Repeals.**—(1) The enactments mentioned in column (2) of the Third Schedule to this Act are (except in relation to arbitrations under arbitration agreements commenced before the operative date) hereby repealed to the extent mentioned in column (3) of that Schedule.

(2) Any enactment or instrument referring to any enactment repealed by this Act shall be construed as referring to this Act.

Part II.

ARBITRATION UNDER ARBITRATION AGREEMENTS.

**9. Authority of arbitrators and umpires to be irrevocable.**—The authority of the arbitrator or umpire appointed by or by virtue of an arbitration agreement shall, unless a contrary intention is expressed in the agreement, be irrevocable except by leave of the Court.

**10. Death of party.**—(1) An arbitration agreement shall not be discharged by the death of any party thereto, either as respects the deceased or any other party, but shall in such an event be enforceable by or against the personal representatives of the deceased.

(2) The authority of an arbitrator shall not be revoked by the death of any party by whom he was appointed.

(3) Nothing in this section shall be taken to affect the operation of any enactment or rule of law by virtue of which any right of action is extinguished by the death of a person.

**11. Provisions in case of bankruptcy.**—(1) In this section the word "assignee" means the Official Assignee in Bankruptcy and includes the assignee (if any) chosen by the creditors to act with the Official Assignee in Bankruptcy.

(2) Where an arbitration agreement forms part of a contract to which a bankrupt is a party, the agreement shall, if the assignee or trustee in bankruptcy does not disclaim the contract, be enforceable by or against him so far as it relates to any difference arising out of, or in connection with, such contract.

(3) Where—

(*a*) a person who has been adjudged bankrupt had, before the commencement of the bankruptcy, become a party to an arbitration agreement, and

(*b*) any matter to which the agreement applies requires to be determined in connection with or for the purposes of the bankruptcy proceedings, and

(*c*) the case is one to which subsection (2) of this section does not apply,

then, any other party to the agreement or the assignee or, with the consent of the committee of inspection, the trustee in bankruptcy may apply to the court having jurisdiction in the bankruptcy proceedings for an order directing that the matter in question shall be referred to arbitration in accordance with the agreement and that court may, if it is of opinion that having regard to all the circumstances of the case, the matter ought to be determined by arbitration, make an order accordingly.

**12. Power to stay proceedings where there is an arbitration agreement.**— [Repealed][1]

**13. Reference of interpleader issues to arbitration.**—Where relief by way of interpleader is granted and it appears to the Court that the claims in question are matters to which an arbitration agreement, to which the claimants are parties, applies, the Court may direct the issue between the claimants to be determined in accordance with the agreement.

*Arbitrators and Umpires.*

**14. When reference is to be to a single arbitrator.**—Unless a contrary intention is expressed therein, every arbitration agreement shall, if no other mode of reference is provided, be deemed to include a provision that the reference shall be to a single arbitrator.

**15. Power of parties in certain cases to supply vacancy.**—(1) Where —

(*a*) an arbitration agreement provides that the reference shall be to two arbitrators, one to be appointed by each party, and

(*b*) either of the appointed arbitrators refuses to act, or is incapable of acting, or dies,

then, unless the agreement expresses a contrary intention, the party, who appointed the arbitrator so refusing to act, becoming incapable of acting or dying, may appoint a new arbitrator in his place.

(2)(*a*) Where —

---

[1] See ss. 4 and 5 of the Arbitration Act 1980 (p. 198, *post*).

(i)  an arbitration agreement provides that the reference shall be to two arbitrators, one to be appointed by each party, and

(ii)  on such a reference one party fails to appoint an arbitrator, either originally or by way of substitution under subsection (1) of this section, for seven clear days after the other party, having appointed his arbitrator, has served the party making default with notice to make the appointment,

then unless a contrary intention is expressed in the agreement, the party who has appointed an arbitrator may appoint that arbitrator to act as sole arbitrator in the reference, and his award shall be binding on both parties as if he had been appointed by consent.

(*b*) The Court may set aside any appointment made under paragraph (a) of this subsection.

**16. Umpires.**—(1) Unless a contrary intention is expressed therein, every arbitration agreement shall, where the reference is to two arbitrators, be deemed to include a provision that the two arbitrators shall appoint an umpire immediately after they are themselves appointed.

(2) Unless a contrary intention is expressed therein, every arbitration agreement shall, where such a provision is applicable to the reference, be deemed to include a provision that if the arbitrators have delivered to any party to the arbitration agreement, or to the umpire, a notice in writing stating that they cannot agree, the umpire may forthwith enter upon the reference in lieu of the arbitrators, but nothing in this subsection shall be construed as preventing the umpire from sitting with the arbitrators and hearing the evidence.

(3) At any time after the appointment of an umpire, however appointed, the Court may, on the application of any party to the reference and notwithstanding anything to the contrary in the arbitration agreement, order that the umpire shall enter upon the reference in lieu of the arbitrators and as if he were a sole arbitrator.

**17. Agreements for reference to three arbitrators.**—(1) Where an arbitration agreement provides that the reference shall be to three arbitrators, one to be appointed by each party and the third to be appointed by the two appointed by the parties, the agreement shall have effect as if it provided for the appointment of an umpire, and not for the appointment of a third arbitrator, by the two arbitrators appointed by the parties.

(2) Where an arbitration agreement provides that the reference shall be to three arbitrators to be appointed otherwise than as is mentioned in subsection (1) of this section, the award of any two of the arbitrators shall be binding.

**18. Power of Court in certain cases to appoint an arbitrator or umpire.**—In any of the following cases —

(*a*) where —

(i)  an arbitration agreement provides that the reference shall be to a single arbitrator, and

(ii)  all the parties do not, after differences have arisen, concur in the appointment of an arbitrator;

(*b*) if —

(i)  an appointed arbitrator refuses to act, or is incapable of acting or dies, and

(ii)  the arbitration agreement does not show that it was intended that the vacancy should not be supplied, and

(iii)  the parties do not supply the vacancy;

(*c*) where the parties or two arbitrators are at liberty to appoint an umpire or

189

third arbitrator and do not appoint him;

(*d*) where two arbitrators are required to appoint an umpire and do not appoint him;

(*e*) where —
  (i) an appointed umpire or third arbitrator refuses to act, or is incapable of acting, or dies, and
  (ii) the arbitration agreement does not show that it was intended that the vacancy should not be supplied, and
  (iii) the parties or arbitrators do not supply the vacancy,

the following provisions shall have effect —

(1) any party may serve the other parties or the arbitrators, as the case may be, with a written notice to appoint or, as the case may be, concur in appointing an arbitrator, umpire or third arbitrator,

(2) if the appointment is not made within seven clear days after the service of the notice, the Court may, on the application of the party who gave the notice, appoint an arbitrator, umpire or third arbitrator, who shall have the like powers to act in the reference and make an award as if he had been appointed by consent of all parties.

*Witnesses, Security for Costs, Discovery of Documents, etc.*

**19. Powers of arbitrators and umpires as to witnesses.**—(1) Unless a contrary intention is expressed therein every arbitration agreement shall, where such a provision is applicable to the reference, be deemed to contain a provision that the parties to the reference, and all persons claiming through them respectively, shall, subject to any legal objection, submit to be examined by the arbitrator or umpire, on oath or affirmation, in relation to the matters in dispute and shall, subject to any legal objection, produce before the arbitrator or umpire all documents (other than documents the production of which could not be compelled on the trial of an action) within their possession or power respectively which may be required or called for, and do all such other things which during the proceedings on the reference the arbitrator or umpire may require.

(2) Unless a contrary intention is expressed therein, every arbitration agreement shall, where such a provision is applicable to the reference, be deemed to contain a provision that the witnesses on the reference shall, if the arbitrator or umpire thinks fit, be examined on oath or affirmation.

(3) An arbitrator or umpire shall, unless a contrary intention is expressed in an arbitration agreement, have power to administer oaths to, or take the affirmations of, the parties to and witnesses on a reference under the agreement.

**20. Powers of parties to a reference to compel attendance of witnesses.**— Any party to a reference under an arbitration agreement may sue out an order in the nature of a writ of subpoena ad testificandum or of a writ of subpoena duces tecum, but no person shall be compelled under any such order to produce any document which he could not be compelled to produce on the trial of an action.

**21. Power of Court to compel attendance of prisoner as a witness.**—The Court may order that an order in the nature of a writ of habeas corpus ad testificandum shall issue to bring up a prisoner for examination before an arbitrator or umpire.

**22. Orders by Court in relation to security for costs discovery of documents, etc.**—(1) The Court shall have, for the purpose of and in relation to a reference, the same power of making orders in respect of —

(*a*)   security for costs;

(*b*)   discovery and inspection of documents and interrogatories;

(*c*)   the giving of evidence by affidavit;

(*d*)   examination on oath of any witness before an officer of the Court or any other person, and the issue of a commission or request for the examination of a witness out of the jurisdiction;

(*e*)   the preservation, interim custody or sale of any goods which are the subject matter of the reference;

(*f*)   securing the amount in dispute in the reference;

(*g*)   the detention, preservation or inspection of any property or thing which is the subject of the reference or as to which any question may arise therein, and authorising for any of the purposes aforesaid any persons to enter upon or into any land or building in the possession of any party to the reference, or authorising any samples to be taken or any observation to be made or experiment to be tried which may be necessary or expedient for the purpose of obtaining full information or evidence; and

(*h*)   interim injunctions or the appointment of a receiver,

as it has for the purpose of and in relation to an action or matter in the Court.

(2) Nothing in subsection (1) of this section shall be taken to prejudice any power which may be vested in an arbitrator or umpire of making orders with respect to any of the matters mentioned in the said subsection.

*Provisions as to Awards.*

**23. Time for making an award.**—(1) Subject to subsection (2) of section 36 of this Act and anything to the contrary in the arbitration agreement, an arbitrator or umpire shall have power to make an award at any time.

(2) The time, if any, limited for making an award, whether under this Act or otherwise, may from time to time be enlarged by order of the Court or by agreement in writing of the parties, whether that time has expired or not.

**24. Removal of arbitrator or umpire on failure to use due dispatch.**—
(1) The Court may, on the application of any party to a reference, remove an arbitrator or umpire who fails to use all reasonable dispatch in entering on and proceeding with the reference and making an award.

(2) An arbitrator or umpire who is removed by the Court under subsection (1) of this section shall not be entitled to receive any remuneration in respect of his services.

(3) For the purposes of this section the expression "proceeding with a reference" includes, in a case where two arbitrators are unable to agree, giving notice of that fact to the parties and to the umpire.

**25. Interim awards.**—Unless a contrary intention is expressed therein, every arbitration agreement shall, where such a provision is applicable to the reference, be deemed to contain a provision that the arbitrator or umpire may, if he thinks fit, make an interim award.

**26. Specific performance.**—Unless a contrary intention is expressed therein, every arbitration agreement shall, where such a provision is applicable to the reference, be deemed to contain a provision that the arbitrator or umpire shall have the same power as the Court to order specific performance of any contract other than a contract relating to land or any interest in land.

**27. Awards to be final.**—Unless a contrary intention is expressed therein, every arbitration agreement shall, where such a provision is applicable to the reference, be deemed to contain a provision that the award to be made by the arbitrator or umpire shall be final and binding on the parties and the persons claiming under them respectively.

**28. Power to correct slips.**—Unless a contrary intention is expressed in the arbitration agreement, the arbitrator or umpire shall have power to correct in an award any clerical mistake or error arising from any accidental slip or omission.

*Costs, Fees and Interest.*

**29. Costs of reference and award to be in the discretion of the arbitrator or umpire.**—(1) Unless a contrary intention is expressed therein, every arbitration agreement shall be deemed to include a provision that the costs of the reference and award shall be in the discretion of the arbitrator or umpire who may direct to and by whom and in what manner those costs or any part thereof shall be paid, and may, with the consent of the parties, tax or settle the amount of costs to be so paid or any part thereof, and may award costs to be paid as between solicitor and client.

(2) Where an award directs any costs to be paid, then, unless the arbitrator or umpire, with the consent of the parties, taxes or settles the amount thereof —

   (a) the costs shall be taxed and ascertained by a Taxing Master,

   (b) the procedure to obtain taxation and the rules, regulations and scales of costs of the Court relative to taxation and to the review thereof shall apply to the costs to be so taxed and ascertained as if the award were a judgment or order of the Court.

**30. Avoidance of certain provisions as to costs in arbitration agreements.** —(1) Any provision in an arbitration agreement to the effect that the parties or any party thereto shall in any event pay their or his own costs of the reference or award or any part thereof shall be void, and this Part shall, in the case of an arbitration agreement containing any such provision, have effect as if that provision were not contained therein.

(2) Nothing in subsection (1) of this section shall invalidate any such provision as is mentioned in that subsection when it is part of an agreement to submit to arbitration a dispute which has arisen before the making of that agreement.

**31. Application to arbitrator or umpire to give directions as to costs where award contains no provisions.**—If no provision is made by an award with respect to the costs of the reference, any party to the reference may, within fourteen days of the publication of the award or such further time as the Court may direct, apply to the arbitrator or umpire for an order directing by and to whom those costs shall be paid, and thereupon the arbitrator or umpire shall, after hearing any party who may desire to be heard, amend his award by adding thereto such directions as he may think proper with respect to the payment of the costs of the reference.

**32. Application of section 3 of Legal Practitioners (Ireland) Act, 1876, to solicitors' costs in arbitration.**—Section 3 of the Legal Practitioners (Ireland) Act, 1876, (which empowers a court before which any proceeding has been heard or is pending to charge property recovered or preserved in the proceeding with the payment of solicitors' costs) shall apply as if an arbitration were a proceeding in the Court, and the Court may make declarations and orders accordingly.

**33. Taxation of arbitrator's or umpire's fee.**—(1) If in any case an arbitrator or umpire refuses to deliver his award except on payment of the fees demanded by him, the Court may, on an application for the purpose, order that the arbitrator or umpire shall deliver the award to the applicant on payment into Court by the applicant of the fees demanded, and further that the fees demanded shall be taxed by a Taxing Master and that out of the money paid into Court there shall be paid out to the arbitrator or umpire by way of fees such sum as may be found reasonable on taxation and that the balance of the money, if any, shall be paid out to the applicant.

(2) An application for the purpose of this section may be made by any party to the reference unless the fees demanded have been fixed by a written agreement between him and the arbitrator or umpire.

(3) A taxation of fees under this section may be reviewed in the same manner as a taxation of costs.

(4) The arbitrator or umpire shall be entitled to appear and be heard on any taxation or review of taxation under this section.

**34. Interest on awards.**—A sum directed to be paid by an award shall, unless the award otherwise directs, carry interest as from the date of the award and at the same rate as a judgment debt.

*Special Cases, Remission and Setting Aside of Awards, Removal of Arbitrator or Umpire, and Relief where Arbitrator not Impartial or Questions of Fraud Involved.*

**35. Statement of case by arbitrator or umpire.**—(1) An arbitrator or umpire may, and shall if so directed by the Court, state —
(a) any question of law arising in the course of the reference, or
(b) any award or any part of an award,
in the form of a special case for the decision of the Court.

(2) A special case with respect to an interim award or with respect to a question of law arising in the course of a reference may be stated, or may be ordered by the Court to be stated, notwithstanding that proceedings under the reference are still pending.

**36. Power of Court to remit award.**—(1) In all cases of reference to arbitration, the Court may from time to time remit the matters referred or any of them to the reconsideration of the arbitrator or umpire.

(2) Where an award is remitted, the arbitrator or umpire shall, unless the order otherwise directs, make his award within three months after the date of the order.

**37. Power of Court to remove arbitrator or umpire on ground of misconduct.**—Where an arbitrator or umpire has misconducted himself or the proceedings the Court may remove him.

**38. Power of Court to set aside award on ground of misconduct.**—(1) Where—
(a) an arbitrator or umpire has misconducted himself or the proceedings, or
(b) an arbitration or award has been improperly procured,
the Court may set the award aside.

(2) Where an application is made to set aside an award, the Court may order that any money made payable by the award shall be brought into Court or otherwise secured pending the determination of the application.

**39. Power of Court to give relief where arbitrator is not impartial or dispute referred involves question of fraud.**—(1) Where—
(a) an agreement between any parties provides that disputes which may arise in the future between them shall be referred to an arbitrator named or designated in the agreement, and

(b) after a dispute has arisen any party, on the ground that the arbitrator so named or designated is not or may not be impartial, applies to the Court for leave to revoke the authority of the arbitrator or for an injunction to restrain any other party or the arbitrator from proceeding with the arbitration,

it shall not be a ground for refusing the application that the said party at the time when he made the agreement knew, or ought to have known, that the arbitrator, by reason of his relation towards any other party to the agreement or of his connection with the subject referred, might not be impartial.

(2) Where—

(a) an agreement between any parties provides that disputes which may arise in the future between them shall be referred to arbitration, and

(b) a dispute which so arises involves the question whether any party has been guilty of fraud,

the Court shall, so far as may be necessary to enable the question to be determined by the Court, have power to order that the agreement shall cease to have effect and power to give leave to revoke the authority of any arbitrator or umpire appointed by or by virtue of the agreement.

(3) In any case where by virtue of this section the Court has power to order that any arbitration agreement shall cease to have effect or to give leave to revoke the authority of any arbitrator or umpire, the Court may refuse to stay any action brought in breach of the agreement.

**40. Power of Court where arbitrator is removed or authority of arbitrator is revoked.**—(1) Where an arbitrator (not being a sole arbitrator) or two or more arbitrators (not being all the arbitrators) or an umpire who has not entered on the reference is or are removed by the Court, the Court may, on the application of any party to the arbitration agreement, appoint a person or persons to act as arbitrator or arbitrators or umpire in place of the person or persons so removed.

(2) Where—

(a) the authority of the arbitrator or arbitrators or umpire is revoked by leave of the Court, or

(b) a sole arbitrator or all the arbitrators or an umpire who has entered on the reference is or are removed by the Court,

the Court may, on the application of any party to the arbitration agreement, either —

(i) appoint a person to act as sole arbitrator in place of the person or persons removed, or

(ii) order that the arbitration agreement shall cease to have effect with respect to the dispute referred.

(3) A person appointed under this section by the Court as an arbitrator or umpire shall have the like power to act in the reference and to make an award as if he had been appointed in accordance with the terms of the arbitration agreement.

(4) Where it is provided (whether by means of a provision in an arbitration agreement or otherwise) that an award under an arbitration agreement shall be a condition precedent to the bringing of an action with respect to any matter to which the agreement applies, the Court, if it orders (whether under this section or any other enactment) that the agreement shall cease to have effect as regards any particular dispute, may further order that the provision making an award a condition precedent to the bringing of an action shall also cease to have effect as regards that dispute.

*Enforcement of Award.*

**41. Enforcement of award.**—An award on an arbitration agreement may, by

194

leave of the Court, be enforced in the same manner as a judgment or order to the same effect and, where leave is so given, judgment may be entered in terms of the award.

*Limitation of Time for Commencing Arbitration Proceedings.*

**42. Application of statutes of limitation to arbitration under arbitration agreements.**—The statutes of limitation shall apply to an arbitration under an arbitration agreement as they apply to actions in the Court.

**43. Accrual for purposes of statutes of limitation of right of action in respect of matters required by arbitration agreement to be referred to arbitration, where agreement provides that arbitration shall be a condition precedent to commencement of action.**—Notwithstanding any term in an arbitration agreement to the effect that no cause of action shall accrue in respect of any matter required by the agreement to be referred until an award is made under the agreement, a cause of action shall, for the purposes of the statutes of limitation (whether in their application to arbitrations or to other proceedings), be deemed to have accrued in respect of any such matter at the time when it would have accrued but for that term in the agreement.

**44. Power of Court to extend period of limitation where it sets aside award or orders arbitration to cease to have effect.**—Where the Court orders that an award be set aside or orders, after the commencement of an arbitration, that the arbitration should cease to have effect with respect to the dispute referred, the Court may further order that the period between the commencement of the arbitration and the date of the order of the Court shall be excluded in computing the time prescribed by the statutes of limitation for the commencement of the proceedings (including arbitration) with respect to the dispute referred.

**45. Power of Court to extend time for commencing arbitration proceedings, where agreement provides that claims are to be barred unless proceedings are commenced within a specified time.**—Where—

(a)  the terms of an agreement to refer future disputes to arbitration provide that any claims to which the agreement applies shall be barred unless notice to appoint an arbitrator is given or an arbitrator is appointed or some other step to commence arbitration proceedings is taken within a time fixed by the agreement, and

(b)  a dispute arises to which the agreement applies,

the Court, if it is of opinion that in the circumstances of the case undue hardship would otherwise be caused, and notwithstanding that the time so fixed has expired, may on such terms, if any, as the justice of the case may require, but without prejudice to section 42 of this Act, extend the time for such period as it thinks proper.

**46. Extension of section 496 of the Merchant Shipping Act, 1894.**—In subsection (3) of section 496 of the Merchant Shipping Act, 1894 (which requires a sum deposited with a wharfinger by an owner of goods to be repaid unless legal proceedings are instituted by the shipowner) the references to legal proceedings shall be construed as including references to arbitration.

*Terms of Orders.*

**47. Terms of orders.**—(1) Any order made under this Part by a court may be made on such terms as to costs or otherwise as that court thinks just.

(2) Subsection (1) of this section shall not apply to an order made under subsection (2) of section 12 of this Act.

Part III.

ARBITRATION UNDER OTHER ACTS.

**48. Application of Parts I and II to arbitrations under other Acts.**—(1) In this section, the expression "the excluded provisions" means the following provisions of this Act, subsection (1) of section 10, section 11, subsection (2) of section 12, and sections 13, 30, 39, 40, 45 and 46.

(2) Parts I and II of this Act (except the excluded provisions) shall apply to every arbitration under any other Act as if the arbitration were pursuant to an arbitration agreement and as if that other Act were an arbitration agreement, except in so far as Part II of this Act is inconsistent with that other Act or with any rules or procedure authorised or recognised thereby.

Part IV.

REFERENCES UNDER ORDER OF THE COURT.

**49. Power of Court and Circuit Court to refer in certain cases.**—(1) If, in any cause or matter (including any cause or matter to which a State authority is a party, but excluding a criminal proceeding at the suit of the Attorney General), the question in dispute consists wholly or in part of matters of account, the Court or the Circuit Court may at any time order the whole cause or matter or any question or issue of fact arising therein to be tried before an arbitrator agreed on by the parties or before an officer of the Court or the Circuit Court (as the case may be), upon such terms as to costs or otherwise as the Court or Circuit Court (as the case may be) thinks just.

(2) The references in sections 50 and 52 of this Act and the first and second references in section 51 of this Act to the Court shall be construed as including references to the Circuit Court.

**50. Powers of arbitrators in references under section 49.**—(1) In all cases of references to an arbitrator under an order of the Court under section 49 of this Act, the arbitrator shall be deemed to be an officer of the Court, and, subject to rules of court, shall have such authority and conduct the reference in such manner as the Court may direct.

(2) The award of an arbitrator on any reference under section 49 of this Act shall, unless set aside by the Court, be equivalent to the verdict of a jury.

(3) The remuneration to be paid to an arbitrator to whom any matter is referred under section 49 of this Act shall be determined by the Court.

**51. Court to have powers as in references under arbitration agreements.**—The Court shall, in relation to references under an order of the Court made under section 49 of this Act, have all the powers which are by Part II of this Act conferred on the Court in relation to references under arbitration agreements.

**52. Statement of case pending arbitration.**—An arbitrator on any reference under section 49 of this Act may at any stage of the proceedings under the reference, and shall, if so directed by the Court, state in the form of a special case for the opinion of the Court any question of law arising in the course of the reference.

**53. Powers of Supreme Court.**—The Supreme Court shall have all such powers as are conferred by this Part on the Court.

Part V.

## ENFORCEMENT OF CERTAIN FOREIGN AWARDS.

**54. "Foreign award".**—(1)—

(a) The Government, if satisfied that any State which has ratified the Convention of 1927 has made such reciprocal provisions as will enable the Convention of 1927 to be operative in any territory to which the Convention of 1927 is applicable, may by order declare—
   (i) that State to be a party to the Convention of 1927,
   (ii) that territory to be a territory to which the Convention of 1927 applies.

(b) The Government may by order vary or revoke any order made under this subsection.

(2) In this Part, "foreign award" means any award made after the commencement of this Part—

(a) in pursuance of an agreement for arbitration to which the Protocol of 1923 applies, and

(b) between persons—
   (i) of whom one is subject to the jurisdiction of a State which is declared by an order under subsection (1) of this section to be a party to the Convention of 1927, and
   (ii) of whom the other is subject to the jurisdiction of another such State, and

(c) in a territory which is declared by an order under subsection (1) of this section to be a territory to which the Convention of 1927 applies.

**55. Effect of foreign awards.**—(1) A foreign award shall, subject to the provisions of this Part, be enforceable in the State either by action or in the same manner as an award of an arbitrator is enforceable by virtue of section 41 of this Act.

(2) Any foreign award which would be enforceable under this Part shall be treated as binding for all purposes on the persons as between whom it was made, and may accordingly be relied on by any of those persons by way of defence, set-off or otherwise in any legal proceedings in the State, and any references in this Part to enforcing a foreign award shall be construed as including references to relying on an award.

The following Sections and Schedules correspond to those of the English Arbitration Act 1950 as noted:—

| | | |
|---|---|---|
| 56 | *Conditions for enforcement of foreign awards* | English s. 37. |
| 57 | *Evidence* | English s. 38. |
| 58 | *Meaning of "final award"* | English s. 39. |
| 59 | *Saving for other rights etc.* | English s. 40. |

FIRST SCHEDULE
Geneva Protocol of 24th September, 1923      English First Schedule.[1]

SECOND SCHEDULE
Geneva Convention of 26th September, 1927      English Second Schedule.[2]

---

[1] See Mustill & Boyd's *Commercial Arbitration*, pp. 643–644.
[2] *Ibid.*, pp. 644–647.

*Statute law applicable to the Republic of Ireland*

## Arbitration Act, 1980 (Number 7 of 1980)

An Act to enable effect to be given to the Convention on the Recognition and Enforcement of Foreign Arbitral Awards done at New York on the 10th day of June, 1958, and to certain provisions of the Convention on the Settlement of Investment Disputes between States and Nationals of Other States opened for signature in Washington on the 18th day of March, 1965, and otherwise to amend the Arbitration Act, 1954.

Part I

## PRELIMINARY AND GENERAL

*Short title and collective citation*

**1.**—(1) This Act may be cited as the Arbitration Act, 1980.

(2) The Arbitration Act, 1954, and this Act may be cited together as the Arbitration Acts, 1954 and 1980.

*Definitions*

**2.**—In this Act—

"arbitration agreement" means an agreement in writing (including an agreement contained in an exchange of letters or telegrams) to submit to arbitration present or future differences capable of settlement by arbitration;

"the Principal Act" means the Arbitration Act, 1954.

*Commencement*

**3.**—Parts III and IV of this Act shall come into operation on such day or days as the Minister for Justice may by order appoint.

*Repeal*

**4.**—Section 12 of the Principal Act is hereby repealed.

Part II

## EFFECT OF ARBITRATION AGREEMENT ON COURT PROCEEDINGS

*Staying court proceedings where party proves arbitration agreement*

**5.**—(1) If any party to an arbitration agreement, or any person claiming through or under him, commences any proceedings in any court against any other party to such agreement, or any person claiming through or under him, in respect of any matter agreed to be referred to arbitration, any party to the proceedings may at any time after an appearance has been entered, and before delivery of any pleadings or taking any other steps in the proceedings, apply to the court to stay the proceedings, and the court, unless it is satisfied that the arbitration agreement is null and void, inoperative or incapable of being performed or that there is not in fact any dispute between the parties with regard to the matter agreed to be referred, shall make an order staying the proceedings.

(2) Nothing in this section shall be construed as limiting or otherwise affecting the power conferred on the High Court pursuant to section 39(3) of the Principal Act to refuse to stay any action brought in breach of an arbitration agreement.

Part III

## ENFORCEMENT OF NEW YORK CONVENTION AWARDS

The following sections correspond to those of the English Arbitration Act 1975 as noted:—

| | | |
|---|---|---|
| 6 | *Interpretation* | English s. 7. |
| 7 | *Effect of awards* | English s. 3. |
| 8 | *Evidence* | English s. 4. |
| 9 | *Refusal of enforcement* | English s. 5. |
| 10 | *Non-application of Part V of Principal Act* | No English equivalent. |
| 11 | *Saving for other rights* | English s. 6. |

Part IV

## ENFORCEMENT OF WASHINGTON CONVENTION AWARDS
(Ss. 12 to 17 inclusive)[1]

[*Note* There is at present no equivalent to this part of the Eire 1980 Act applicable to the United Kingdom.]

---

[1] See article under "Ireland" by M. W. Abrahamson in the *International Handbook on Commercial Arbitration*, Suppl. 2, ICCA, Aug., 1984.

# *Appendix III*

# ARBITRATION CLAUSES

**ICE Conditions of Contract (5th edition), June, 1973**

SETTLEMENT OF DISPUTES[1]

*Settlement of Disputes—Arbitration.*

66. (1) If any dispute or difference of any kind whatsoever shall arise between the Employer and the Contractor in connection with or arising out of the Contract or the carrying out of the Works including any dispute as to any decision opinion instruction direction certificate or valuation of the Engineer (whether during the progress of the Works or after their completion and whether before or after the determination abandonment or breach of the Contract) it shall be referred to and settled by the Engineer who shall state his decision in writing and give notice of the same to the Employer and the Contractor. Unless the Contract shall have been already determined or abandoned the Contractor shall in every case continue to proceed with the Works with all due diligence and he shall give effect forthwith to every such decision of the Engineer unless and until the same shall be revised by an arbitrator as hereinafter provided. Such decisions shall be final and binding upon the Contractor and the Employer unless either of them shall require that the matter be referred to arbitration as hereinafter provided. If the Engineer shall fail to give such decision for a period of 3 calendar months after being requested to do so or if either the Employer or the Contractor be dissatisfied with any such decision of the Engineer then and in any such case either the Employer or the Contractor may within 3 calendar months after receiving notice of such decision or within 3 calendar months after the expiration of the said period of 3 months (as the case may be) require that the matter shall be referred to the arbitration of a person to be agreed upon between the parties or (if the parties fail to appoint an arbitrator within one calendar month of either party serving on the other party a written notice to concur in the appointment of an arbitrator) a person to be appointed on the application of either party by the President for the time being of the Institution of Civil Engineers. If an arbitrator declines the appointment or after appointment is removed by order of a competent court or is incapable of acting or dies and the parties do not within one calendar month of the vacancy arising fill the vacancy then the President for the time being of the Institution of Civil Engineers may on the application of either party appoint an arbitrator to fill the vacancy. Any such reference to arbitration shall be deemed to be a submission to arbitration within the meaning of the Arbitration Act 1950 or the Arbitration (Scotland) Act 1894 as the case may be or any statutory re-enactment or amendment thereof for the time being in force. Any such reference to arbitration may be conducted in accordance with the Institution of Civil Engineers' Arbitration Procedure (1973) or any amendment or modification thereof being in force at the time of the appointment of the arbitrator and in cases where the President of the Institution of Civil Engineers is requested to appoint the arbitrator he may direct that the arbitration is conducted in accordance with the aforementioned Procedure or any amendment or modification thereof. Such arbitrator shall

---

[1] See p. 207, *post*, for the new 1985 form.

have full power to open up review and revise any decision opinion instruction direction certificate or valuation of the Engineer and neither party shall be limited in the proceedings before such arbitrator to the evidence or arguments put before the Engineer for the purpose of obtaining his decision above referred to. The award of the arbitrator shall be final and binding on the parties. Save as provided for in sub-clause (2) of this Clause no steps shall be taken in the reference to the arbitrator until after the completion or alleged completion of the Works unless with the written consent of the Employer and the Contractor. Provided always:–

(a) that the giving of a Certificate of Completion under Clause 48 shall not be a condition precedent to the taking of any step in such reference;

(b) that no decision given by the Engineer in accordance with the foregoing provisions shall disqualify him from being called as a witness and giving evidence before the arbitrator on any matter whatsoever relevant to the dispute or difference so referred to the arbitrator as aforesaid.

*Interim Arbitration.*

(2) In the case of any dispute or difference as to any matter arising under Clause 12 or the withholding by the Engineer of any certificate or the witholding of any portion of the retention money under Clause 60 to which the Contractor claims to be entitled or as to the exercise of the Engineer's power to give a certificate under Clause 63(1) the reference to the arbitrator may proceed notwithstanding that the Works shall not then be or be alleged to be complete.

*Vice-President to Act.*

(3) In any case where the President for the time being of the Institution of Civil Engineers is not able to exercise the functions conferred on him by this Clause the said functions may be exercised on his behalf by a Vice-President for the time being of the said Institution.

## APPLICATION TO SCOTLAND[1]

*Application to Scotland.*

67. If the Works are situated in Scotland the Contract shall in all respects be construed and operate as a Scottish contract and shall be interpreted in accordance with Scots law.

---

## FCEC Form of Sub-Contract (as amended, March, 1973)[2]

*Disputes.*

18. (1) If any dispute arises between the Contractor and the Sub-Contractor in connection with this Sub-Contract, it shall, subject to the provisions of this clause, be referred to the arbitration and final decision of a person agreed between the parties, or failing such agreement, appointed upon the application of either of the parties by the President for the time being of the Institution of Civil Engineers.

(2) If any dispute arises in connection with the Main Contract and the Contractor is of opinion that such dispute touches or concerns the Sub-Contract Works, then provided that an arbitrator has not already been agreed or appointed in pursuance of the preceding sub-clause, the Contractor may by notice in writing to the Sub-

---

[1] See p. 208, *post*, for the new 1985 form.
[2] See p. 208, *post*, for the September 1984 version.

Contractor require that any dispute under this Sub-Contract shall be referred to the arbitrator to whom the dispute under the Main Contract is referred and if such arbitrator (hereinafter called "the joint arbitrator") be willing so to act, such dispute under this Sub-Contract shall be so referred. In such event the joint arbitrator may, subject to the consent of the Employer, give such directions for the determination of the two said disputes either concurrently or consecutively as he may think just and convenient and provided that the Sub-Contractor is allowed to act as a party to the dispute between the Employer and the Contractor, the joint arbitrator may in determining the dispute under this Sub-Contract take account of all material facts proved before him in the dispute under the Main Contract.

(3) If at any time before an arbitrator has been agreed or appointed in pursuance of sub-clause (1) of this clause any dispute arising in connection with the Main Contract is made the subject of proceedings in any court between the Employer and the Contractor and the Contractor is of opinion that such dispute touches or concerns the Sub-Contract works, he may by notice in writing to the Sub-Contractor abrogate the provisions of sub-clause (1) of this clause and thereafter no dispute under this Sub-Contract shall be referable to arbitration without further submission by the Contractor and Sub-Contractor.

---

## FIDIC Conditions of Contract (3rd edition), March, 1977

### SETTLEMENT OF DISPUTES

*Settlement of Disputes—Arbitration.*

67. If any dispute or difference of any kind whatsoever shall arise between the Employer and the Contractor or the Engineer and the Contractor in connection with, or arising out of the Contract, or the execution of the Works, whether during the progress of the Works or after their completion and whether before or after the termination, abandonment or breach of the Contract, it shall, in the first place, be referred to and settled by the Engineer who shall, within a period of ninety days after being requested by either party to do so, give written notice of his decision to the Employer and the Contractor. Subject to arbitration, as hereinafter provided, such decision in respect of every matter so referred shall be final and binding upon the Employer and the Contractor and shall forthwith be given effect to by the Employer and by the Contractor, who shall proceed with the execution of the Works with all due diligence whether he or the Employer requires arbitration, as hereinafter provided, or not. If the Engineer has given written notice of his decision to the Employer and the Contractor and no claim to arbitration has been communicated to him by either the Employer or the Contractor within a period of ninety days from receipt of such notice, the said decision shall remain final and binding upon the Employer and the Contractor. If the Engineer shall fail to give notice of his decision, as aforesaid, within a period of ninety days after being requested as aforesaid, or if either the Employer or the Contractor be dissatisfied with any such decision, then and in any such case either the Employer or the Contractor may within ninety days after receiving notice of such decision, or within ninety days after the expiration of the first-named period of ninety days, as the case may be, require that the matter or matters in dispute be referred to arbitration as hereinafter provided. All disputes or differences in respect of which the decision, if any, of the Engineer has not become final and binding as aforesaid shall be finally settled under the Rules of Conciliation and Arbitration of the International Chamber of Commerce by one or more arbitrators appointed under such Rules. The said

arbitrator/s shall have full power to open up, revise and review any decision, opinion, direction, certificate or valuation of the Engineer. Neither party shall be limited in the proceedings before such arbitrator/s to the evidence or arguments put before the Engineer for the purpose of obtaining his said decision. No decision given by the Engineer in accordance with the foregoing provisions shall disqualify him from being called as a witness and giving evidence before the arbitrator/s on any matter whatsoever relevant to the dispute or difference referred to the arbitrator/s as aforesaid. The reference to arbitration may proceed notwithstanding that the Works shall not then be or be alleged to be complete, provided always that the obligations of the Employer, the Engineer and the Contractor shall not be altered by reason of the arbitration being conducted during the progress of the Works.

---

## JCT Standard Form of Building Contract (April, 1980 revision)

ARTICLE 5

*Settlement of disputes—Arbitration*

5·1     In case any dispute or difference shall arise between the Employer or the Architect/Supervising Officer on his behalf and the Contractor, either during the progress or after the completion or abandonment of the Works, as to

5·1  ·1     the construction of this Contract, or

5·1  ·2     any matter or thing of whatsoever nature arising hereunder or in connection herewith including any matter or thing left by this Contract to the discretion of the Architect/Supervising Officer or the withholding by the Architect/Supervising Officer of any certificate to which the Contractor may claim to be entitled or the adjustment of the Contract Sum under clause 30·6·2 or the rights and liabilities of the parties under clauses 27, 28, 32 or 33 or unreasonable withholding of consent or agreement by the Employer or the Architect/Supervising Officer on his behalf or by the Contractor, but

5·1  ·3     excluding any dispute or difference under clause 19A, under clause 31 to the extent provided in clause 31·9 and under clause 3 of the VAT Agreement,

then such dispute or difference shall be and is hereby referred to the arbitration and final decision of a person to be agreed between the parties to act as Arbitrator, or, failing agreement within 14 days after either party has given to the other a written request to concur in the appointment of an Arbitrator, a person to be appointed on the request of either party by the President or a Vice-President for the time being of the Royal Institute of British Architects.

5·1  ·4     Provided that if the dispute or difference to be referred to arbitration under this Contract raises issues which are substantially the same as or connected with issues raised in a related dispute between

the Employer and a Nominated Sub-Contractor under Agreement NSC/2 or NSC/2a as applicable or

the Contractor and any Nominated Sub-Contractor under Sub-Contract NSC/4 or NSC/4a as applicable or

the Contractor and/or the Employer and any Nominated Supplier whose contract of sale with the Contractor provides for the matters referred to in clause 36·4·8, and if the related dispute has already been referred for determination to an Arbitrator, the Employer and Contractor hereby agree that the dispute or difference under this Contract shall be referred to the Arbitrator appointed to determine the related dispute; and such Arbitrator shall have power to make such directions and all necessary awards in the same way as if the procedure of the High Court as to joining one or more defendants or joining co-defendants or third parties was available to the parties and to him;

5·1 ·5 save that the Employer or the Contractor may require the dispute or difference under this Contract to be referred to a different Arbitrator (to be appointed under this Contract) if either of them reasonably considers that the Arbitrator appointed to determine the related dispute is not appropriately qualified to determine the dispute or difference under this Contract.

5·1 ·6 Articles 5·1·4 and 5·1·5 shall apply unless in the Appendix the words "Articles 5·1·4 and 5·1·5 apply" have been deleted.

5·2 Such reference, except

5·2 ·1 on article 3 or article 4; or

5·2 ·2 on the questions

whether or not the issue of an instruction is empowered by the Conditions; or

whether or not a certificate has been improperly withheld; or

whether a certificate is not in accordance with the Conditions; or

5·2 ·3 on any dispute or difference under clause 4·1 in regard to a reasonable objection by the Contractor, and clauses 25, 32 and 33,

shall not be opened until after Practical Completion or alleged Practical Completion of the Works or termination or alleged termination of the Contractor's employment under this Contract or abandonment of the Works, unless with the written consent of the Employer or the Architect/ Supervising Officer on his behalf and the Contractor.

5·3 Subject to the provisions of clauses 4·2, 30·9, 38·4·3, 39·5·3 and 40·5 the Arbitrator shall, without prejudice to the generality of his powers, have power to direct such measurements and/or valuations as may in his opinion be desirable in order to determine the rights of the parties and to ascertain and award any sum which ought to have been the subject of or included in any certificate and to open up, review and revise any certificate, opinion, decision, requirement or notice and to determine all matters in dispute which shall be submitted to him in the same manner as if no such certificate, opinion, decision, requirement or notice had been given.

5·4 The award of such Arbitrator shall be final and binding on the parties.

5·5 Whatever the nationality, residence or domicile of the Employer, the Contractor, any sub-contractor or supplier or the Arbitrator, and wherever the Works or any part thereof are situated, the law of England shall be the proper law of this Contract and in particular (but not so as to derogate from the generality of the foregoing) the provisions of the Arbitration Acts 1950 (notwithstanding anything in S·34 thereof) to 1979 shall apply to any arbitration under this Contract wherever the same, or any part of it, shall be conducted.

# JCT Intermediate Form of Building Contract (September, 1984)

ARTICLE 5

*Settlement of Disputes—Arbitration*

5·1   If any dispute or difference concerning this Contract shall arise between the Employer or the Architect/the Supervising Officer on his behalf and the Contractor (other than a dispute or difference under clause 5·7, or under Supplemental Condition A7 or Supplemental Condition B8) such dispute or difference shall be and is hereby referred to the arbitration and final decision of a person to be agreed between the parties or, failing agreement within 14 days after either party has given to the other a written request to concur in the appointment of an arbitrator, a person to be appointed on the request of either party by the President or a Vice-President for the time being of the Royal Institute of British Architects or of the Royal Institution of Chartered Surveyors as stated in the Appendix. The proper law of this Contract shall be English law.

5·2   Subject to the provisions of clauses 3·5·2 (*Architect's/Supervising Officer's instructions*), 4·7 (*Effect of final certificate*) and Supplemental Conditions C4·3 (*Tax etc. fluctuations*) or Supplemental Conditions D8 (*Formulae fluctuations*) the Arbitrator shall, without prejudice to the generality of his powers, have power to direct such measurements and/or valuations as may be desirable in order to determine the rights of the parties and to ascertain and award any sum which ought to have been the subject of or included in any certificate and to open up, review and revise any certificate, opinion, decision, requirement or notice and to determine all matters in dispute which shall be submitted to him in the same manner as if no such certificate, opinion, decision, requirement or notice had been given.

5·3   Where this Article 5·3 is stated in the Appendix to apply, the parties hereby agree and consent pursuant to Sections 1(3)(a) and 2(1)(b) of the Arbitration Act 1979 that either party
      (*a*)  may appeal to the High Court on any question of law arising out of an award made in an arbitration under the Arbitration Agreement and
      (*b*)  may apply to the High Court to determine any question of law arising in the course of the reference;
      and the parties agree that the High Court should have jurisdiction to determine any such questions of law.

5·4   Where this Article 5·4 is stated in the Appendix to apply, if the dispute or difference to be referred to arbitration under this Contract raises issues which are substantially the same as or connected with issues raised in a related dispute under a sub-contract entered into in accordance with the provisions of clause 3·3 and if the related dispute has already been referred for determination to an Arbitrator, the Employer and Contractor hereby agree that the dispute or difference under this Contract shall be referred to the Arbitrator appointed to determine the related dispute; and such Arbitrator shall have power to make such directions and all necessary awards in the same way as if the procedure of the High Court as to joining one or more defendants or joining co-defendants or third parties was available to the parties and to him.

# ICE Conditions of Contract (5th edition) as revised, March, 1985[1]

## SETTLEMENT OF DISPUTES BY ARBITRATION

66(1) If a dispute or difference of any kind whatsoever shall arise between the Employer and the Contractor in connection with or arising out of the Contract or the carrying out of the Works including any dispute as to any decision opinion instruction direction certificate or valuation of the Engineer (whether during the progress of the Works or after their completion and whether before or after the determination abandonment or breach of the Contract) it shall be referred in writing to and be settled by the Engineer who shall state his decision in writing and give notice of the same to the Employer and the Contractor.

(2) Unless the Contract shall have already been determined or abandoned the Contractor shall in every case continue to proceed with the Works with all due diligence and the Contractor and Employer shall both give effect forthwith to every such decision of the Engineer unless and until the same shall be revised by an arbitrator as hereinafter provided. Such decisions shall be final and binding upon the Contractor and the Employer unless and until the dispute or difference has been referred to arbitration as hereinafter provided and an award made and published.

(3)(a) Where a Certificate of Completion of the whole of the Works has not been issued and

    (i)   either the Employer or the Contractor be dissatisfied with any such decision of the Engineer or

    (ii)  the Engineer shall fail to give such decision for a period of one calendar month after such referral in writing

then either the Employer or the Contractor may within 3 calendar months after receiving notice of such decision or within 3 calendar months after the expiration of the said period of one month (as the case may be) refer the dispute or difference to the arbitration of a person to be agreed upon by the Parties by giving notice to the other Party.

(b) Where a Certificate of Completion of the whole of the Works has been issued and

    (i)   either the Employer or the Contractor be dissatisfied with any such decision of the Engineer or

    (ii)  the Engineer shall fail to give such decision for a period of 3 calendar months after such referral in writing

then either the Employer or the Contractor may within 3 calendar months after receiving notice of such decision or within 3 calendar months after the expiration of the said period of 3 months (as the case may be) refer the dispute or difference to the arbitration of a person to be agreed upon by the Parties by giving notice to the other Party.

(4)(a) If the Parties fail to appoint an arbitrator within one calendar month of either Party serving on the other Party a written Notice to Concur in the appointment of an arbitrator the dispute or difference shall be referred to a person to be appointed on the application of either Party by the President for the time being of the Institution of Civil Engineers.

(b) If an arbitrator declines the appointment or after appointment is removed by order of a competent court or is incapable of acting or dies and the Parties do not within one calendar month of the vacancy arising fill the vacancy then either Party may apply to the President for the time being of the Institution of Civil Engineers to appoint another arbitrator to fill the vacancy.

(c) In any case where the President for the time being of the Institution of Civil Engineers is not able to exercise the functions conferred on him by this Clause the

---

[1]   For discussion, see Chapter 6.

said functions may be exercised on his behalf by a Vice-President for the time being of the said Institution.

(5)(a) Any reference to arbitration shall be conducted in accordance with the Institution of Civil Engineers' Arbitration Procedure (1983) or any amendment or modification thereof being in force at the time of the appointment of the arbitrator. Such arbitrator shall have full power to open up review and revise any decision opinion instruction direction certificate or valuation of the Engineer and neither party shall be limited in the proceedings before such arbitrator to the evidence or arguments put before the Engineer for the purpose of obtaining his decision above referred to.

(b) Any such reference to arbitration shall be deemed to be a submission to arbitration within the meaning of the Arbitration Act 1950 or any statutory re-enactment or amendment thereof for the time being in force. The Award of the arbitrator shall be binding on the parties.

(c) Any reference to arbitration may unless the parties otherwise agree in writing proceed notwithstanding that the Works are not then complete or alleged to be complete.

(6) No decision given by the Engineer in accordance with the foregoing provisions shall disqualify him from being called as a witness and giving evidence before the arbitrator on any matter whatsoever relevant to the dispute or difference so referred to the arbitrator as aforesaid.

## APPLICATION TO SCOTLAND[1]

67(1) If the Works are situated in Scotland the Contract shall in all respects be construed and operate as a Scottish contract and shall be interpreted in accordance with Scots Law and the provisions of this Clause shall apply.

(2) In the application of Clause 66 the word 'arbiter' shall be substituted for the word 'arbitrator'. Any reference to the Arbitration Act 1950 shall be deleted and for any reference to the Institution of Civil Engineers' Arbitration Procedure (1983) there shall be substituted a reference to the Institution of Civil Engineers' Arbitration Procedure (Scotland) (1983).

---

# FCEC Form of Sub-Contract (revised September, 1984)[2]

18. (1) If any dispute arises between the Contractor and the Sub-Contractor in connection with or arising out of this Sub-Contract or the carrying out of the Sub-Contract Works including any dispute as to any decision, opinion, instruction or direction of the Contractor and/or Engineer or any dispute as to payment under Clause 15 it shall, subject to the provisions of this clause, be referred to the arbitration and final decision of a person agreed between the parties, or failing such agreement, appointed upon the application of either of the parties by the President for the time being of the Institution of Civil Engineers and any such reference to arbitration may be conducted in accordance with the Institution of Civil Engineers' Arbitration Procedure 1983 or any amendment or modification thereof in force at the time of the appointment of the arbitrator.

(2) If any dispute arises in connection with the Main Contract and the Contractor is of the opinion that such dispute touches or concerns the Sub-Contract Works, then provided that an arbitrator has not already been agreed or appointed in

---

[1]  For discussion, see Chapter 11.

[2]  For discussion, see Chapter 6.

pursuance of the preceding sub-clause, the Contractor may by notice in writing to the Sub-Contractor require that any such dispute under this Sub-Contract shall be dealt with jointly with the dispute under the Main Contract in accordance with the provisions of Clause 66 thereof. In connection with such joint dispute the Sub-Contractor shall be bound in like manner as the Contractor by any decision of the Engineer or any award by an arbitrator.

(3) If at any time before an arbitrator has been agreed or appointed in pursuance of sub-clause (1) of this clause any dispute arising in connection with the Main Contract is made the subject of proceedings in any court between the Employer and the Contractor and the Contractor is of opinion that such dispute touches or concerns the Sub-Contract Works, he may by notice in writing to the Sub-Contractor abrogate the provisions of sub-clause (1) of this clause and thereafter no dispute under this Sub-Contract shall be referable to arbitration without further submission by the Contractor and Sub-Contractor.

(4) Notice of any dispute under this Agreement shall be given by the Sub-Contractor to the Contractor in writing as soon as practicable after the event giving rise to the dispute. The Sub-Contractor shall be bound by the time limits imposed on the Contractor by Clause 66 of the Main Contract in respect of any decision given by the Engineer thereunder insofar as such decision affects the Sub-Contract Works.

# NOTICES

**Form ArbICE (revised)** issued by
## The Institution of Civil Engineers

These Forms are intended for use with the *ICE Arbitration Procedure* in connection with arbitrations under the *ICE Conditions of Contract* or the *FCEC Form of Sub-Contract*. They are, however, easily adapted for use in other arbitrations.

## Part 1: THE CONTRACT(S)

Title of (Main) Contract:

Date of (Main) Contract:

Brief description of the Works:

Employer's name:

Employer's address:

(Main) Contractor's name:

(Main) Contractor's address:

Engineer's name:

Engineer's address:

Title of Sub-Contract (if any):

Date of Sub-Contract:

Brief description of the Sub-Contract Works:

Sub-Contractor's name:

Sub-Contractor's address:

Please state the form of the Arbitration Clause:

Clause 66 of the *ICE Conditions of Contract*

Clause 18 of the *FCEC Form of Sub-Contract*

Clause 67 of the *FIDIC Conditions of Contract*

Other (please state, and attach a copy hereto):

## Part 2: NOTICE TO REFER DISPUTE(S) OR DIFFERENCE(S) TO ARBITRATION

WHEREAS dispute(s) or difference(s) as hereinafter described have arisen between the Parties to the Main Contract/Sub-Contract (as described in Part 1 hereto) in connection with or arising out of the said Contract or the carrying out of the Works

Now we the undersigned hereby give notice requiring the said dispute(s) or difference(s) to be referred to arbitration.

Dated this          day of          19

Signed

for and on behalf of

the Employer/(Main) Contractor/Sub-Contractor

Brief description of the dispute(s) or difference(s) to be referred to arbitration

To be completed where Clause 66 of the *ICE Conditions of Contract* or Clause 67 of the *FIDIC Conditions of Contract* apply.

The above dispute(s) or difference(s) were referred to the Engineer in accordance with Clause 66/67 of the Conditions of Contract in letter(s)
from          dated

Notice of the Engineer's decision thereon was given in the Engineer's

letter(s) to          dated

The Engineer has so far failed to give notice of his decision thereon.

## Part 3: NOTICE TO CONCUR IN THE APPOINTMENT OF AN ARBITRATOR

To:

Address:

WE HEREBY call upon you to concur in the appointment of an Arbitrator to hear and determine the dispute(s) or difference(s) between us as set out in Part 2 hereof.

WE PROPOSE the following person for your consideration and require you within 14 days of the service of this Notice
(i)  to agree in writing to his appointment; or
(ii) to propose an alternative person for our consideration
failing which we intend to apply to the President of the Institution of Civil Engineers to appoint an Arbitrator.

Name of person proposed as Arbitrator:

Address of person proposed as Arbitrator:

Dated this          day of          19

for and on behalf of:

the Employer/(Main) Contractor/Sub-Contractor

## Part 4: APPLICATION TO THE PRESIDENT OF THE INSTITUTION OF CIVIL ENGINEERS TO APPOINT AN ARBITRATOR

To: The President, the Institution of Civil Engineers,
    Great George Street, London SW1P 3AA

IN THE MATTER OF THE DISPUTE(S) OR DIFFERENCE(S) referred to in Part 2 of this Form and since the Parties have failed to agree upon an Arbitrator we hereby apply to you to appoint an Arbitrator.

We enclose a cheque for £      plus VAT in respect of the charge made by the Institution towards administrative costs in connection with this application.

We think it desirable that the Arbitrator should if possible be skilled/have experience in the following fields or professions:

The amount at issue is approximately £

Dated this     day of     19

Signed:

for and on behalf of:

the Employer/(Main) Contractor/Sub-Contractor

## Part 5: APPOINTMENT OF AN ARBITRATOR BY THE PRESIDENT OF THE INSTITUTION OF CIVIL ENGINEERS

From the President:

To:

Copies for information to:

and:

I hereby appoint:

of:

Arbitrator in this matter and I hereby direct that the Arbitration be conducted in accordance with the *ICE Arbitration Procedure 1983* (England & Wales) or (Scotland).

Dated this     day of     19

----------------------------
PRESIDENT/VICE PRESIDENT

*Appendix V*

# PLEADINGS AND PRECEDENTS

## Form 1: Points of claim (conventional pleading)

IN THE MATTER OF THE ARBITRATION ACTS 1950 TO 1979
AND IN THE MATTER OF AN ARBITRATION

BETWEEN:

|  |  |
|---|---|
| A. B. CONTRACTORS LIMITED | *Claimants* |
| and | |
| C. D. DISTRICT COUNCIL | *Respondents* |

POINTS OF CLAIM

1. By a contract in writing made the 1st January 1982 incorporating the ICE Conditions of Contract, Fifth Edition, the Claimants (as Contractor) undertook to carry out certain sewerage and ancillary works for the Respondents (as Employer).

2. The Claimants have carried out and completed the said works but the Respondents failed to pay the balance of the Claimants' final account namely £150,000, which sum has been certified by the Engineer one E. F.

3. Further, during the course of the said works the Claimants encountered unforeseen physical conditions which greatly hampered the progress of the works and caused considerable loss and expense to the Claimants.

PARTICULARS

Between manholes 15 and 22, the Claimants encountered running sand conditions at depths between 3.5 and 7.5 metres. These conditions could not have been foreseen from any of the tender documents or other information available to the Claimants.

4. Further or alternatively, upon discovering the said conditions, the Engineer instructed the Claimants to employ well point dewatering. In the premises, the Claimants are entitled to payment for such dewatering and for the loss and expense consequent thereon pursuant to Clauses 13 and/or 51 of the Conditions of Contract.

5. Full particulars of the sums claimed under paragraphs 3 and 4 are set out in the Schedule hereto.

AND THE CLAIMANTS CLAIM:

(1) Under paragraph 2:  £156,237.00
(2) Under paragraph 5:  £551,826.00
(3) Interest.

SERVED the        day of        19

## Form 2: Points of defence and of counterclaim (conventional pleading)

IN THE MATTER OF THE ARBITRATION ACTS 1950 TO 1979
AND IN THE MATTER OF AN ARBITRATION

BETWEEN:

A. B. CONTRACTORS LIMITED  *Claimants*

and

C. D. DISTRICT COUNCIL  *Respondents*

POINTS OF DEFENCE AND COUNTERCLAIM

1.   The Respondents admit paragraph 1 of the Points of Claim.

2.   Paragraph 2 is admitted, save that the Respondents are entitled to set off their Counterclaim against the sum otherwise due to the Claimants.

3.   It is admitted that the Claimants encountered running sand conditions as alleged, save that the Conditions existed between manholes 17 to 21 only, and between depths of 3.5 and 4.5 metres only. The conditions could and should have been foreseen by an experienced contractor including the Claimants for the following reasons:

   (i) Boreholes B, C and D, in the vicinity of manholes 17 to 21 each showed a sand strata together with a high water-table.
   (ii) Ordnance Survey maps showed springs in the vicinity of the works.

4.   It is denied that E. F. instructed the Claimants to use any particular method of construction. It is admitted that E. F. stated verbally that he had no objection to the Contractor's employing well point dewatering. This did not constitute an instruction either under Clause 13 or 51.

5.   Subject to the foregoing denials, it is admitted the Claimants have suffered some loss and expense. The Claimants' claim document is grossly exaggerated. The Engineer has assessed the actual loss suffered in the sum of £78,120.00

6.   By way of Counterclaim, the Contract required the works to be completed by 31st December 1982 and provided for liquidated damages at the rate of £5,000 per week. The Claimants completed their work 30 weeks late, and in the premises the Respondents are entitled to withhold the sum of £150,000.

AND THE RESPONDENTS COUNTERCLAIM:

   £150,000.00.


SERVED the          day of          19

## Form 3: Request for further and better particulars (conventional pleading)

IN THE MATTER OF THE ARBITRATION ACTS 1950 TO 1979
AND IN THE MATTER OF AN ARBITRATION

BETWEEN:

A. B. CONTRACTORS LIMITED      *Claimants*

and

C. D. DISTRICT COUNCIL      *Respondents*

REQUEST FOR FURTHER AND BETTER PARTICULARS OF THE
POINTS OF CLAIM

*Under Paragraph 3*

Please state how the conditions encountered are alleged to vary from those shown in boreholes B, C and D.

*Under Paragraph 4*

Please state whether the instruction relied on was given orally or in writing.

If the instruction was in writing identify the document containing it. If the instruction was oral state when and where it was given and the substance of the words alleged to constitute the instruction.

SERVED the      day of      19

## Form 4: Points of claim (standard form)

*Note* This form may be reproduced and filled in if desired; or it may be adapted to suit a particular case.

## IN THE MATTER OF THE ARBITRATION ACTS 1950 TO 1979 AND IN THE MATTER OF AN ARBITRATION

[Heading optional]

BETWEEN:

A. B. CONTRACTORS LIMITED          *Claimants*

and

C. D. DISTRICT COUNCIL          *Respondents*

POINTS OF CLAIM

1. *Particulars of Contract*
   Date of Contract
   Parties
   Brief Description of Works
   Approximate Value of Works
   Appointed Engineer
   Start and Completion Dates

2. *The Works* were completed on or about          /are anticipated to be completed on or about

3. *Particulars of Payment*
   Has all measured work been paid for?
   If not, state amount of dispute and brief particulars (attach Schedule if necessary):
   Is there any other dispute about the value of work carried out?
   If so, give details or attach separate sheet:

4. *Particulars of Claims*
   Has a claim already been submitted?
   If so, give date of documents and reference (attach copies of claim documents if possible):
   Clauses of contract relied on (attach copies of any special conditions):
   Sum paid on account (if any) (state date of payment):

5. *Other Disputes*
   Is the arbitrator required to adjudicate on any matter other than those above?
   If so, give details of precisely what the Claimants ask for:

6. *Summary of Claims*
   Total of money claims:
   Any other awards sought (it is assumed that interest and costs are claimed):

DATED the          day of          19

## Form 5: Points of defence and of counterclaim (standard form)

*Note*   This form may be reproduced and filled in if desired; or it may be adapted to suit a particular case.

### IN THE MATTER OF THE ARBITRATION ACTS 1950 TO 1979 AND IN THE MATTER OF AN ARBITRATION

[Heading optional]

BETWEEN:

A. B. CONTRACTORS LIMITED                   *Claimants*

and

C. D. DISTRICT COUNCIL                   *Respondents*

POINTS OF DEFENCE AND COUNTERCLAIM

A.   *Defence*
Set out (with paragraph references) any disagreement with the Points of Claim:

B.   *Counterclaim*
1.   Set out details of any cross-claim against the Claimant:

(Attach copies of any claim document already submitted by the Respondents)

2.   *Summary of Counterclaims*
State total of sums counterclaimed.
State any other relief sought by Respondents.


DATED the          day of          19


## Form 6: Request for particulars (informal)

To: A. B. Contractors Limited.

Dear Sirs,

*Re: Sewerage Scheme Arbitration*

With reference to your Points of Claim, there are two matters which we cannot understand.

(1) Your claim states that running sand could not be foreseen from the tender documents. The Engineer considers this condition was readily apparent from boreholes B, C and D. In the light of this information, would you please explain how you consider that the condition was unforeseeable.

(2) You have not explained how the alleged instruction to use well point dewatering was given. The Engineer is not aware of having given such an instruction.

Will you please supply us with further particulars of the above matters?

Yours faithfully,

## Form 7: Claimants' statement of case (Short Procedure)

IN THE MATTER OF THE ARBITRATION ACTS 1950 TO 1979
AND IN THE MATTER OF AN ARBITRATION

BETWEEN:

A. B. CONTRACTORS LIMITED *Claimants*

and

C. D. DISTRICT COUNCIL *Respondents*

CLAIMANTS' STATEMENT OF CASE

1.  The Claimants seek the following awards:

    (i) £150,000 for work done under the Contract
    (ii) £551,826 for claims made under Clause 12 or under Clauses 13 or 51 of the ICE Conditions.

2.  The Claimants are entitled to these awards for the following reasons.

    (i) The money has been certified by the Engineer and the Respondents have refused to pay. They allege that they are entitled to liquidated damages. But the delay was caused entirely by the matters which are the subject of the claim below. The Claimants are therefore entitled to extensions of time covering this delay.

    (ii) Running sand conditions were encountered between manholes 15 and 22 at depths between 3.5 and 7.5 metres. These conditions fall under Clause 12 of the ICE Conditions. When rejecting the claim, the Engineer told the agent that he ought to use well point dewatering. It is contended this was an instruction under Clause 13 or a Variation Order. The Claimants therefore contend that they are entitled to be paid for their claim whether or not the conditions fall under Clause 12.

3.  The Claimants attach the following documents:

    (*a*) A copy of the Contract, including Bill of Quantities specification and drawings.
    (*b*) A copy of the site investigation report.
    (*c*) A copy of the claim under Clause 12.
    (*d*) Copies of correspondence passing between the parties and the Engineer, including the Engineer's Certificate of Payment.
    (*e*) A signed statement by the Claimants' site agent.

DATED the          day of          19

**Form 8: Respondents' statement of case (Short Procedure)**

IN THE MATTER OF THE ARBITRATION ACTS 1950 TO 1979
AND IN THE MATTER OF AN ARBITRATION

BETWEEN:

A. B. CONTRACTORS LIMITED       *Claimants*

and

C. D. DISTRICT COUNCIL       *Respondents*

RESPONDENTS' STATEMENT OF CASE

1.  The Respondents ask for findings as follows.

    (i) The Respondents are entitled to deduct £150,000 as liquidated damages.
    (ii) The Claimants are not entitled to any claim under Clause 12 or under Clauses 13 or 51. If they are, the amount of the claim should be £78,120.

2.  The Respondents' reasons are as follows.

    (i) There were 30 weeks' delay to the Contract, and the Claimants had no grounds for extensions of time.
    (ii) The condition alleged to fall under Clause 12 was foreseeable from the borehole data. The Engineer did not give an instruction for dewatering. He approved the work which the Claimants themselves proposed.

3.  There is attached hereto the following:

    (a) Copies of correspondence passing before the date of the Contract between the parties relating to soil conditions.
    (b) An Ordnance Survey Map and the local geological memoir.
    (c) Additional correspondence relating to the claim.
    (d) A signed statement by the Engineer.
    (e) A signed statement by the Engineer's representative.


DATED the       day of       19

## Form 9: Claimants' statement of case (Special Procedure for Experts)

IN THE MATTER OF THE ARBITRATION ACTS 1950 TO 1979
AND IN THE MATTER OF AN ARBITRATION

BETWEEN:

|  |  |
|---|---|
| A. B. CONTRACTORS LIMITED | *Claimants* |
| and | |
| C. D. DISTRICT COUNCIL | *Respondents* |

CLAIMANTS' STATEMENT OF CASE

1.  The Claimants ask for findings that running sand conditions between manholes 15 and 22 at depths between 3.5 and 7.5 metres could not reasonably have been foreseen under Clause 12 of the ICE Conditions.

2.  A report by the Claimants' expert is attached.

3.  There is also attached to this statement:

   (*a*) A copy of the site investigation report.
   (*b*) A report of further investigations made by the Claimants during the course of the works.
   (*c*) A signed statement by the site agent.


DATED the     day of     19

## Form 10: Respondents' statement of case (Special Procedure for Experts)

IN THE MATTER OF THE ARBITRATION ACTS 1950 TO 1979
AND IN THE MATTER OF AN ARBITRATION

BETWEEN:

|  |  |
|---|---|
| A. B. CONTRACTORS LIMITED | *Claimants* |
| and | |
| C. D. DISTRICT COUNCIL | *Respondents* |

RESPONDENTS' STATEMENT OF CASE

1.  The Respondents ask for findings that the running sand was limited in extent to manholes 17 to 21 and to depths of 3.5 to 4.5 metres, and that these conditions were reasonably foreseeable under Clause 12.

2.  A report by the Respondent's expert is attached.

3.  The following further documents are attached:

   (*a*) A copy of the Ordnance Survey Map and geological memoir.
   (*b*) A signed statement by the Engineer.


DATED the     day of     19

# Appendix VI

# ORDERS AND AWARDS

## ORDERS FOR DIRECTIONS (GENERAL)

*Note* In the interests of clarity, several versions are given. However, most of the elements are readily interchangeable, and there should be no difficulty in assembling and adapting Orders appropriate to most situations.

Words in italics should be replaced with others appropriate to the Order being drafted. Words and phrases in square brackets may be included or omitted as necessary.

### Form 11: Order following preliminary meeting

IN THE MATTER OF THE ARBITRATION ACTS 1950 TO 1979
AND IN THE MATTER OF AN ARBITRATION

BETWEEN:

|  |  |
|---|---|
| A. B. CONTRACTORS LIMITED | *Claimants* |
| and | |
| C. D. DISTRICT COUNCIL | *Respondents* |

ORDER FOR DIRECTIONS
On hearing Mr Black, *Solicitor* for the Claimants, and Mr White, *Solicitor* for the Respondents, at a Preliminary Meeting on *Monday, 19th March, 1984*, at *23, High Street, Hometown, Mudshire*, the following directions are given:
1.   The Claimants shall serve their Points of Claim on or before *Monday, 16th April, 1984* [to include full details of their case as to          ].
2.   The Respondents shall serve their Points of Defence [and Points of Counterclaim (if any)] within *28* days from service of the Points of Claim [to include etc.].
3.   The Claimants shall serve their Reply (if any) [and Points of Defence to Counterclaim] within *28* days from service of the Points of Defence [and of Counterclaim].
4.   Each party shall give discovery of documents relating to the matters at issue by [preparing and serving upon the other party a list of all such documents in his possession, custody or power][1] within *14* days of close of pleadings,[2] and inspection shall be completed within 7 days thereafter.
5.   There shall be full leave to apply.

In *HOMETOWN* this          day of          19

X. Y.
Arbitrator

---

[1]   Alternative methods include "preparing . . . a list of files and indexes thereto" or "delivering copies of all such documents to the other party".
[2]   Pleadings are "closed" when the Claimant's Reply and/or Defence to Counterclaim has been served, or he confirms that he does not intend to serve a Reply. It is helpful if the Arbitrator informs the parties when he considers pleadings to have been closed.

## Form 12: Order following procedural meeting

IN THE MATTER OF THE ARBITRATION ACTS 1950 TO 1979
AND IN THE MATTER OF AN ARBITRATION

BETWEEN:

A. B. CONTRACTORS LIMITED      *Claimants*

and

C. D. DISTRICT COUNCIL      *Respondents*

*SECOND* ORDER FOR DIRECTIONS

Having heard the parties appearing by *Counsel* at a Procedural Meeting on *Friday, 25th May, 1984,* in *Gray's Inn in the County of London,* I hereby ORDER as follows:

1. The *Claimants* shall serve on or before *Monday, 11th June, 1984,* the Further and Better Particulars requested in the *Respondents'* letter of *16th May, 1984.*

2. The *Respondents* shall serve Further and Better Particulars of [the following matters] on or before *Monday, 18th June, 1984.*

3. [Each party shall serve with the said Further Particulars copies of the documents relating thereto upon which they intend to rely. Thereafter, either party may serve requests for discovery of further documents or classes of documents within *14* days of service of the relevant Particulars].

4. The time for service of the Claimants' Reply and Defence to Counterclaim is extended until *Friday, 29th June, 1984* [and the timetable thereafter as laid down in my first Order for Directions is amended accordingly].

5. Costs of the meeting on *25th May, 1984,* shall be costs in the arbitration, and are certified fit for Counsel.

IN *HOMETOWN* this      day of      19

X. Y.
Arbitrator

## Form 13: Order without a preceding meeting

IN THE MATTER OF THE ARBITRATION ACTS 1950 TO 1979
AND IN THE MATTER OF AN ARBITRATION

BETWEEN:

| | |
|---|---|
| A. B. CONTRACTORS LIMITED | *Claimants* |
| and | |
| C. D. DISTRICT COUNCIL | *Respondents* |

ORDER FOR DIRECTIONS [No.   ]

[On the application of the Claimants] [by agreement between the parties] the following [further] directions are given:

IN *HOMETOWN* this      day of      19

X. Y.
Arbitrator

## Form 14: Order convening a meeting

IN THE MATTER OF THE ARBITRATION ACTS 1950 TO 1979
AND IN THE MATTER OF AN ARBITRATION

BETWEEN:

| | |
|---|---|
| A. B. CONTRACTORS LIMITED | *Claimants* |
| and | |
| C. D. DISTRICT COUNCIL | *Respondents* |

[Preamble as appropriate]

1.   The parties shall appear before me [by their *Solicitors*] on *Tuesday, 17th April, 1984,* at 4.30 o'clock[1] at *my office in Victoria Street, London, SW1,* to consider [whether orders should be made for      and      ] [the *Claimants'* application for an order for      ].

2.   Each party shall give notice to me and to the other party of their views on the said matters not less than *14* days before the said meeting.

3.   The Engineer to the Contract, *Mr Grey*, is requested to attend the meeting.

4.   Should either party wish any other matter to be dealt with at the meeting they shall give notice thereof [in accordance with paragraph 2 above] [not later than noon on the day preceding the meeting].

DATED the      day of      19

X. Y.
Arbitrator

---

[1]   The former practice of adding "in the forenoon" or "in the afternoon" is seldom followed now. It is, however, still not conventional to utilise the 24-hour clock.

## ORDERS FOR DIRECTIONS (PRE-HEARING)

### Form 15: Hearing of all issues

IN THE MATTER OF THE ARBITRATION ACTS 1950 TO 1979
AND IN THE MATTER OF AN ARBITRATION

BETWEEN:

A. B. CONTRACTORS LIMITED      *Claimants*

and

C. D. DISTRICT COUNCIl      *Respondents*

[Preamble as appropriate]

1. A Hearing of all matters at issue in this arbitration shall take place at the *Institution of Civil Engineers, Great George Street, London,* over *5* [working] days starting on *Monday, 15th October, 1984.*

2. Not less than 7 days before the Hearing the Claimants shall prepare and serve on the Respondents and on the Arbitrator a written summary of their case together with a list of the documents upon which they seek to rely.

3. Proofs of evidence of all witnesses of fact shall be exchanged not less than *14* days before the Hearing.

4. The *Claimants* shall have leave to call *Mr Green* as an expert on    . [*Mr Green* will be examined on his written report by the Arbitrator.] The *Respondents* may call *Mr Brown* as an expert only if his written report is served on or before *Friday, 5th October, 1984.*

5. Messrs *Puce and Scarlett*, Quantity Sureyors for the parties, shall meet on or before *Monday, 8th October, 1984*, to agree facts and figures so far as is possible and to prepare a list of matters still in difference between them.

6. A copy of the agreed bundle of documents for use at the Hearing shall be delivered to the Arbitrator at *his London office* by *Friday, 8th October, 1984.*

7. [Costs etc.]


DATED the      day of      19

X. Y.
Arbitrator

**Form 16: Hearing of some issues only**

IN THE MATTER OF THE ARBITRATION ACTS 1950 TO 1979
AND IN THE MATTER OF AN ARBITRATION

BETWEEN:

A. B. CONTRACTORS LIMITED          *Claimants*

and

C. D. DISTRICT COUNCIL          *Respondents*

[Preamble as appropriate]

1.   The issues[1] [listed in the Appendix to this Order] [set out in paragraphs *3, 8 and 10 to 15 inclusive* of the Points of Claim and paragraphs *5, 6 and 8* of the Points of Defence] shall be heard first.

2.   For this purpose a Preliminary Hearing will open in *Courtroom 1 of the Chartered Institute of Arbitrators, 75, Cannon Street, London, EC4,* at 10.0 o'clock on *Monday, 15th October, 1984.*

3.   At the Preliminary Hearing the Claimants shall open their case first and the Arbitrator will make and publish an Interim Award on the [above issues] [issue of liability] before the Hearing continues.

4.   Thereafter [all remaining issues] [the issues set out in          ] shall be heard [at a final Hearing on          at          ] at which the Respondents shall open their case first.


DATED the          day of          19          .

X. Y.
Arbitrator

---

[1]   Where appropriate, a more general form may be used, such as "The issues of liability shall be heard first".

*AWARDS*

## Form 17: The Award (general or Interim)

IN THE MATTER OF THE ARBITRATION ACTS 1950 TO 1979
AND IN THE MATTER OF AN ARBITRATION

BETWEEN:

A. B. CONTRACTORS LIMITED      *Claimants*

and

C. D. DISTRICT COUNCIL      *Respondents*

[*SECOND*] [INTERIM] AWARD
WHEREAS
    1.   The parties entered into a contract dated      for the construction of    ,
which contract was subject to the ICE Conditions of Contract;
    2.   Certain disputes arose between the parties and [, at their request,] the
President of the ICE appointed Mr *X. Y. of 23, High Street, Hometown, Mudshire,*
as sole arbitrator pursuant to Clause 66 of the said ICE Conditions;
  [ 3.   A *first* Interim Award was made on      in respect of certain of the matters
at issue;]
NOW I, the said X. Y. having [further] heard the parties and having [further]
considered the pleadings, documents and evidence DO HEREBY MAKE AND
PUBLISH this my [*second*] [Interim] Award as follows:
    1.   The Claimants' claims in paragraphs     of the Points of Claim are
dismissed.
    2.   The Claimants' claims in paragraphs     of the Points of Claim succeed,
and the Respondents are liable to the Claimants thereon in the sum of £    .
    3.   The Respondents' Counterclaim succeeds in part, and the Claimants are liable
to the Respondents thereon in the sum of £    .
  [ 4.   The reasons for the above awards are set out in Appendix 1 attached hereto.][1]
ACCORDINGLY I direct as follows:
    5.   The Respondent shall pay to the Claimant the sum of £    .
    6.   The parties shall bear their own costs and shall each pay half the costs of this
my Award, which I hereby tax and settle in the sum of £   . Provided that if
one party shall have paid the whole of the costs of the Award [whether on taking
up the Award or otherwise] the other party shall forthwith reimburse it on
demand. [I reserve the right to vary this order upon hearing the parties on the
issue of costs.]
    7.   Certified fit for Counsel.
MADE AND PUBLISHED in [place] this    day of    19

X.Y
Arbitrator
In the presence of:
  [signature]
  [name of witness]
  [occupation]
  [address]

---

[1]  Reasons may be (a) appended to the Award, as here; (b) published separately (in which case
paragraph 4 should be amended accordingly); (c) published separately, but *not* as part of the
Award (in which case paragraph 4 should be deleted); or (d) written into the Award itself
(see Form 18 below).

**Form 18: Reasons integral with the Award**

IN THE MATTER OF THE ARBITRATION ACTS 1950 TO 1979
AND IN THE MATTER OF AN ARBITRATION

BETWEEN:

A. B. CONTRACTORS LIMITED      *Claimants*

and

C. D. DISTRICT COUNCIL      *Respondents*

[*SECOND*] [INTERIM] AWARD

WHEREAS

1.   The parties entered into a contract dated      for the construction of     , which contract was subject to the ICE Conditions of Contract;

2.   Certain disputes arose between the parties and [, at their request,] the President of the ICE appointed Mr *X. Y. of 23, High Street, Hometown, Mudshire,* as sole arbitrator pursuant to Clause 66 of the said ICE Conditions;

[3.   A *first* Interim Award was made on      in respect of certain of the matters at issue;]

NOW I, the said X. Y. having [further] heard the parties and having [further] considered the pleadings, documents and evidence DO HEREBY MAKE AND PUBLISH this my [*second*] [Interim] Award as follows:

[*Narrative*

   *The disputes or differences* ⎤
   *The Parties' claims*       ⎥ [All in informal language,[1] with
   *Discussion*            ⎥ paragraphs numbered consecutively.]
   *Conclusions*][2]       ⎦

Accordingly I FIND AND HOLD[3]

   (*a*) ⎤ [Formal language. Each item should
   (*b*) ⎥ follow logically from the last,
   (*c*) ⎦ so far as is possible.]
   etc.

AND I AWARD AND ADJUDGE[4]

   (i)  ⎤ [Formal language; see paragraphs 1–3
   (ii) ⎥ of the operative part of Form 17.]
   (iii) ⎦
   etc.

AND I FURTHER DIRECT[4]

                  [as paragraphs 5, 6 and 7 of the operative part of
                  Form 17.]

MADE AND PUBLISHED . . . [as in Form 17]

---

1   Reasons should be in a clear style such as that used by Engineers for ordinary reports to their Clients.

2   These headings are suggestions only. Any other logical arrangement would be equally acceptable.

3   The Arbitrator "finds" facts and "holds" matters of law. It may sometimes be appropriate to list "findings" and "holdings" separately.

4   These two sections can, alternatively, be combined under the rubric "AND I AWARD ADJUDGE AND DIRECT", in which case it may be convenient to separate directions as to costs under a further heading "AND I FURTHER DIRECT".

## Form 19: Summary Award

## IN THE MATTER OF THE ARBITRATION ACTS 1950 TO 1979 AND IN THE MATTER OF AN ARBITRATION

BETWEEN:

A. B. CONTRACTORS LIMITED *Claimants*

and

C. D. DISTRICT COUNCIL *Respondents*

SUMMARY AWARD

WHEREAS

1.   The parties entered into a contract dated        for the construction of        , which contract was subject to the ICE Conditions of Contract;

2.   Certain disputes arose between the parties and [, at their request,] the President of the ICE appointed Mr *X. Y of 23, High Street, Hometown, Mudshire*, as sole arbitrator pursuant to Clause 66 of the said ICE Conditions;

3.   The [President directed] [parties agreed] that the arbitration should proceed subject to the ICE Arbitration Procedure (1983);

4.   Upon application by the Claimants I agreed and directed that the Claimants should make application for a Summary Award under Rule 14 of the said Procedure.

NOW I, the said X. Y., having heard the parties and having considered the pleadings documents and affidavits placed before me DO HEREBY make and publish this my [first] Summary Award as follows:

1.   The Respondents shall pay to the Claimants the sum of £        .

2.   The Respondents shall pay the further sum of £        to a stakeholder to be agreed between the parties or if not agreed to be nominated by me. Should this sum not be so paid within 28 days of the date of this my Summary Award it shall thereupon become payable directly to the Claimants and may be retained by them.

3.   The Respondents shall forthwith pay to the Claimants the sum of £        being a contribution towards the costs of these Summary proceedings.

4.   This Award may be varied by any subsequent award which I may make.

5.   Certified fit for Counsel.

MADE AND PUBLISHED in [place] this        day of        19

X. Y.
Arbitrator
In the presence of:
  [signature]
  [name of witness]
  [occupation]
  [address]

## Form 20: Award (Interim Arbitration)

IN THE MATTER OF THE ARBITRATION ACTS 1950 TO 1979
AND IN THE MATTER OF AN ARBITRATION

BETWEEN:

A. B. CONTRACTORS LIMITED       *Claimants*

and

C. D. DISTRICT COUNCIL       *Respondents*

AWARD

WHEREAS

1.   The parties entered into a contract dated          for the construction of          ,
which contract was subject to the ICE Conditions of Contract;

2.   Certain disputes arose between the parties and [, at their request,] the
President of the ICE appointed Mr *X. Y. of 23, High Street, Hometown, Mudshire*,
as sole arbitrator pursuant to Clause 66 of the said ICE Conditions;

3.   The [President directed] [parties agreed] that the arbitration should proceed
subject to the ICE Arbitration Procedure (1983);

4.   At the date of commencement of this arbitration the said Works were not
complete and the parties agreed that the arbitration should be an Interim
Arbitration;

5.   Directions were given that certain issues should be heard and determined in
accordance with Part G of the said Procedure;

6.   Notice was given during the Hearing that it was intended to make an Interim
Decision (as defined in the said Procedure) in respect of the issues in paragraph
          below.

NOW I the said X. Y., having heard the parties and their experts and having
considered the pleadings documents and evidence and having inspected the said
Works in progress DO HEREBY MAKE AND PUBLISH the following awards
findings and decisions in accordance with the Rules of the said Procedure as severally
indicated:

1.   *Interim Award under Rule 24.5(a)*
     Under paragraphs          of the Points of Claim I award and direct that the
Respondents shall pay to the Claimants the sum of £          [subject to paragraph
          below].

2.   *Findings of fact under Rule 24.5(b)*
     In respect of paragraphs          of the Points of Counterclaim I make the
following findings of fact:
     (i) . . .
     (ii) . . .

3.   *Summary Award under Rules 24.5(c) and 14*
     In respect of paragraphs          of the Points of Counterclaim I award and direct
that the Claimants shall pay to the Respondents the sum of £          [this sum to be
set off against and deducted from the sum ordered to be paid under paragraph

above, giving a balance due to the Claimants of £     ].

4.   *Interim Decision under Rule 24.5(d)*
In respect of paragraphs      of the Points of Claim I [find] [award and direct] as follows:

(i) . . .
(ii) . . .

5.   The Respondents shall pay to the Claimants simple interest on the nett amount to be paid hereunder at the rate of      per cent from [date] to the date of this Award.

6.   The Respondents shall pay half of the Claimants' costs incurred to date, to be taxed if not agreed.

MADE AND PUBLISHED in [place] this      day of      19

X. Y.
Arbitrator
In the presence of:
  [signature]
  [name of witness]
  [occupation]
  [address]

# MISCELLANEOUS

**Form of oath**[1]

I swear by Almighty God that the evidence I shall give touching the matters in difference in this reference shall be the truth, the whole truth, and nothing but the truth.

**Form of affirmation**[1]

I solemnly, sincerely and truly affirm and declare that I will true answers make to all such questions as shall be asked of me touching the matters in difference in this reference.

**Form of exclusion agreement under the Arbitration Act 1979**

It is hereby agreed for the purposes of Section 3 of the Arbitration Act 1979 that the jurisdiction of the High Court under Sections 1 and/or 2 of the said Act in respect of this Arbitration [or in respect of specified issues thereunder] shall be excluded.

---

[1]   Oaths Act 1909.

# Appendix VIII

# CHECK LIST OF ENGINEERS' DUTIES

**Institution of Civil Engineers**

ADVISORY COMMITTEE ON CONTRACT ADMINISTRATION
AND LAW

*CHECK LIST ON THE DUTIES OF ENGINEERS DESIGNATED
AS "THE ENGINEER" IN CONTRACTS UNDER THE ICE
CONDITIONS OF CONTRACT (FIFTH EDITION)*

As a result of criticism that Engineers are not acting independently when considering contract matters which involve the interests of both their Employers and the Contractors, the Committee wishes to emphasize the different roles the Engineer must assume under the ICE Conditions of Contract (5th Edition), first in pre-contract matters where he is the Employer's agent and professional advisor, and later, once the Contract has come into existence by the acceptance of a tender, his additional and quite separate duty to act impartially in the administration of the Contract and his quasi-judicial role as between the Employer and the Contractor.

The Committee has prepared this check list with references[1] to remind those named as "the Engineer" in construction contracts carried out under the ICE Conditions of Contract[2] of their duties and obligations. The list should not be taken as a set of rules, but the items listed should be carried out where appropriate.

The Committee strongly recommends that "the Engineer" should always be a specific, named individual.

*Pre-contract duties*
1. Ensure that the Employer is aware of the financial, managerial and advisory resources required for the Contract, and that he carries the financial risk for unforeseen events.
2. Warn the Employer of the decisions and actions which will be required of him, giving programme dates for finalisation of designs, for the provision of access, for construction and for taking over the completed Works.
3. Design and detail the Contract Works and, as far as possible, prepare clear working drawings and a concise specification.
4. Prepare accurate Bills of Quantities, detailing the work required and complying with the Civil Engineering Standard Method of Measurement where possible. Keep provisional items to a minimum.
5. Ensure that the Employer and his staff understand the role of the Engineer under the ICE Conditions of Contract in ensuring fair dealing between the Contractor and the Employer.
6. Adopt the ICE Conditions of Contract (or, for ancillary works, national and

---

[1] For references, see below, at p. 237.
[2] Or under similar forms, such as FIDIC (see Appendix III).

well-understood Conditions of Contract) in full, without variation or deletions, and draw the Employer's attention to the powers and duties of the Engineer under these contracts.

7. Ensure that the Employer and his Auditors are aware of and fully accept the ICE/CIPFA "Joint Statement: Engineers and Auditors" on the correct relationship between Engineer and Auditor, and in particular that they accept that the Engineer has quasi-judicial powers to make decisions that are final and binding upon Employer and Contractor alike, subject only to reference to arbitration.

8. Ensure that the Employer has a defined and readily understood method of selecting Tenderers and recommend that the number of tenders invited should be limited.

9. Ensure that all Tenderers receive the same tendering information and are given a sufficient period for the proper preparation of their tenders.

10. Make all site and service information in the possession of the Employer and of the Engineer available to those invited to tender.

11. Ensure that tenders are delivered in specifically marked envelopes to the Employer or to the Engineer by a fixed date and time, and that they are opened in the presence of witnesses at a declared and fixed time.

12. Check each tender carefully and correct any errors in extension of items (rates × quantities). Notify the Tenderer of any resulting change in the total of the priced Bills of Quantities and in the tender sum.

   Review all tenders received with particular regard to the proposed construction methods, the degree of risk involved, the implications of sectional completion dates on the Employer's and the Contractor's cash flows, and the anticipated final contract price.

   Submit to the Employer a report on each tender, pointing out any rate that is less than the known cost of carrying out the work, and recommending (with reasons) acceptance of a particular tender. If any tender rates are in doubt, recommend that the Tenderer be invited to stand by his rates or to withdraw.

13. Advise the Employer that Tenderers should be given the name of the successful Tenderer at the earliest opportunity, and that the list of values of tenders received should be circulated.

## Post-contract duties

14. On the appointment of a Contractor, confirm the appointment by letter.

15. Give by letters to the Contractor and to the Engineer's Representative details of the powers and responsibilities which are to be delegated to the latter. Name the Engineer's Representative and the members of the project team, and give a date for the commencement of the Works.

16. Agree the extent and methods of payment for variations and extras, and how dayworks are to be supervised and recorded (preferably before work is commenced), and confirm these matters in writing.

17. Do not exceed the powers granted by the Employer. (For example, do not take on responsibility for re-design, significant variations or extra works without the Employer's prior agreement both to the works concerned and to the provision of the necessary finance.)

18. Make decisions on extensions of time at the stages and times required under the Contract.

19. Ensure that a site diary and site records are properly kept and agreed with the Contractor where appropriate, and arrange for regular progress photographs to be taken.

20. Ensure that site meetings are held at least monthly, and that minutes of such

meetings are kept and agreed.
21. Issue certificates for payments promptly after interim measurements.
22. Visit the site regularly, at least once a month. Inspect works in progress and keep compliance with the contract programme under review.
23. Ensure that nominated Sub-Contractors are properly appointed by the Main Contractor and that appropriate Sub-Contract Conditions of Contract are applied.
24. Agree measurements and quantities for completed work as the work proceeds, and agree that such measurements and quantities shall be carried unaltered to the Final Account.
25. Ensure that all Claims are properly detailed and the sums due thereon (if any) are settled as soon as possible.
26. Ensure that Certificates of Completion and of Maintenance are issued to the Contractor promptly at the proper time.
27. Ensure that the Employer is aware of his new insurance liability when the Maintenance Certificate is issued.
28. When asked for an Engineer's decision under Clause 66, review all the evidence available and arrange for the Contractor to put his case and (if possible) for the Engineer's Representative to put the Employer's case, so that a clear judgement may be made upon the issues.
29. Should any matter go to arbitration, keep the dispute within the scope of the issues covered in arriving at the Clause 66 decision, and present your evidence fairly and concisely.

## Generally

The guiding principles for the Engineer and his staff are that the Contract is a joint enterprise for the benefit of both parties; the Employer is entitled to a project well executed and the Contractor is entitled to fair dealing and a fair profit. Remember always that the Contractor could only price and plan resources for the Works as they were defined at the time he tendered.

## References

| | | |
|---|---|---|
| Item 4 | ICE Conditions of Contract | Clause 57 |
| Item 5 | Conditions of Contract Standing Joint Committee Guidance Note 2A—"Functions of the Engineer under the ICE Conditions of Contract". | |
| Items 8 to 14 | These are dealt with in greater detail in the Conditions of Contract Standing Joint Committee document "Guidance on the preparation, submission and consideration of Tenders for Civil Engineering Contracts in the United Kingdom". | |
| Item 15 | ICE Conditions of Contract | Clauses 2 and 41 |
| Item 16 | ditto | Clause 51 |
| Item 17 | ditto | Clause 44 |
| Item 18 | ditto | Clause 44 |
| Item 21 | ditto | Clause 60 |
| Item 23 | ditto | Clause 59 |
| Item 24 | ditto | Clause 48 |
| Item 25 | ditto | Clause 52 |
| Item 26 | ditto | Clause 48 |
| Item 27 | ditto | Clause 21 |
| Item 28 | ditto | Clause 66 |
| Item 29 | ICE Arbitration Procedure (1983); see also "The ICE Arbitration Practice" (Thomas Telford Ltd.), 1986. | |

# ACKNOWLEDGMENTS

Acknowledgment is made to the Controller of Her Majesty's Stationery Office for permission to reproduce parts of the Arbitration Act 1950, the Arbitration Act 1975, the Arbitration Act 1979, Rules of the Supreme Court (Order 73), the Arbitration (Scotland) Act, 1894, the Administration of Justice (Scotland) Act, 1972, and the Arbitration Act (Northern Ireland) 1937.

Further acknowledgment is made to the Controller, Stationery Office, Dublin, for permission to reproduce part of the Arbitration Act 1954 and the Arbitration Act 1980.

# INDEX